A TIDY UNIVERSE
OF ISLANDS

DR. WILLIAM M. PECK

Funded by
Commonwealth of the Northern Mariana Islands
Council for the Humanities
and National Endowment for the Humanities
and
Commonwealth of the Northern Mariana Islands
Council for Arts and Culture

First Printing, June 1997
1 2 3 4 5 6 7 8 9

ISBN 1-56647-117-6

Design by Jane Hopkins

Mutual Publishing
1127 11th Avenue, Mezz. B
Honolulu, Hawaii 96816
Telephone (808) 732-1709
Fax (808) 734-4094
e-mail: mutual@lava.net

Dr. Bill Peck has had a wonderfully rich and varied life. As a young physician, he was a pioneer in the treatment of tuberculosis with strepto-mycin, and later an official (and horrified) observer of the nuclear tests in the Pacific. He was one of the first to see the greatly heightened incidence of thyroid cancer, leukemia and miscarriages following these. As commissioner of health for the Trust Territory of the Pacific Islands (as Micronesia was called then), he built up a desperately needed service, attracted energetic physicians from all over the world, and trained native nurses to be patients' aides.

Having lived in the Pacific for thirty-five years now, intensely conscious of the ancient traditions and myths of the Micronesian peoples, he has dedicated his life's work to preserving and translating the songs and myths of Chuuk and other Micronesian cultures.

Bill Peck is himself a mystic, a poet, and a storyteller no less than a grand physician, and every aspect of his extraordinary life is brought together in this remarkable and beautiful collection, *A Tidy Universe of Islands*.

—*Oliver Sacks, MD, New York City*

ACKNOWLEDGMENTS

The final compilation of my last 38 years into a book could not have been accomplished without positive and creative action by many friends, and I want to give special credit to: Tim Bruce, Lynn Michael, Dr. Mark Durand, Gerald Calvo, Dr. Oliver Sacks, Dirk Ballendorf, Jackie Bussell, Paul Strauss, Father Francis S. Hezel. And, of course, I must give special credit to the Pacific Island storytellers themselves whose stories have given substance and continuity to everything I have written.

The new dispensary on Northern Truk (Chuuk). Inside, a complicated women's dance is taking place.

TABLE OF CONTENTS

PROLOGUE

Reader, this is an honest book. It warns you at the very outset that in it I have met for myself no other goal than a domestic and private one. I have given no consideration in it either to your service or to my glory. My powers are not capable of such an aim. I have dedicated it to the personal use of my relatives and friends, so that when they have lost me (which they must soon do), they may find again some traits of my habits and humor and may by this means keep more intact and more alive the knowledge they have had of me. If I had intended to seek the favor of the world, I should have adorned myself better and should present myself in a studied bearing. I wish to be seen in my simple, natural, and ordinary fashion, without effort or artifice, for it is myself that I portray. My defects will here be read to the life, and my natural form, as far as respect for the public has permitted. Had I lived among those nations which are said to live still in the sweet liberty of the first laws of nature, I assure you I should very gladly have portrayed myself here at full length and entirely naked. Thus, reader, I am myself the matter of my book; there is no reason for you to spend your pleasure on so frivolous and vain a subject. So farewell, from Montaigne, this first day of March, fifteen hundred and eighty.

Montaigne's Introduction to his *Essays*
[orig., *(Fr.,)* Michel de Montaigne,
Livre de poche classique (1533-1592)].

⊕ ⊕ ⊕

When I started writing this series of articles and poems, some thirty years ago, I had no expectation that I might be recording the antics of a quiet, house-broken physician who was unwittingly on the verge of abandoning the 20th Century for the excitement and pain and joy and flamboyance of 'jousting' with islands and the shadows of past centuries that hover over them. But that's the way it turned out and I think I had little to do with selecting the kind of life I would live—all this dashing about the world—for I was an humble fellow who accepted his fate as it appeared...I sit at my desk in Rota, here in the Western Pacific, writing these remarks, contemplating and weighing those long, chaotic years, and I decided in retrospect that I would not, even if I could, have eliminated any of them—even the nasty ones—at risk of distorting the destiny that has finally placed me here on this comfortable, friendly island.

I shall start with introductory notes on 'Cultural Adaptation,' that I once gave in speeches to prepare newcomers for the shock and joy and adventure of existence on small Pacific islands. I'll then include articles that record the details of bomb testings as I participated in them in the Marshall Islands (glorious when they occurred but painful now to reconstitute and impossible to justify,) and then I'll include favorite sketches of my adventure in Guam where I lived through the worst typhoon ever recorded up to that time. Africa, where I spent three years, I shall try to reduce to island size by including just one short chapter and a poem. Then I shall include five and one half years of adventures in the old, now-defunct Trust Territory, and an account of three years I spent in Truk (*Chuuk*); and finally I shall feature stories from the Northern Marianas, especially the verbal histories of Japanese occupation and of the war that are recounted with reverence by Rota's eager, elder citizens almost as if they had occurred yesterday...And at this point, now being 86 years old and retired on this 'blessed' island of Rota I'll seek no new adventures for myself other than those that are permitted by nostalgia.

I should add that I have had two purposes in writing *A Tidy Universe of Islands.* Number one: to put down on paper my activities on the Pacific Islands that have thrilled and awed me which I want to share with my friends and relatives (just as Montaigne wanted to share his Essays); and Number two: I want to cite incidents that affirm the honor and dignity and soundness of traditional ways of life that, over many centuries, have been slowly crafted and adapted to the essentials for survival on these isolated, stark, rocky, jungle islands; for it was here that I first came to understand that cultures are usually fundamentally sound for the situations in which they have been created and should be respected, and that the term 'uncivilized' should be used with discretion. Learning this principle was a slow, often painful process, and I've tried to recount the process step by step that I went through before I realized that the mere possession of complicated technology in no way prepared me (nor others of my ilk) to dominate and 'correct' human values that have slowly evolved on islands.

GREENPEACE NUCLEAR MAP OF THE PACIFIC

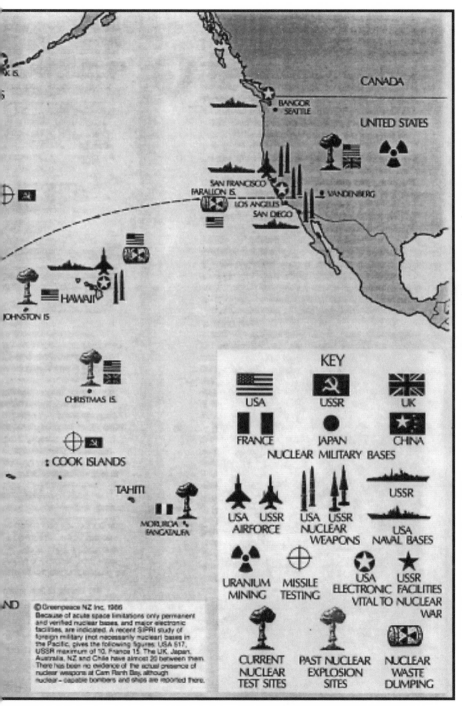

CANADA

UNITED STATES

BANGOR
SEATTLE

SAN FRANCISCO
FARALLON IS.
LOS ANGELES
SAN DIEGO

VANDENBERG

HAWAII

JOHNSTON IS

CHRISTMAS IS.

: COOK ISLANDS

TAHITI

MORUROA &
FANGATAUFA

KEY

USA

USSR

UK

FRANCE

JAPAN

CHINA

NUCLEAR MILITARY BASES

USA USSR
AIRFORCE

USA USSR
NUCLEAR
WEAPONS

USSR

USA
NAVAL BASES

URANIUM
MINING

MISSILE
TESTING

USA   USSR
ELECTRONIC FACILITIES
VITAL TO NUCLEAR
WAR

CURRENT
NUCLEAR
TEST SITES

PAST NUCLEAR
EXPLOSION
SITES

NUCLEAR
WASTE
DUMPING

Map used with permission from Greenpeace New Zealand

During a trip to a northern Chuukese island, we dedicated a new dispensary. This photo was taken inside the new dispensary where the women are executing a complicated, sitting-down dance. Ordinarily all women on the island go bare-breasted, but to prepare for the elegance of their dance, they ordered commercial brassieres to wear during the dance. But, as soon as the dance was complete and we were all applauding, they removed their brassieres and became normally bare-breasted.

CHAPTER ONE

HINTS ON CULTURAL ADAPTATION
A Lecture for Newcomers to Islands

To a landlubber statesider who has never seen nor smelled an island, nor been injured by one, an island is a treasured dream that can be splendidly recreated by coming to the Western Pacific. This, I firmly believe, is an expectation that is universal among new arrivals. There is a belief, even among those who should know better, that an island's ways are simple, quaint and controllable and lacking only the civilized insights and amenities that anyone of us can bring to it. There is a conviction, subliminal in most of us, that a few primal instincts determine the course of events on an island and that by immersing ourselves in simple island ways we can avoid the complications, the stresses and agonies of an over-wrought civilization and thus benevolently renew our lives. By this interpretation an island is a refuge and a beatitude.

But the reverse is true. Do not be deluded into thinking that because an island is small and has a small population that it is a simple place. People who have made this mistake have labeled tropical island life as paradise—which it is not. An island is a miniature universe, complete unto itself. It is a compressed universe with all the complexities of our disordered world: its treacheries, its conflicting ambitions, its dishonesties, its follies, as well as its kindnesses and pleasures, all brought unrelentingly into one's daily life. Few of these events are important enough to interest the world, but when one reduces one's perspectives and expectations to island size, these miniature events loom large, become personal, always portentous and sometimes threatening.

Traditionally, these once self-contained island populations built their own system for resolving their frequent and intense conflicts so that they could live in close proximity without killing each other off. In cases of physical violence or thievery, for instance, the two families or clans involved would come together, discuss the matter at great length and end up by making satisfactory reparations without recourse to police or to courts...a sort of miniature world diplomacy at its best. Remnants of the system remain and often infuriate newcomers who assume they represent the breakdown of modern law enforcement; but actually, though not always, they serve to stabilize an island's social order better than our judicial and prison systems.

An ancient Chuukese *samol* (chief) once defined the traditional indigenous system of customary law in these stern, transcendental terms:

> Confuse
> Confuse thy Samol no more
> Confuse thy Samol
> At thy Life's peril
> For I, Samol,
> Know the difference between Night and Day
> I, Samol, know
> When Nights shorten
> Days become longer
> And my heart recalls an ancient Truth:
> 'Day cuts Night
> Night cuts Day'
> For such is the way of this island
> Such is the way things accommodate themselves
> One to another and exact their price
> On this island
> On this earth
> Since the Beginning

The principle stated metaphorically in this poem is that quarrels must be resolved in ways that do not disrupt life in a small, closed community.

This system also acts as a forum for judging newcomers such as ourselves and for deciding who should be accorded close social relations and who should be kept at a distance, whose opinions should be respected and whose should be ignored. For American physicians coming here the system will determine, far more than their medical abilities, which ones succeed and which ones fail.

Traditional island life style, as you can see, is elaborate and fulfills most island needs, but it is perplexing to anyone who comes suddenly onto it. This is especially true for a new physician, for he comes directly into the maelstrom of island life where matters of death and disability, despair and panic, dominate all other considerations, and he must establish the community's faith in his skills and integrity even as he steps off the plane.

How is this to be done? If, indeed, I had the wisdom to construct for you an unfailing itinerary of proper behavior and if you were to follow it, I think I would be doing you a disservice, for a large part of the charm and value of cross-cultural experience will be from the mistakes you will make and the frantic efforts at innovation you must make to recover from them. Indeed, my most cherished memories, now that my novice days are over, are not of my several successes, but of my many faux pas; accordingly, I will dare offer only generalities. I speak specifically to physicians but my remarks are meant to include all newcomers.

First, I would like to disabuse you of any idea that you may have during your short two year assignment that it is your responsibility to affect social, political, or administrative changes beyond the narrow purview of your day-to-day and week-to-week professional responsibilities. This sounds like a recantation of a paramount American commitment, but it is not. I am simply saying: do not let your good intentions carry you into areas beyond your competence where, unwittingly, you may do harm. These areas, these non-professional areas, are mine fields and numerous physicians, with the best intentions, have found their undoing in them, or at least have found basis for despair with their assignment. Uncontrolled missionary impulses, Boy Scout impulses, even Peace Corps impulses are the most common causes of physician failure.

To be successful on any of these islands you must develop a tolerance for chaos, for you will be immersed in chaos: the chaos of acculturation, the chaos of our 20th century compressed within the reef of whatever island you are on. And I enjoin you to see these changes objectively as if you were seeing them in a movie and not as a personal challenge; or to see them as the inescapable destiny of an island people that is unfolding before your eyes, but involving you only briefly or not at all. Become nostalgic or paternal about these islands and your pleasure in them will vanish.

The work ethic! It will bother you just as it bothered me and still does. Just the other day I heard a teacher explain why he missed many school days. "You must realize," he said, "that I am both a teacher and a farmer, and I have to divide my responsibilities between my cattle and my classroom."

And here is an article from the *Pacifica* that was written tongue-in-cheek by an excellent young Marshallese correspondent. In it, Akio

Heinie gives 'rational Marshallese' reasons why one should work for the government of the Marshall Islands:

"Free slot and other gambling machine time during working hours. Extended coffee break hours (early morning, mid-morning, early afternoon and mid-afternoon). Free use of government vehicles for transporting coconuts, firewood and/or relatives. If you ever get into trouble, no problem—you are usually hired back to your job after committing crimes (e.g. cheating, forgery, embezzlement, and what not). Somehow or other through plea bargaining you end up with a light sentence (so light, in fact, that you are encouraged to cheat again) and you are usually back at your job or transferred to a better paying one than before. It is as though the government is rewarding you for the shame and suffering you and your family went through when you got caught."

I thought this was a remarkable dissertation and I showed it around to my Chamorro neighbors and collected these remarks:

First person: This is just like the Northern Marianas.
Second person: This is not at all like the Northern Marianas.
Third person: That guy ought to be assassinated.
Fourth person: That's the way I like it. I'm going to try to get a job in the Marshalls.

Of course these statements are somewhat exaggerated and you will find some government employees who are splendid exceptions to them; but in general the work ethic is very much less stringent than the one that motivated you through medical school and residency. I call this dismal work ethic to your attention and note that it is contradictory: though there is tolerance for Micronesians who abuse it, you will be condemned if you follow their example.

Paradoxically, we Americans must take responsibility for this poor work ethic, for during the Japanese Mandate, discipline was strict and devotion to the job was high; and that was the way things were when we took over.

I speak with some authority on this matter for I have worked with the Micronesian Area Research Center of the University of Guam on a project to document the consequences of Japanese education and cultural contact on citizens of the Northern Marianas; we did this by taking oral histories from those who grew up, went to school and worked under the Japanese. Those elder citizens whom we studied all deplored the fact that the American education system and American contacts (notably Peace Corps and Trust Territory personnel) have introduced attitudes that have destroyed the disciplined way of life they grew up with and which they admired. "There was almost no crime in those days," they said, "and children were obedient. We all worked hard and we liked it."

But there is ambivalence in their attitude, for when we asked them which were the best days of their lives—Japanese times, Trust Territory times, or Commonwealth times —they said Commonwealth times and they said it with conviction. "Why?" we asked them. "Because now we have more money and we have freedom to do what we want to do and to think." "And what times were the next best?" And they answered "Trust Territory times."

You will find contradictions to this assessment among politicians. Politicians going to Washington to ask for more funds decry the present situation as impoverished and say that Japanese times were better. But this is nothing more than ritual posturing brought on by budget discussions, and it is wrong. I can document the fact, at least for the Northern Marianas.

I am using the Northern Marianas as a prototype because this is what I know best. Let me add several observations based on these interviews which, I think, will improve the prototype by focusing on sociological implications. The Japanese system was an easy one to fit into for there were predetermined niches in the social hierarchy into which one knew one must fit and once in it, one knew what he amounted to, how he must act and whom he must obey and respect. Of the four ethnic groups, Japanese were first, the Okinawans were second and the Chamorros and Koreans alternated between third and fourth place depending on the situation. The Chamorros understood their place in the system, were content with it and they worked hard and loyally. Yet, when American troops came to Saipan, some Chamorro men ran to meet and embrace them. Japanese loyalty and culture were thrown off that easily!

Why? Recently I have been reading books and articles by American, British and Japanese scholars who point out that Japanese, because of their powerful self-image, have shown themselves incapable of empathy: friendliness, yes; but empathy, no! They were powerful, devoted and persuasive colonizers but their influence was short-lived and disappeared the moment their authority was lost. They have gone from the Northern Marianas leaving almost no trace of their thirty one years of intense occupation except for a few forgotten, jungle artifacts.

I mention this in somewhat more detail than the subject of cultural adaptation would seem to justify, and I do this because of the word "empathy" which I would like for you to keep in mind as you go to work with your Micronesian counterparts. For if any of your efforts remain after you leave, it will be because of the empathy you have developed with coworkers, the sense of equality and of true brotherhood.

This brings us to the matter of your public relations that you must establish and I want to give you several examples to avoid. But before I do this I want to emphasize that acculturation—or perhaps I should say Americanization—is such a powerful force that you will go wrong if you rely on familiar stateside standards, and I urge you to approach all questions carefully and with readiness to improvise and compromise.

Examples: A middle-aged physician on Rota whom I liked and regarded as competent. Just before Rota's annual fiesta, a Korean fishing vessel full of frozen fish got itself stranded on Rota's rocky shore and for a few days everyone, including me, lived high on fish. The mayor decided to use the remaining fish for the annual fiesta, but the physician thought otherwise and condemned the lot. He felt so strongly about it that he personally took on the task of searching for the fish and destroying them. There were public discussions about it and one meeting in which the physician, carried away by his own eloquence, called the mayor an asshole. That did it! Whatever support the physician had was then lost and he began to receive threats, even threats to his life. I spoke to the mayor about the threats and received this very revealing answer: "Threats, threats are nothing," he said, "I have my life threatened all the time. It is just the way we communicate!" Nevertheless, the physician hastily decided to leave Rota.

Arrogance is sometimes the cause of defeat and one young physician on Saipan, just before leaving, published a statement in a local paper to vent his spleen and to express his disappointment: "I have been on Saipan for a year," he lamented, "and I have never been consulted by the governor!" And gathering his skirt about him, he left.

Obviously these situations were mishandled. How should they have been handled? Knowing no more details than I have presented, we can't say. But very generally I would say to you: Don't take leadership in public matters, rely on experts. And who are your experts? They are your local colleagues—local physicians, nurses, technicians, sanitarians—who know the social and political structure of the island and who, I hope, will have become your close friends who empathize with you and have become just as concerned over professional standards and ethics as you.

Obviously, an ethical physician cannot sit quietly by and see patients suffer and die needlessly, and sometimes you will be forced to take prompt action. But do this cautiously and with full knowledge that there will be local backlash to anything you do that contradicts local customs or authority. Weigh the odds carefully before you act and know that local martyrdom may be the price you will pay. And abolish from your consciousness any fantasy you may have brought with you that you are a white knight who is itching to jump on his charger and gallop into battle to save Micronesia.

Chaos! That word chaos again! It is the only word I can think of when I approach the subject of politics. Island politics mirrors the restlessness and moral decay of the rest of the world, I suppose, but also it comes from the introduction of our democratic process. This has been accepted with incredible enthusiasm. Sometimes I suspect that politics has been thus frantically grasped to fill the void left by the weakening clan and family and religious structures; perhaps it is a new kind of faith to cling to. Also, political campaigns have come to serve as entertainment—rough and lively and far into the night. In a political speech a citizen can say (or, rather, shout at the top of his voice) any insulting remark he wants to about the opposing candidates and their wives and children and relatives, and somehow not be held accountable. Good clean fun, perhaps, but it carries over into violent acts, none for which the perpetrators ever seem to be apprehended or   punished. Consider these political events: A president's office was bombed; a president assassinated; the motor of a mayor's new car shot full of bullets; a senator's ranch house burned down. I can extend the list for a couple of pages, but do I need to say more to warn you to stay out of politics and not reveal your political affiliations to anyone?

I have said nothing about the details of your adaptation to local customs: should you, when in Yap, feel that it is mandatory for you, if you are a male, to wear a *thu* or if you are a woman to go bare breasted, and in Chuuk should you learn to eat dog without nausea? How far is it necessary to go? I would say, not very far, for local people do not admire the spectacle of statesiders trying to go 'native.'

I will illustrate this by example, but first let me quote Dr. Charlie Jones, an excellent older surgeon who worked eight years in Chuuk and was adored. He once told me: "When I am with Chuukese, especially when I am in a Chuukese home, I follow local precepts as if they were my Bible, but when I am in my home or about my business I am as thoroughly American as if I were still in Pennsylvania. That is the way my wife and I and the Chuukese have learned to respect each other. Despite being in his late 50s, Jones learned to speak Chuukese, not fluently, but sufficiently to show that he respected the language.

I would like to add to Charlie Jones' statement by saying that the essence of successful adaptation, as I see it, is in making certain that those around you are comfortable with you and are at ease. You must be able to cross all barriers of race and all barriers that superior educational advantages may have put in your way so that you can inspire your colleagues with feelings of equality and brotherhood that will endure. But I would hastily add that you have brought with you your rights as a human being. These you must maintain. Let no one take them from you for no one expects you to kowtow and no one will respect you if you do. Charlie Jones would have agreed with this.

Now to cite an example of how not to go 'native' whole hog. This concerns a young physician who affronted Yapese, society by going 'whole hog.' To him the essence of Yapese society was nudity, for he did not realize that to Yapese a *thu* is a complete and modest form of clothing; so at a party in his house for leading Yapese citizens, he came into his living room bearing a tray of martinis, wearing nothing, no *thu*, stark naked. The Yapese were as shocked, so I have been told, as if they had been Southern Methodists at a prayer meeting. He left soon after that and commenced a residency in psychiatry…belatedly, I would say.

The freedom of living your own private life pretty much as you are accustomed to living it is important, and I urge you to take advantage of your spare time to cultivate your stateside interests and hobbies, or to develop new ones: if you are a musician, continue to be one. I, for instance, am fond of baroque music, and I take a harpsichord and a clavichord and recorders with me and play them every day. And, of course, if you are a swimmer and a diver or a fisherman or a hiker you can extend these interests ad infinitum and you should. If you have scientific research interests, they can be pursued profitably providing you design them to fit the limitations of your situation. If you are interested in writing, you will never have a better opportunity to try out and polish your skills. You can write about your personal adventures, or you can dip into Micronesian history and lore, including ancient poetry. Poetry was once a common and respected means of communication and sometimes reached true literary heights. Unearthing and preserving these poems in the vernacular and in the best, most sensitive English you are capable of is an important and enduring contribution you can make to local culture.

I think back over what I have written, especially the earlier sections and I am afraid that most of it is too heavily loaded with threats and negative admonitions. But this is not the way I feel at all, otherwise I would have fled the area long ago. Please accept all those nasty things I have been saying, all that 'pessimism' as a sort of essential purgation and ritual of purification, as an evocation of the spirit of adventure you must have if you are to enjoy island life, and, most of all, as a Rite of Passage to an experience that will be memorable to you and a blessing that will enlarge your concept of yourselves and of human values. I think I have emphasized the hardships, embarrassments and frustrations because I am actually hoping you will have some of them; otherwise the experience might add up to nothing more than a pleasant afternoon on the beach...Culture shock, if you survive it, can be a blessing and a kind of enlightenment, at least in retrospect.

I have almost finished, but I pause to hark back to the Peace Corps Volunteers I worked with in Africa whose subsequent careers I have been able to follow for many years: green kids when they started, fresh out of college, but who, from their African experience and during it, matured wonderfully, and nearly all of them are now in the midst of highly successful, mostly socially-oriented careers: five became physicians, two of whom are frequently invited as consultants by impoverished Third World governments; one ranks high as a career diplomat; and one, actually a Peace Corps teacher but closely associated with our program, has become one of America's leading novelists (Paul Theroux).

Cross-cultural experience did not cause them, nor should it cause you, to lose sense of direction nor to lose personal identity; rather, it should expand these qualities and give new dignity and scope. Such experience should, if you give it a chance, teach you sensitivity to fellow men, patience, compassion, a kindly sort of existentialist attitude and good humor...I truly believe that this experience you are now undertaking should be as profitable to you as to the population you have come to serve. I give you my best wishes and my highest hopes.

⊕ ⊕ ⊕

Island cemetery on Rongelap. Always room
for one more grave, for once a ghost
disappears and is no longer a danger, its
space can be cleared for another occupant.

CHAPTER TWO

NUCLEAR BOMB TESTING IN MICRONESIA

INTRODUCTION
The Radiation Catastrophe

In April, 1958 the United States Public Health Service sent me to participate in bomb testing in the Marshall Islands. This was the first series of tests since the devastating 1954 series in which a Bikini bomb spewed its radiation across Rongelap killing (eventually) many of its inhabitants, and rendering Rongelap temporarily unfit for habitation. Rongelapese had been returned to their atoll in July, 1957 just months before I arrived and tests were renewed. Those were strange times, for neutron bombs were regarded with almost spiritual reverence, at least in Washington where they had been ordained the device that would forever establish peace on earth, and bomb blasts began to seem like trumpets from heaven proclaiming this Truth.

So I volunteered. Suddenly I, aged forty-seven, who knew nothing and cared nothing about the military was given the rank of Commander, awarded a rating of 'top security' and dropped off by seaplane in Rongelap Lagoon. My duty was to give medical care to the 180 islanders, to discipline 30-some GIs who had been assigned to assist me, to monitor fallout radiation and, if this should once again rise to dangerous heights, to lead everyone into the lagoon and stay there as nearly submerged as possible until a destroyer could rescue us. But I was not ready for the immense responsibilities that immediately overpowered me: interpreting terse radio instructions for the next day's detonation and planning the action I should take for each level of possible catastrophe; trying to understand the quirky, changing patterns of wind directions and velocities up through the troposphere that would determine our next day's radiation fate. Never before nor since have I spent so many sleepless nights. Thirty-three bombs were detonated on Bikini or Eniwetok during my four months' assignment. On cloudless nights they had the grandeur of an arctic aurora borealis as they flashed and flushed the western sky; and sometimes, when we had not been notified of their schedule, they shook us in our beds.

It was the four months I spent sharing the dangers of bomb testing with these Rongelap people (they the victims, I a perpetrator) that gave me admiration and respect for them, and that has sent me scurrying about the earth ever since to find people with whom I could experience such empathy and confidence.

When I had completed my four months' tour on Rongelap and returned to my home in Raleigh, North Carolina, I started writing about the experience, and after finishing a number of chapters I sent them to a leading publisher who encouraged me to continue by sending me a contract to extend those chapters into a book. Unfortunately my high security rating got in the way and Washington officials insisted on imposing severe censorship that had nothing to do with security but that confirmed the righteousness of bomb testing and that converted every official bomb tester into a hero. I refused to cooperate and the book was not completed…. Here I shall seek to preserve only those portions that now have personal appeal and which seem to explain how bomb testing on Rongelap changed my life. I shall begin by describing the 1954 radiation catastrophe as it was reconstructed for me by its victims as we sat about campfires at night on Rongelap.

ATOM WINTER
Marshallese Recollections

Early on a Monday morning in February, 1954, a bomb by the name of *Bravo* was detonated on Bikini. Many minutes later and one hundred miles away, Jimaco and Tina were washing clothes by the Rongelap lagoon, squatting and teetering on their young haunches, facing westward. When the shock wave hit, enveloping them in its rifle-crack, enfolding them for an instant of pressure—more like an implosion than an explosion—mouthing them almost tenderly and spitting them out, they sat down suddenly. Later, when they tried to recreate the event—just as everyone on Rongelap tried to preserve and magnify in time this one split second—they maintained that the earth had been jerked from under them like a mat snatched in play, although others believed that it was only the surprise that sent them sprawling.

They looked at each other in amusement, then tensed themselves as they waited for it to happen again. They sat there listening but heard only the lap of lagoon wavelets on the gravel and the rasp of palm fronds. No sound came from the village, and they began to comb their black, wavy hair, still listening, combing faster and faster as their tension mounted. Then, Jimaco, who was older and more determined, said in Marshallese. "This is funny," and laughed and they ran as fast as they could into the village.

There was an appearance of delayed action slightly behind that on the beach, for all was quiet. Groups of island people, dressed like the missionaries had 'taught' them to dress, sat as usual in the shade of trees or in the cool space inside palm-thatched houses, but their hands were transfixed in the act of mending nets or weaving baskets as they listened intently. When Jimaco and Tina, hair flying and breathless, laundry strewing the path behind them, dashed exuberantly into the village and shouted, "This is funny," they all jumped up and began to laugh and to pantomime the experience as if they had rehearsed it many times and knew just what to do. Others, as they recovered from their surprise, spilled out of the houses until the space about the council house moved with excitement; everyone chattering at once, their Marshallese consonants exploding like fire-crackers, all asking what had happened, but sometimes laughing and saying, "It is funny" before they asked. When everyone was there and excitement was at its peak, someone thought to beat on the bell that hung at the entrance of the council house. For a moment this quieted them, for it seemed to announce a disaster…like the time someone rang it years before when a tidal wave swept across the island, and the bell ridiculously kept proclaiming the catastrophe that all of them knew as they clung for their lives to trees heeling in the tide. But soon they began to laugh and chatter again, and to feel happy that, after Sunday's prayer-pierced piety, a new week had started so gaily. None of them knew what had caused the disturbance except to suspect that it had something to do with the Americans whose activities at Eniwetok, Bikini and Kwajelein they comprehended vaguely. That a bomb on Bikini could have produced such an effect did not occur to them because they knew the distance involved, and, from World War II experience, they knew the limitations of conventional armaments, so they decided that a jet plane or a destroyer, just out of sight, must have performed in some enormous manner. And with that explanation they went back to work or to laze, as they preferred, thinking a little more favorably about a conqueror who could perform so magnificently.

The trade winds continued to bear, as always from east to west toward Bikini, but the upper winds shifted until they carried directly across Rongelap, shearing somewhat tangentially, however, so that the atomic cloud centered over the northern, unoccupied side of the atoll, dragging its heavy fringe over the village. The fall-out started four to six hours after the detonation and appeared first as an indefinite haze, rapidly changing to a white, sifting powder: like snow, some of them said who had seen movies at Kwajelein. Jimaco and Tina romped through the village with a troop of younger children, exulting in the miracle, and shouting, "Look, we are like a Christmas picture, we play in snow," and they pointed with glee at the sticky powder that smeared their skin, whitened their hair, and rimed the ground with hoarfrost. But the younger children soon tired of the game since snow meant nothing to them, and becoming resentful of the stickiness of the flakes, ran frequently into the lagoon to bathe.

John, the solemn young Magistrate who had been elected two years before and wore his responsibility with unusual concern, found it difficult to be amused. He laughed with others at the strange events but worried about them as he walked along the beach alone trying to find an explanation. Once he noted a plane flying high among the big shouldered clouds, its motors echoing distantly, and it occurred to him that it might be fogging for mosquitoes in some new manner. A slight tingle and itching of his skin seemed to go along with this explanation, and he returned to the village partially reassured, scratching his exposed skin from time to time, but wondering why anyone should fog for mosquitoes during the dry season.... The possibility that the fall-out and the detonation might be related never occurred to him.

Others in the village had seen the plane, paying little attention to it at the time since planes were not unusual, but with John's explanation, they recalled certain peculiar details of its flight—such as avoidance of clouds—which seemed to indicate that it had been fogging. And they recalled that two frigate birds, high-hovering in mating-play, had taken fright as if from the smell of poisonous mosquito spray, and headed with slow-arcing beat for the horizon. Thus a satisfactory explanation was evolved.

As evening came on the visible fall-out diminished until finally all that remained was a little unnatural luster in the moonlight. And the itching. Almost everyone was scratching. Even as they strummed guitars and sang softly to each other about love and heroism and moonlight, they would scratch without breaking rhythm, smiling about it, though, for it seemed strange that they, instead of the mosquitoes, should have been fogged.

In the morning they were still itching and several of them had weeping eyes. The flakes had become grimy and adherent from sweat, and attempts to wash them off in cold water failed. Everyone felt a little sick and three of them vomited. But no one was seriously ill and no one worried.

In the middle of the morning a plane flew low over the island, and, banking widely, returned to make several more slow passes over it. Someone joked that the crew was probably looking for dead mosquitoes, and they waved listlessly for not even a good joke seemed funny that day. Then, with motors roaring, the plane raced away.

About four hours later a seaplane appeared suddenly from the west, swept the lagoon briefly and splashed to a landing. Men in military uniforms, carrying small box-like instruments, came on shore looking worried. They ignored the welcome as they took rapid readings on their instruments and inspected the necks and scalps of several of the Marshallese—Jimaco was one of these, for she stepped forward boldly for examination as soon as she understood their intent, then in embarrassment at her boldness, combed her hair with furious concentration and sudden bursts of giggling. None of the visitors smoked, and that amazed John who had thought all Americans smoked constantly; and they held their hands at their sides as if they were covered with filth.

After a nervous consultation with each other, the Americans called for the head man and a translator. John came forward with the school-teacher, all the other Rongelapese crowding close behind to watch and listen. He stood very erect, proud of his position as magistrate and waited. A tall, sweating officer, who towered over him and looked uncomfortable, started to reach for a cigarette but changed his mind, then, suddenly in an unnatural, loud voice, said "Now I don't want any of you to get worried." John recoiled from the sudden volume, listened to the school teacher's translation, then smiled and said very softly in Marshallese that they weren't worried. They liked visitors and hoped they would all return frequently with their little boxes.

No, no, that wasn't what the officer meant. Something terrible had happened, and they were all in great danger. They must all leave the island, and a destroyer would come tomorrow to take them to Kwajelein. John looked jarred but replied in the same quiet voice, smiling a little so that no offense could be implied, that they loved their atoll, but, if it were necessary, they would go. He even managed to add, as an after-thought, that they had many friends on Kwajelein.

This seemed too easy for the officer who had expected refusal and hysteria. He began to doubt if he had been thoroughly understood, and in his uncertainty launched into a prolonged discussion of the nature of fall-out, the necessity of decontamination, the chagrin that he, in fact all

Americans, felt for such an unfortunate accident. In his effort to be understood he spoke loudly, repeating the key words many times and rearranging them into untranslatable pigeon-English. John understood none of it except to learn one of his first words in English, the same word that Jimaco and Tina and many of the other Rongelapese learned. This word was *radiation*.

After the Americans left, the adults went into the council house for formal discussion. They understood that they had been ordered to leave the atoll for sake of their own safety, and that it had something to do with this new, very beautiful word they had just learned. But reaction to the order was mixed. Many of them concealed their bewilderment by a show of stoicism; a few became hysterical; most of the older people asserted their right to stick to their land, to take their chances with it just as their ancestors had done for the last thousand years or so—who would take care of their pigs and chickens that wandered freely through the village? Who would chase them out of the houses? A few of the more adventurous, mostly the younger men who were always in opposition to the old people, welcomed it as a fine opportunity for an excursion. (Who cared what happened to the live-stock? It was scrawny and miserable now from lack of attention.) Together they spent hours developing these points of view, those with strong feelings speaking tirelessly and with superb oratory, but, as usual in their council meetings, convincing no one; yet each knew that he would simply follow directions when the destroyer arrived.

That night, the last one on the atoll, was a little better. The itching and nausea were less apparent, and, as they lay on the floors of their houses, close together in the light of smoking kerosene lanterns, the comfort and security of their lives seemed as unchangeable as the surf itself, shuddering and growling at the head-lands.

In the morning, they ate with relish and went to church, Wednesday being a church day. They were in church when the destroyer felt its way through the South Pass and moved cautiously among the coral heads toward the village, anchoring about a mile off-shore in the bright lagoon. Church broke up then, and everyone hurried to the beach, laughing and joking, almost festive as they attempted to arrange themselves into a formal receiving line. Several of them wore perfumed *lei*, and Tina carried one that she hoped to give to the officer in command.

The Americans were in a hurry and took little time for handshaking, but they did seem to be concerned with the welfare of the Rongelapese for the first question was, "Has anyone vomited? Any diarrhea?" But without waiting for answers, "Where are your belongings? We've got to get you off this island."

John said that they had made no preparation for leaving, and that he would call a council meeting so that the elders could decide what each should take.

No, there would be no time for a council meeting. Each one
could carry an armload of possessions.
How about live-stock?
No animals.
Could they take lanterns?
Yes, but they wouldn't need them. Why on earth did they want
to take lanterns anyway?

It was the Rongelap custom. They couldn't go without lanterns. And the prospect of being lanternless on a strange atoll in a strange darkness filled them with uneasiness.

Tina shyly handed the perfumed *lei* to the officer who seemed to be in charge, but he accepted it without comprehension and carried it in his hand; finally gave it to a subordinate, saying "Better check this for radiation."

The Rongelap people went to their houses for their belongings and returned in a few minutes, each with a sleeping mat, a change of clothes, a Bible and a hymnal; each family with a few cooking pots and a lantern. This was all they had expected to take, and, except for the atoll and its weathered huts, a few canoes, and a few miserable pigs and chickens, this represented their entire material wealth…Actually the stipulation of an armload per person had been liberal.

For the next hour a little motor launch shuttled back and forth to the destroyer, cramming it with Rongelapese. Every storage space in the destroyer, every walk-way, every cranny large enough for a sleeping mat became a dormitory. The deck, all hallways, even the deep entrails of the destroyer seethed with sudden village life as excited Rongelapese constantly extended themselves, appropriating this space after that locker room, the mess hall, gun housing—with the ebbing and flowing of ameboid proto-plasm. Individuals grouped and regrouped themselves noisily, hilariously and with an appearance of complete chaos and indecision; yet, actually sifting themselves, family by family and clan by clan, into the strictest of feudalistic social structures wherein subtle distinctions between locker room and deck space were acknowledged according to property rights and blood lines. The members of the crew stepped cautiously and with disgust over them, and said, "It's a mess."

As the destroyer got under way the crew set up decontamination stations on the deck and called the Rongelapese, a few at a time, for close scrutiny and scrubbing. The flakes came off with difficulty, particularly from the scalp, so that oftentimes the hair had to be clipped. There were interminable series of scrubbing, checking with Geiger counters, and more scrubbing.

When the destroyer entered the ocean it began to plunge strangely and unpredictably in the great seas. To these sea-going islanders who knew the buffeting and smack of out-rigger canoes, the slow lurch of the destroyer, its confining walls, and its stagnate spaces seemed unnatural. A few women at first, finally all of the women, began to get seasick. The men smiled indulgently since they believed that Marshallese men are immune to seasickness, but the smell of vomitus, the contagion of misery, and, perhaps, some of the nausea remaining from the previous day finally overcame them, too, and there began a general retching, a general waiting for the next rise and fall of the destroyer, a general self-perpetuation of misery and stench.

But despite sea-sickness, decontamination went on through the night as a few Marshallese at a time, emesis basins in hand, sat under brilliant lights while crewmen searched, monitored, clipped hair and scrubbed. Thus the trip continued to the base at Kwajelein, three hundred nautical miles and many emesis basins south of Rongelap.

The Rongelapese walked giddily onto the dock at Kwajelein, looked apathetically at the noisy activity of the base, and climbed into trucks that shuttled them to long, low barracks. Carpenters were completing improvised partitions as they arrived, and dark-skinned Polynesian porters were making beds, turning the sheets under skillfully according to military standards. The Rongelapese watched them in awe, admiring their deftness and their familiarity with civilized ways. But when the porters had finished and were out of sight, they tried out the beds, bouncing somewhat dubiously on their springs, pressing the mattresses, and inspecting the sheets. "Very fine," they agreed, but they spread their sleeping mats on the floor, and always slept on them, huddled about their kerosene lanterns.

About nine days later, while physicians and scientists from government bureaus and major universities watched the Rongelapese with increasing apprehension, made notes, drew blood, speculated on the dosage of radiation, the first beta burns appeared—first as areas of redness and then as actual ulcers. Sometimes these were excruciatingly painful lesions on the feet, sometimes on the neck where the collar had rubbed, often in the scalp where coconut oil had gummed the fall-out. Lesions were confined almost wholly to adults and older children, and rarely occurred in those younger children who had thought fallout a nuisance and bathed it off. But more alarming, at least to the physicians, were the white blood counts which fell with partially reassuring slowness at first, and then fluctuated erratically and menacingly on the verge of disastrous levels. There were conferences, consultations and arguments about antibiotics and transfusions. Extensive plans were discussed for every conceivable complication; but, just as things looked their worst and before the crises had really gotten much beyond that of laboratory reports, the blood counts began to rise. And it seemed to a score or so of worried scientists and physicians that the most beautiful and exciting thing in the entire Pacific was the phenomenon of a white blood count rising—rising as if preordained, rising inexorably—toward normal. About this time the beta burns began to heal, and the immediate problems of radiation illness faded with them.

The next problems were those of logistics. Rongelap Atoll had become uninhabitable and would remain so for at least several years, and the military barracks at Kwajelein did not yield readily to native village life. So Majuro Atoll, also in the southern Marshalls and the headquarters of the Trust Territory's District office, was selected. Houses were built off to one side of Majuro village, and the Rongelap Islanders moved into them. This solved the problem of housing but confounded the socio-economic situation since Marshallese customs—which are immutable, at least so far as American officials are concerned—had already fixed the ownership of every coconut palm and every breadfruit tree on the island, of every fish in the lagoon. So now the entire Rongelap population was without food or means of obtaining it, and, as a result of this sudden poverty, socially debased. Officials reasoned, cautioned, issued edicts, held conferences, and scratched their heads in dismay, but it made no difference. There was no alternative but to place the entire Rongelap population on dole for an indefinite duration.

At first there was considerable doubt among the officials as to their acceptance of dole. Wouldn't it offend their millennial pride in self-reliance and their dignity? Surely it would be antagonistic to Marshallese customs, and would humiliate the islanders even more than poverty. But they hadn't learned much about Rongelap islanders, who, indeed, agreed that security and sufficiency were desirable states of affairs, even at the cost of self-sufficiency—providing that it required no worry, no planning, and little if any physical effort. Thrift and hard work had no meaning on their atoll in terms of survival (who could make the rains come or the fish run?), and were regarded with suspicion and contempt. In a way, the idea of a dole was merely an extension of nature's bounty, a further evidence that they were well-favored. It had enormous appeal to them; and in the eyes of their envious neighbors, as well as their own, it elevated them to the status of aristocracy. Those who were marriageable, were sought after and married. Distant relatives, who could be recognized as relatives nowhere on earth except here where relationships were unfathomable, moved in. The little colony of 'expatriates' boomed cozily over-crowding its housing facilities as it doubled, trebled and quadrupled its size, riding high on the wonderful innovation of dole. And everyone, except the officials was delighted.

After several years the radiation levels on Rongelap appeared to subside to acceptable levels and Washington officials began to talk of returning the Rongelap people to their home atoll. But the palm-thatched houses had fallen apart by then, and underbrush had taken over. Holmes and Narver, the contractor for the AEC in the Western Pacific, undertook the job of reconstructing the Rongelap village, an exercise in diplomacy and group-process that was astounding.because the AEC, the Trust Territory, the Navy, the Rongelapese, and the contractor each had ideas of what an ideal 20th Century native village should be. The result were houses built high on stilts as in jungle Borneo (although Rongelap houses had been ground-level); constructed of American plywood sides and corrugated metal roofs; equipped with strong ghost-proof shutters and doors; and painted battle-ship gray. There was a seaworthiness about their construction and the way they were anchored in concrete that suggested they could survive a tidal wave. And there was pride about them, for these neat, gray cottages nestling under palm trees seemed to set standards for orderliness and cleanliness that had never before been obtained on any atoll. In addition each house had a modern cistern, well-screened and protected from flies and rats, and a privy that recalled the best days of the WPA privy builders. In the center of the village was a church, charmingly constructed along contemporary architectural lines, although somewhat surprisingly—until one realized there could be no ghosts problem here—having its lower walls completed by chicken wire. It, too, was painted battleship gray.

Evacuation had been simple, but moving back was different. The colony had more than quadrupled in size. It had become affluent, influential and complex. Now it required special handling and ceremony, and hours of conferences and planning. All of the livestock on Rongelap Island had died except one old sow by the name of Bessie which had lived on to achieve local, and even scientific fame of a sort. So new, but equally under-endowed hogs and chickens were purchased at Majuro to replace them. There had been several deaths among the islanders and these bodies had to be exhumed for return to the home burying ground. New out-rigger sailing canoes had to be built, and a 28-foot sloop was bargained for and purchased from the new 'fat' treasury. There were bicycles now and sewing machines, new clothes, supplies of canned goods and pharmaceuticals to be transported. The destroyer that had brought Rongelapese to Majuro Atoll would not do at all for the return trip, for now they required the capacity and loading facilities of a vessel that would have been suitable to move a small army.

In July, 1957, after months of preparation, repatriation was actually accomplished, formally, factually, and ceremonially. A large military landing craft was loaded, the Rongelap Islanders came on board with the entire Majuro population. There was a prolonged church service; the Majuro high school band played a noisy farewell; there were tearful partings; a fearful last-minute rash of indecision as to who were to go and who were to remain; the visitors were shooed off; and the LST, exuding a little of the aura of the Mayflower, headed north for Rongelap.

A professional photographer on board for the contractor, snapped his shutter busily to document this trip which everyone in the Western Pacific regarded as being historic, so now there are more than six hundred photographs of Rongelap repatriation on file in the Holmes and Narver home office. These show the excitement on arrival at Rongelap, the repatriates throwing themselves on the ground to caress their ancestral soil and to offer prayers of thanksgiving; their amazement as they inspected the new houses, the church, the immaculate cisterns brimming with water, the privies (which, incidentally, were never to be desecrated by use); Jimaco posing languorously on the beach with a ukulele and looking like a Hawaii tourist poster.

Then the LST left and Washington officials speculated somewhat fearfully how the Rongelap people would return to primitive, subsistence life, and how they 'caged' on their atoll, would react to bomb-testing that was already scheduled for the next spring.

⊕   ⊕   ⊕

As stated above, the Rongelap people, because of residual soil radiation from the 1954 tests were removed from their atoll and taken to Majuro in the southern Marshall Islands where they lived for four years until 1958. Then, shortly before the 1958 bomb tests that have just been described, they were returned to Rongelap Atoll where they survived another four months of bomb testing. But in 1986 scientific tests showed that radiation, presumably from the 1954 tests, persisted in potentially dangerous quantity in Rongelap soil and at the urging of Green Peace, they were once again evacuated from Rongelap, this time to unpopulated Majatto Island in the Kwajelein Atoll where they have been living ever since, paying a sizable rent for the privilege.

TRIP TO BOMB TESTING

On April 2nd, 1958 I left Raleigh, North Carolina. I took leave from my position in the State Board of Health, tried unsuccessfully to convince my wife and daughter that they didn't really want to go with me, and hoped to high heaven that none of those peculiar people I used to know had been communists, for this was soon after the McCarthy days. Then I took the plane to Washington DC, and I was on the first leg of my trip to the Pacific Proving Grounds for Bomb Testing in the Marshall Islands. In my bag I had my orders—specific, awe-inspiring orders which explained almost nothing. Fortunately, they had left me so bemused and befuddled that I had no difficulty at all in staying well within security regulations, and in so doing had created an agreeable neighborhood myth of mystery and secret mission.

Generally, I knew that I would be in the active United States Public Health Service Reserve with the rank of Commander, a rank that was established on the basis of certain medical attainments, and that seemed very satisfying indeed to one whose previous military experience had been confined to that of private in a broken down National Guard Cavalry unit. It was to startle many persons who expected it to be associated with a 'naval sort of person,' and, I might add as the horizon tilts a little and my 'stomach turns over,' one who never, never would become seasick. I knew that I was going to Rongelap Atoll—wherever and whatever that might be—and that I would have responsibility for the command of the Joint Task Force personnel on the atoll; but I had no idea whether this would consist of a thousand men or just me and the cook—I was inclined to suspect the latter. A sub-topic in my orders conferred on me the authority to imprison personnel, and I was intrigued with the possible diversion of imprisoning the cook from time to time—say between meals—in event there were just the two of us. I knew that I was to have responsibility for medical care on the island, and at times I visualized bright shining wards with alert corpsmen or mission-trained natives, but vacillated also with the image of participating somewhat awkwardly in voodoo dances and circumcision rituals. I knew that I was to be responsible for radiation hazards on the island, but was considerably chilled by an attendant statement that in case radiation from fall-out reached dangerous levels, I (who couldn't swim) and all people on the island should go under water in the lagoon and stay there until a destroyer could rescue us.

Thus tantalized and curious I arrived in Washington, DC about 10 a.m. to begin my tour of duty. There were renewals of old friendships and briefings by Public Health officials. All seemed quite routine except for two developments which suggested that Fate might be taking an unnatural interest in my assignment. I learned that the FBI had not completed its report on me, so that my security status was still unknown; and that somehow I had never been issued an identification card, a procedure which through the magic maze of bureaucracy requires several weeks. So here I was preparing to enter a zone of intense secrecy equipped with little more acceptable identification than the men on the Golden Rule who, I read in the papers, were headed westward across the Pacific, to destroy themselves under a bomb to assert their disapproval of the tests. Since my appearance—which I can do nothing about—suggests a conscientious-objector-type of person, I wondered if we did not have about equally slim chances for getting to the Proving Grounds. The briefing in Washington required only a couple of hours and my plane for Los Angeles did not leave until after midnight. For me, waiting is an ordeal. I can do nothing productive with such time: can't read, won't go to a movie, and I usually end up pacing the floor. So I walked up and down corridors—miles of bitter, hard corridors—retracing my steps so often that office girls came out offering to direct me to my destination; but since they knew even less about Rongelap than I, or so I presumed, I continued my lonely pacing. After dinner, I waited at the airport trying to read a little but still too excited to wait calmly, and I spent most of my time pacing the aisles.

Finally the plane came, and we proceeded non-stop through the night to Los Angeles. It was a pleasant flight, uneventful except for my seat partner, a man in his fifties, obviously a salesman since he spent considerable time memorizing sales talks. Occasionally, though, he would become animated and involve me in conversation. I don't remember what we said, the remarkable thing being the way we said it. He had his larynx removed and now breathed through a tracheotomy tube in his neck. After having had these operative procedures which, of course, deprived him of his larynx for speaking, he had learned to talk by so-called frog-breathing, that is by swallowing air and then forming it into words as he belched it forth; thus he talked on the wings of a controlled burp, sounding, though, more like a frog croaking than like a man belching. Since flying conditions placed him at considerable disadvantage, our first few attempts at conversation were disastrous and provoked the poor man into such agonized coughing attacks that he had to stop and clean out his tracheotomy tube. Finally, I got the hang of it and rounded out my remarks so that he could reply in terse, one-burp sentences. That solved our communication difficulty and we became friends. I admired the man with this tremendous handicap for continuing a pretty nearly normal life, and for working in a competitive field.

At Los Angeles I stood up to deplane and noted a peculiar pain in the calf of my right leg which became more marked as I walked down the ramp and into the terminal. "This," I told myself without conviction, "is surely nothing but a cramp caused by all the walking I had done in hallways" The grotesqueness of having a vascular accident at this time obsessed me. The pain continued to get worse, and when I got on a commercial plane for Hawaii a few hours later, it was with a guilty conscience for misusing tax-payers' money on a purposeless trip. Fortunately, I had no seat companion on that portion of the trip so that with pillows, ingenuity and incredulous looks from other passengers, I managed to get my leg elevated and reasonably comfortable. But my apprehension over it continued during the flight.

Fortunately, this incident was not really important, for the pain gradually subsided over the course of the next few weeks, and finally disappeared altogether when I started swimming regularly and walking many miles over rough, coral beaches. But I have become a little fond and protective of the incident since, in retrospect, it has taken on a new significance: here was a sincere and manly protest of seldom-used muscles against Washington corridors, a parting cry against the architecture and the tensions of our civilization, a sort of ceremonial act of dismay with the flabbiness of our times...and a final shudder.

In Honolulu I left civilian life, and positively and irrevocably assumed my rank which I wore like a misplaced halo. But my transfiguration was not complete, and, for that matter, never did meet the standards of professional warriors. My civilian clothes I would shed at the Proving Grounds, but my look of piety, my appearance of mild bewilderment and imminent seasickness, I was to keep forever. (Sometimes I think I would have done better as a chaplain in Special Services). For the moment both my clothes and appearance were against me and kept publicly contradicting the military orders which I carried with me for sustenance and which I reread frequently with a measure of disbelief and secret pride.

At Hickam Field I went to the Joint Task Force Office, where I, a tired, disheveled person was trying to muster enough gall to get by without identification. There I announced myself as Commander Peck, but the sergeant didn't understand, or perhaps didn't believe my weakly muttered rank, and continued to call me 'mister.' He rifled through his files and found just what he appeared to expect: nothing. He asked to see my identification card, but when I said I had none, he began to quiz me suspiciously. It helped not at all when somehow the subject of my tape recording-dictating device was introduced for, at this point, he ceased looking harried and became marvelously alert, and marvelously supple, too, as simultaneously he tried to reassure me sufficiently so that I would not run away, and at the same time to confide to a major in the next office that he had just uncovered something dark, devious, and smelling of espionage. The major came hastily. With him we discussed the strange coincidence of my having no identification with me or in their files, and the logic of their suspicions began to weigh so heavily that I sneaked a rapid survey of my motives to reassure myself of their purity. Fortunately, at this time another sergeant appeared who remembered filing my name under another category, and I thought to show them my travel orders. These turned the tables, and from that time on the Commander from Headquarters received special consideration: living quarters convenient to the Officers' Club, chauffeuring to Waikiki Beach, special deference in address. Yet I could see them scratching their heads and muttering as they pondered my strange situation.

Once I threw care to the wind and walked over to Pearl Harbor to get skin diving equipment. If I had known there would be a guard at the gate, I wouldn't have gone. As it was I discovered him, or he discovered me, after it was too late to turn back without creating suspicion. So there I was standing in front of a spic-and-span, alert young sailor who was holding out his hand for my identification card, while other pedestrians lined up behind us wondering why I was so slow. In a rush to get the whole thing over I tried to explain in two seconds my entire existence and my reason for being there. He looked frustrated and annoyed and I could see him looking about for reinforcements in case of a sneak attack. But this time I was prepared: in my musette bag I had my travel orders. I reached for them but they were misplaced, and I ended up kneeling in the street as I went over paper by paper. His irritation increased, but finally when I found them and handed them to him, I heard a gasp above me as he jerked violently to attention and salute, aghast at the enormity of the thing he had done. And this was the explanation for the strange sight at the gates of Pearl Harbor on April 4th, 1958 when a superb young seaman stood at rigid, horrified attention over a middle-aged, pious-appearing man who knelt at his feet, fumbling and looking perplexed.

Clerks in the PX also turned out to be a very suspicious lot, and I lived in terror of the power they exerted over my simple needs. When I would finally get up enough courage to buy tooth paste, I knew I would have to undergo a grilling about my identification card, and I would be lucky to get by without the military police being called.

I stayed in Honolulu for three days waiting for a MATS airplane going to the Proving Grounds. It came on April 5th, late Saturday night, a huge, thunderous contraption that shook the terminal as it landed. Departure occurred a little after midnight on April 6th, Easter

Sunday, a day that by prodigy of the International Date Line never was to materialize.

MATS airliners are constructed solely for utilitarian purposes with no interest at all in competing with niceties of commercial overseas airliners such as champagne and hors d'oeuvres. The management makes only one concession, and it can be thoroughly pleasing to only one passenger on each trip. There is a little formality at loading time when the passengers' names are called in order of rank with a suitable pause after the Number One passenger's name to indicate this unusual honor. As you crowd up to the loading gate there is a moment of tenseness and silent prayer while you wait to see where some sergeant has rated you. Since this was my first experience with the gentle ceremony, I was standing at the back of the crowd, looking the wrong direction, when suddenly a woman clerk at the gate shouted triumphantly as if announcing the winner of a raffle, "Number one! Number one is Commander Peck!"

It took me a little while to absorb this information, turn around, and elbow my way through the crowd. By the time I reached her she had already repeated the announcement several times, and she and most of the crowd were looking about for the missing commander. I felt happy that I was about to relieve their concern as I announced, "Here I am." She looked startled, and suspicious as if she thought someone was pulling her leg, and a little hysterically she screamed, "What, you aren't really Commander Peck are you?" I nodded stubbornly and she, a little crushed with this turn of events, said, "Well, I guess you go first."

My lone walk under flood lights with the aura of trumpet flourishes and red carpets, seemed a little flat after that, and I climbed dismally into the cavern of the huge plane. I waited near the entrance for some petite stewardess to lead me to my seat and make me comfortable. But, of course, there was none. The tunnel of the plane stretched far ahead into gloomy shadows and reminded me of a poorly lighted mine shaft. On the walls all types of gear—collapsible boats, ditching equipment, litters—were secured; seats, uncompromisingly for support and not comfort, faced backward. And now, as Number One passenger in this climax of protocol, I was allowed a moment of silent survey to determine which of these seventy seats pleased me the most. Decisions involving infinite possibilities have always bothered me, and this was an especially horrid one, for all the seats were exactly the same. I poked a couple of them but they also felt alike. Surely more experienced travelers would recognize a poor choice of seat, would think that I had squandered my splendid prerogative, and that I should really have been rated passenger number sixty-five. In my despair I chose a seat in the middle of the plane. Then I saw lesser passengers come in one at a time, choosing their seats with care, sometimes in front of me, sometimes behind and sometimes on either side of me, but always with a circumspection that made me feel ashamed of my hasty selection.

The seats on MATS airliners are not as uncomfortable as they appear, their only serious disadvantage being an unfortunate inclination of the seat and an absence of footrest, so that the vibration of the plane sifts you slowly toward the floor. To stop this endless sliding you can lower the back of your seat until you achieve complete stability, but by that time you are lying in the lap of the passenger behind you. You feel him stir uncomfortably, hear him grunt in disgust, and for a moment you are torn in indecision between your comfort and his. The way out of this dilemma—you discover these things very rapidly on a MATS airliner—is to let your seat fall all the way back with a thud, apologize to the agonized passenger for your awkwardness, and raise the seat one millimeter at a time until groans and stirring begin to fade but do not quite disappear. This is the end-point, and once achieved by such careful titration, may be safely and comfortably maintained from Honolulu to Timbuctoo or to any destination you can name.

Soon after our departure and I had time to make these observations and watch my seat companion confirm them on the unfortunate wretch behind him, we settled down to the serious business of flying. A sergeant demonstrated how to get into a life preserver and discussed ditching procedures (a horrid term to contemplate when you are flying three miles above the Pacific); the lights were turned out, and we all went to sleep or lay there thinking about ditching. As we gained altitude it became uncomfortably cool, and I spent much of the night exploring for warmth the several positions you can assume in a MATS airliner seat; but I never could make up my mind whether it is colder on the right side or the left.

We awoke on Monday morning, having crossed the International Date Line in darkness. Easter morning was thus eliminated for me just as certainly and completely as if I had suddenly turned Buddhist.

We arrived in Kwajelein—the largest atoll in the world, and the site of heavy fighting with the Japanese—in time for breakfast. Then, after three rain squalls and a reshuffle of the passenger list, we prepared to board the plane. Again I was Number One on the list, but I was prepared for it and marched smartly to the plane almost before the words were out of the announcer's mouth. As I started up the ramp I heard someone running behind me, and along came a naval officer, panting and perspiring in the unaccustomed heat and in the excitement of his curiosity. He held out his hand and said, "I am Lieutenant Commander so and so, the Number Two passenger on the plane, and I want so much to meet you. Tell me, are you traveling incognito?" I looked about stealthily and stage-whispered, "Let us not speak of it here," pinched his arm significantly, and went into the plane ahead of him to choose a seat with unusual deliberation.

An hour and fifty minutes later we landed on Eniwetok, the true gateway to the Proving Grounds, the final winnowing place for the properly identified from the improperly identified. There we were led into an open shed and told to sit on long wooden benches—like judgment benches—in front of a bank of security officers who seemed reluctant to start the inquisition as they compared folders of information on us, exchanged whispered comments, and seemed uncertain of procedure. Probably they were confounded by reports of my misdeeds in Honolulu such as:

Item One. Tried to buy tooth paste without an ID card.

Item Two. Poses as a Commander so as to obtain honored position on MATS airliners.

Item Three. May be a fugitive from the Golden Rule; harmless; probably not worth investigating; simply return by tramp steamer.

Such terrible thoughts afflicted me as I waited. Finally, when one of the officers assumed a solemn look, cleared his throat and prepared to call a name, I started forward; but it was someone else. Incredible! Just as I had succeeded in catching on to the beautiful, easily-remembered system of my being first, someone changed the system. I sat back and waited while tattooed adventurers, grotesquely bearded construction workers, GIs, Hawaiian mess boys were called ahead of me. It was ridiculously easy for them since they all seemed to be naturally endowed with identification cards; and as I sat there, my apprehension mounting and my cunning oozing, I began to envy the happy lot of an identified dish washer. I was nearly last when a tired officer finally got around to calling my name. By that time I was nervous and jumpy, and this was probably what really saved me, for in a rush of over-powering animation I advanced on him, pushing at him my dog tag, my license to operate a government vehicle, my travel orders, all in such bewildering rotation—and threatening him with a whole sheaf of papers under my arm—that his sole interest became the speedy termination of our interview. Somehow in the excitement of my pushing things at him and his pushing them back at me, we never did get around to the question of my identification card, and I was in. Blessed confusion at the gate.

When the officials had finished with us we followed a sergeant out of the shed into a yard where two trucks were waiting. The sudden warmth from the sky and the glare from the coral gravel enveloped us like headaches, and we hurried to the trucks, pushing each other, sweating and swearing as we attempted to find space in them for ourselves and our gear. But the sergeant was dissatisfied by the commotion and ordered us all out; and then, like a fussy housewife loading a shopping cart, placed us one by one in this truck or the other, sizing and grading us according to some preconceived formula of orderliness, muttering and making notes on a clip-board. When he had finished he seemed pleased with his work: he grinned boyishly at the truck drivers, shouted good-natured obscenities at them, and both trucks lumbered northward up the island on a paved road.

At the end of the island two landing crafts were beached in the fine coral sand of the lagoon waiting for us. Scarcely slowing its speed, our truck rumbled into one of them, bucking noisily over its lowered ramp as the landing craft rose and fell with wave action. The ramp clanged shut after us to form the prow of the scow-like craft, which then backed awkwardly and carefully into the lagoon. Then with sudden, exploding intensity like a Waring blender, the landing craft charged northward, slamming its bulk against the smooth-backed waves. Most of us climbed out of the truck and up onto the deck to watch the spectacle, and we got soaked almost at once as cascades of water hurled at us. We were leaving Eniwetok Island behind in our enormous wake. Off to our right about half a mile was the reef at low tide. On it I could see rusted derelicts of bombed-out vessels, and the lone figures of shell hunters picking their way slowly along the high spots as if in a deserted world. And on all sides was the strange blueness of the lagoon that hurt my eyes with its unfamiliar brightness ...a little heathenish to a North Carolinian who thought all water should look like Pamlico Sound.

Ahead, where the reef broadened, was Parry Island, loaded with buildings, observation towers and radar equipment. As we approached it, the traffic began to thicken and we passed among gray naval craft, widely dispersed at anchor as if prepared for combat operations. We roared along a few yards parallel to the shark net of the bathing beach— a water-skier, cavorting over our wake, waved at us, and we beached with a sudden lurch in the sand of Parry Island, just twenty minutes after leaving Eniwetok Island. I climbed down to the truck that was waiting for us and tried to follow the GIs as they jumped into it, but in the panic of the ramp opening, the truck motor starting, and my muscles failing to respond to simple commands, I lost my momentum and had to be hauled into the truck by GIs.

The truck headed up the island, past the airport, through the 'industrial' section with its warehouses, machine shops, and small ship-yards; then through the residential section of neat tents, metal barracks and a few sickly, transplanted palm trees. Occasionally the truck would stop and a GI or a worker would jump out and go to his tent.

When there was only a handful of us left, the truck stopped in front of the badge office and the driver growled, "All of you who ain't got a badge better get one if you wanna stay on this island." This was something I hadn't foreseen, and I knew what I was in for. These recurring crises, which at first had frightened me so badly, were beginning to interest me like a cloak and dagger story perpetually unfolding, and I joined the end of the line, actually feeling a little curious to find how I would get by this time.

A sergeant checked each man's name against a roster, inspected his identification card, and then issued him a badge that had been prepared by the Security Office. This was an impressive three by four inch placard that contained the to-be-wearer's photograph and a classification of the amount of confidence to which he might be exposed: thus some of the badges proclaimed the bearer as 'confidential', some as 'secret,' and one—issued to the most shifty-eyed of the lot of us—as 'top secret.'

My turn came and the sergeant gasped, when he failed to find my name in his roster, "My god, how did you get here. The damnedest things happen here," he confided to me. "Any day now I'm expecting one of them crazies from the Golden Nugget or Golden Rule, or whatever its lousy name is, to turn up here asking me for a badge. Are you sure you came through Honolulu?"

"Sergeant," I said, and I was pleased to hear myself speaking with authority, "suppose we hurry this on. Have you called anyone at Headquarters yet? Anyone like General Luedecke, for instance?"

He looked at me with new interest and made an automatic motion toward the telephone like one following a hypnotic suggestion—the general's name could do queer things to people on Parry Island—and I was afraid that he might actually call him, so hastily I added, "Well, suppose we hold General Luedecke in reserve and start with Major Griffin.

Fortunately the Major knew vaguely of my coming—or that a person corresponding to my description was supposed to come—and he told the sergeant to issue me a temporary badge that would give me access to the dormitory and dining areas, and he promised to send an officer to escort me and to keep me out of trouble.

A few minutes later Lieutenant Darien arrived, young and eager, and proud of having been selected for a difficult assignment. He approached briskly, stopped suddenly a few feet in front of me, and saluted. I watched him with fascination as he froze in position and remained transfixed while he waited for me to acknowledge him. Self-consciously I looked about to see if anyone was watching and made a stealthy, half-hearted effort at returning the salute.

"Oh, Commander," he said, "I'm afraid that was the Boy Scout salute, at least it wasn't regulation. It is most embarrassing and we simply must change it. I will drill you on your salute later when we are alone."

"I have a jeep outside and will take you to your quarters now, Commander." But when I started to pick up my luggage to follow him, he said hastily, "Oh no! Commanders do not carry luggage." But the sergeant had disappeared and Lieutenant Darien, looking somewhat irritated at this turn of events, carried it to the jeep. As we drove away he said, "I can see, Commander, that it's going to take me quite a while to get you into shape."

"Young man, you appear very knowledgeable," I said, becoming impressed with his sureness.

"How long have you been in uniform?"

"Almost a month now, sir," he said and smiled winningly.

Lieutenant Darien stopped the jeep in front of dormitory 105 and said, "Well, Commander, this is home. This is where most of the men from Headquarters live—the real brass. You are fortunate to have quarters with us for this is the best disciplined dormitory on the island. If you stay here any length of time you will be assigned to a morning clean-up squad, and may even be placed on the social committee, that is, of course, after you get on to the hang of things."

All occupants were away at work and we had the dormitory to ourselves. I carried my gear this time, and followed the Lieutenant through the long central corridor into a four-bed room. Then he returned to Headquarters leaving me to unpack my bag into a metal locker that was heated with an electric bulb to keep out the mold.

Dormitory 105 was identical with other metal ones that were lined up with it like a drill team, a few yards from the surf. It—like the others—had been constructed knowledgeably in the ways of the tropics, for it had double roofs that were separated by an air space. There was an abundance of cross-ventilation, and many of the windows opened from the roof to the floor so that trade-winds, fresh and cool from the surf, washed through without interruption. Halfway down the long corridor the partitions gave way and on one side there was a large club room with comfortable chairs and sofas. On one wall, where one might have expected a library, there was a bar stocked with the bounty of tax-free liquor (gin, $0.95 a fifth; scotch, $2.50) that reached triumphantly toward the ceiling. Across the hallway, sharing the same sweep of ventilation and scenery, were shower stalls and wash basins so that it was possible to drink gin and tonic in the lounge, to shower or perform one's ablutions all in the same intimacy and comfort.

At five o'clock a whistle blew. Shortly thereafter there was a rush of men from the offices, and suddenly the dormitory became a crowded and exciting place. Most of the men were career officers in the Air Force, the Marines or the Army, with a sprinkling of university scientists and USPHS officials. All were friendly and attentive to my comfort: one brought a bottle of gin as a gift and made more space for my clothes in his hot locker; another showed me how to get ice; and someone else handed me a can of beer...and no one, not even the security officer with whom I shared my bedroom, seemed to be concerned over my lack of identification.

The uniforms of the test area consisted of khaki shorts and short-sleeved shirts, a blue, base-ball-type cap, blue anklets and blue sneakers. Lieutenant Darien brought a stack of uniforms to me in the morning, and I dressed in one, placing a silver maple leaf in each lapel of my collar, and the USPHS insignia in my cap. Feeling that at last I was indistinguishable from the warriors around me, I went to the lounge to drink coffee with the security officer.

We were having a pleasant conversation, reminiscing about earlier times when we had both been civilians—many years ago for him and a few hours for me—when I noticed an increasing look of disbelief in him as he focused intently on my collar. Finally, he rubbed his eyes, looked again and said, "Doctor, I do believe that your maple leaves must have been displaced for they are both upside down. Do let me adjust them for you." And he turned the stems of the leaves downward where they belonged, locking them securely in place.

Lieutenant Darien hoped to lose no time in my indoctrination, and after breakfast he took me to Headquarters. This was a compound of metal buildings that were set apart behind a high wire fence with armed guards patrolling the gates—a sort of unapproachable Kafka-heaven, a little seedy and overrun with office workers. The guards checked our badges, admitted Lieutenant Darien but refused to let me enter. The Lieutenant argued with them, but they knew their regulations, argued back with a polite flurry of yes-sirs and no-sirs, and were not persuaded. Finally Lieutenant Darien said he would take the matter up with their superiors and for me to wait at the gate for him. But suddenly overwhelmed by doubts, he turned to the guards with whom he had been arguing and said pleadingly, "Please keep an eye on him for me. He's my responsibility. Don't let him go away."

I stood at the gate feeling forlorn as if I had been consigned to limbo, my tattle-tale, temporary badge flapping pariah-like and worthlessly in the wind. Lesser officers and privates came and went freely, eyeing me with surprise as they saluted. I wondered what mysteries were hidden from me in those metal buildings, and I looked closely at each person emerging from the gate, searching for a clue, but their faces were inscrutable, and all I could imagine was a monstrous teaching model of an atom with flashing lights. Finally Lieutenant Darien came out shaking his head: he would not be able to take me into Headquarters, but he did bring me an unclassified book on the Marshall Islands.

Later in the morning I ventured on my own to walk over to the infirmary, hoping that I could learn from the physician something of the medical and surgical facilities I would have to work with in Rongelap. The infirmary was maintained by Holmes and Narver, the civilian contractors for the Test Area. It was a long, low, rambling building, backed up against the surf, not far from Dormitory 105. There I found Dr. John Medved, a darkly handsome young physician, dressed in white shorts and a short-sleeved shirt, efficient and capable, and a charming host to visiting physicians. I stayed for lunch with him while he instructed me in the maze of administrative channels of Holmes and Narver and the military. The infirmary, I realized was the true, informal center of medical activities for the Test Area, for all visiting physicians learned to come to it for news of the area, for socializing, for obtaining current data on epidemics among the islanders, to get the details of an accident, to celebrate a birthday, to consult on a patient. In a way it was a combination of scientific academy, saloon, and private club, pleasantly presided over by Dr. Medved who never seemed to stop working; and whose work and entertainment merged imperceptibly, for a physician guest usually ended up reading X-rays, holding retractors, listening to a chest, or even working as full-time assistant for several weeks. Since there was a flow of medical specialists through the area, it had become the custom to have medical meetings with lectures as frequently as the supply of specialists would permit. "We thought we should give ourselves a name," said Dr. Medved, "and we tried calling ourselves the Atoll Medical Society. This worked very well until an irreverent member started experimenting with puns and came up with The Asshole Medical Society. In the panic that followed we changed the name to the only safe one we could think of at the moment and now we call ourselves the Eniwetok County Medical Society." Dr. Medved thought that I should learn to know the physicians in the Air Force Hospital over on Eniwetok Island, and cutting neatly across my objections about my badge and Lieutenant Darien's responsibilities, he called the Air Force hospital to arrange for an interview that afternoon, reserved a taxi airplane for me, and sent me to the airport in an ambulance.

A little taxi plane flew between the two islands about every twenty minutes, the actual flight requiring only a few minutes in the air. Nevertheless the dispatcher made me buckle on a life-preserver as I climbed into the plane, and I knew that there had been a death two days before in a somewhat similar flight involving a helicopter. I was the only passenger.

Midway between the two islands the pilot turned to me chattily and said, "This sure is a pile of junk we're flying. We've had this damn lemon for six months and couldn't get it off the ground until three days ago. Never can tell when it'll conk out." I looked far down at the reef awash with incoming tide and forming a sinuous skim of white breakers between the two islands that now seemed dangerously far apart.

An Air Force captain met me at the Eniwetok airport and took me in his jeep to the hospital. Several of us worked for an hour or so over a list of medical supplies that I would need on Rongelap and I promised the captain that I would send him a murex shell from Rongelap. Then, after a short tour about the island, the captain took me back to the airport.

That afternoon after work hours, I was relaxing in the lounge of Dormitory 105 when Dr. Medved called me on the telephone. "Come on up to the infirmary for dinner," he said, "The Eniwetok County Medical Society is going into session. Lieutenant Commander Lanpheer is here and we've persuaded him to give us a lecture on diving medicine. A group of Navy divers will come in after dinner to listen to the lecture." I went to dinner and enjoyed meeting Lieutenant Commander Lanpheer who was in charge of diving medicine in the Navy and a co-author of a book on the subject. After dinner about a dozen young divers, an intense and handsome group of youngsters, joined us. Lieutenant Commander Lanpheer spoke in a scholarly way, shaping his material, however, so that it excited all of us: scientists, practicing physicians and divers. Here are some of the highlights as I remember them:

Anyone who enters a tropical ocean accepts certain risks from the flourishing underwater animal life. Stone fish, hideously ugly little creatures, about 6 to 10 inches long, with absurd underslung jaws, are a serious menace. These shy little horrors merely lie in the sand, partially concealed, and elevate thirteen poison-bearing dorsal spines as their defense against bare-foot aggression. They are mud-colored and difficult to see except when they raise their spines flashing brilliant vermillion colors like warning flags hoisted too late. The poison is intensely toxic, perhaps comparable in danger to the venom of a cobra. The GIs in the area were indoctrinated in a very simple, easily-remembered first-aid procedure for a stone fish sting (I don't want to attribute this to Lieutenant Commander Lanpheer for I may have heard it elsewhere); this was to go to the beach, sit down on the sand, light a cigarette, and wait for death.

There was also a gorgeous turkey fish whose poison spines were on swishing, filamentous tendrils. Its poison was said to be comparably serious to that of the stone fish, but somehow no one seemed to become alarmed over these beauties—perhaps they were rare, or were cleverer in avoiding divers, or more probably, simply charmed one into ignoring their menace.

And there was an array of more obvious hazards such as sharks, barracuda, moray eels, Portuguese-man-of-war, killer clams (monstrous clams up to six feet in length, that could, by responding to simple stimuli rather than evil intent, amputate a hand or a foot). Even coral presented certain hazards, its brittle surface and spines wounding easily and causing prolonged infections. Some coral could cause severe itchy, allergic reactions.

The other risks in diving varied with the type of equipment. If one used only a mask and snorkel and fins (skin-diving), the risk was merely that from animal life in the sea or of simple, uncomplicated drowning, which, as Lieutenant Commander Lanpheer looked at it, was of no scientific interest whatsoever. But if one carried his own compressed air tank, the possibilities of death or injury from all manner of complex and distorted physiological processes asserted themselves most beguilingly to the scientific mind; for instance, 'rapture of the depths' in which a diver becomes drunkenly irresponsible and playfully tears off his partner's mask or hacks at his own air hose. This is a function of pressure, and the depth of a dive can be expressed almost as well in martini-equivalents as in feet or meters.

I watched the young divers as Lieutenant-commander Lanpheer explained to them how their lives might be terminated or crippled abruptly at anytime. And I admired them, for they sat forward on their chairs, breathing deeply, fascinated by the intricate horror of their daily routines. They asked intelligent questions, but these seemed to be peripheral to themselves with no implication of personal threat; and as I watched them I fancied a marvelous jeweled jungle of inexpressible delight, a wild blue-under which was calling to them, offering a moment of ecstasy and transport.

"This is something that I will do," I decided, and after the meeting I approached Lieutenant Commander Lanpheer to ask if he would arrange for me to take diving lessons. "Since I am a very poor swimmer," I pointed out to him, "I will have very few preconceived ideas about the importance of remaining on the surface." "Most certainly I will not do such a thing," he said when he had recovered from his surprise. "I have never dived, and I don't intend that either of us will start now at our ages. The Navy has no intention of contributing to our destruction. Next time listen to what I have to say instead of watching those wild kids."

But I had made up my mind.

After several days of indoctrination I packed my bags and went to Rongelap. A captain in the USPHS and a technician, who was loaded with

Geiger-Mueller counters, made the trip with me. Early in the morning we took a taxi plane across to Eniwetok Island where we boarded an Air Force search-rescue amphibious plane. Crates of vegetables, mailbags, pieces of machinery were being loaded with us, and I had a crate of cabbages for a seat companion. We put on life preservers, and the young pilot came to brief us on the flight. For toilet facilities, he told us, there was a bucket, but who ever used it first must, by the immutable law of this flight, empty it and clean it out on arrival at our destination. He told us what we must expect and what we must do in event of a forced landing at sea: "A landing in the open sea is always a calculated risk," he said; and he showed us how to brace ourselves at the moment of impact, how to transfer to a rubber raft, how to use shark repellent, and how to signal a passing aircraft with a small mirror. Then we buckled on our safety-belts and took off into the clouds that lay heavily about us like wilted blossoms in the sunrise.

The morning came on rapidly and we lumbered along at 3,500 feet, pushing barge-like through a brightening dazzle of cloud banks. White-capped waves, from this elevation, looked like fish scales, and in the distance the ocean and the clouds disappeared in a glare of white haze that hurt my eyes. The air was bumpy and we kept our safety belts buckled most of the time. When the flight sergeant poured coffee for us, he sat down squarely on the floor in front of the canteen so as to steady the brown trickle into the paper cups.

After an hour of flying we looked down on Bikini Atoll: flattened out, map-like and bleak, with a twisted rind of reef and treeless, sea-level islands outlining the lagoon. There was an unnaturalness about it as it stretched out into the haze, a suddenness in the perception of it like an after-image or an apparition—a festival of ruin and terror for this was the atoll that would threaten me, and that in 1954 had destroyed a village and a ship's crew. I looked closely for signs of past violence, mutilated islands or wrecked fleets, but there was nothing of the sort; instead, on several of the larger islands there were several large buildings—one looked like a church—and there were many roads, all looking well-ordered and substantial as in a normal community. There was a New England-kind of tweediness about the atoll, and I got to thinking about Nantucket; and, for a moment, some-what implausibly and dreamily, about engulfed cathedrals and villages and their legends of bell-ringing and pious, orderly habits.

My first view of Rongelap was by way of a radar image: meaningless flecks of light that flashed briefly behind the sweeping arm on the airplane's radar screen where it seemed to be hopelessly distracted by all sorts of climatological disturbances. The navigator proudly pointed out the island masses to me as if he had just spawned them, and then waited for my comment. But each fleeting image that I attempted to identify turned out to be a cloud or a rain squall. A little later we were flying over Rongelap Atoll itself, coming in low over the south-western side, following the path, almost, of the great 1954 atomic cloud. There lay Rongelap Atoll unrolled across the Pacific Ocean, sky-washed and desolate, and stretching out of sight into the haze almost to the sea's edge, where a thin rim of reef and sparse island chain separated the deep blue of the ocean from the turquoise of the lagoon. As we flew along the reef I could see its furrowed sides drop steeply into the transparent water, and swarms of great fish on the ocean side nuzzling its coral growths as if they were breasts. Slowly we followed along the reef, passing over narrow islands, some that supported tattered palm groves and others only coral rubble. There was no evidence of human habitation or activity thus far, only a feeling of immensity and emptiness as in a desert or in outer space, and of vast loneliness.

Then we passed over a break in the reef (which I learned later was the four-mile-wide South Pass, the entry to the lagoon for destroyers and copra boats) and on to Rongelap Island itself. It was a long narrow island like the others, but with drumstick ends that gave enough space for a native village at one end and a small military camp at the other, but constricted to a slither of palm trees through its mid-section. On the near point of the island next to the South Pass, I could see the tiny military camp clinging to a sandy spit of bare beach a little precariously as if on a disputed beach head, with waves breaking only a few yards away. Huge radio towers seemed top-heavy. And at the other end, where the island expanded to the width of a half-mile or so, I could see the gleaming metal roofs of the 1954-destroyed island village that had been reconstituted in the image of US military housing just eighteen months before I came.

Slowly we circled the island testing the wind direction and force, made a long sweep of the lagoon in front of the village, banked, and prepared to drop into the water, flying very slowly and cumbrously, seeming almost to hover. When we struck the water, spray flew up until it cascaded across the windows with such force that the cabin became dark and for a moment it seemed as if we had submerged. Obediently I tried to remember the order of things to do in ditching, felt for my bottle of shark repellent, wondered if I could really signal a plane with my mirror, remembered that no matter what happened I must not panic. But suddenly, as if on another day and in another place, we were floating quietly in the lagoon while crewmen moored the plane to a buoy, threw the doors open to the wash of fresh air and joked quietly with each other in the silence of Rongelap Lagoon, a silence that sounded like my heartbeat.

I released my safety belt and the captain and I went to the door. We were about half a mile from shore, and across the bright choppy waves a small motor boat bucked toward us. In it were two men in over-sized orange life preservers, leaning forward in racing posture and ducking spray as the strong breeze and their slight speed whipped it at them. They brought the boat up to the plane and tried to tie up at the door but it plunged so wildly against the hull of the plane that the pilot came running to protest. The technical sergeant succeeded in jumping into the boat and the three of them held it in appropriate position long enough for the younger boatman to shout to me, "Better make a jump for it, Commander. It's the only way you're ever goin' to make it." I jumped, stumbled against the opposite gunwale and sat down hard on the bottom of the boat.

"My God," said the young boatman. "You jumped like an old woman. We're goin' ta have ta get ya over that, Commander. We'll make a man out of ya on this island." And he grinned happily as he helped me to a seat as if I were his great aunt.

Then the captain jumped in, someone tossed my luggage and the mailbags into the boat, and we shoved off. I sat in the front between the two boatmen. Waves sloshed me in the face and soaked my shirt. Over the roar of the little motor, we tried to carry on a conversation. The younger boatman, who was steering, said, "I'm Bill Bailey, the assistant camp manager. I'm real glad ta see ya. An' that's Doc Farrington, the camp manager, sitting on the other side of ya. He don't talk much so ya'll probably never know if he's glad ta see ya or not. That right, Doc Farrington?"

"Uh," said Doc Farrington looking self-conscious and a little coy as he got busy bailing.

"We work for Holmes and Narver and not the military," said Bill Bailey, "an' that's the reason we c'n run around almost naked like this, even when we're meeting planes. Ya oughta see the real brass—not just commanders an' captains, I mean the real brass like admirals and generals—ya oughta see them when we go running around like this in front of them. They almost has cats, an' write memos and SOPs an' all that crap. But nothin happens. Ain't that right, Doc.?"

"Ya," said Doc and he looked very pleased with his performance.

Doc was in his early fifties, tough looking and sinewy, heavily tattooed over his arms and torso, burned as brown as a coconut husk, and silent. I watched him intently and wondered if this was a tower of strength or an idiot. But he gave me little material for decision because he just sat there bailing the slosh out of the boat and occasionally spitting a torrent of tobacco juice into the spray. Only once did he show interest when he leaned toward me and said, "See here, on this island they all call me Doc and you're a doctor. We got a real problem about this. Now here's how it puts it. Which one gets called Doc?"...."You do," I said with relief.

A small motor boat passed us heading for the plane. "It's goin' after the freight, an' the fresh fruit," Bill Bailey explained, looking after it a little hungrily.

We were approaching the beach in front of the village. Great palm trees came down to the water's edge, leaning perilously over the water, their fronds waving wildly. (They were like one-legged flag-wavers leaning out to welcome us, and probably hired flag-wavers at that for there was a professional crassness in the way they went about it). And back under the trees on the sand beach we could see little knots of islanders sitting about as if in a tableaux, scarcely aware of our exciting activities in the waves or of the pandemonium of the palms, as they talked to each other, mostly looking in the opposite direction as we came nearer. Other details of the beach were becoming clearer: outrigger canoes, delicately contoured and painted, their masts slanting forward, were drawn up in windrows on the sand, and there was a good-sized sloop anchored just off-shore. Back of the beach itself, were shacks of corrugated metal, some of them obviously improvised from scrap materials, and pieced by bits of plywood, cardboard or thatch— "A far cry," I thought, "from the AEC-dream-village that I thought I was coming to." And from the water-front came a strong odor of rotting fish and a strange, heady sweetness that later I learned to identify as the odor of copra.

We beached the boat at water's edge, jumped out into ankle-deep water and struggled to heave the boat up on the sand. But suddenly many dusky young men replaced us on either side of the boat and without apparent effort slid it beyond the grasp of the tide, then, without a single wasted motion, transferred my gear and mail bags to the rear of a quarter-ton weapons carrier. All this was done quietly as if under strict orders, but at that point, all changed, for then, suddenly jostling and laughing, they skipped a few feet to shore to form a formal receiving line with villagers who had been waiting for us in the shade, all neatly arranged by age, the solemn old men up front; giggling, wriggling children in the rear. For a moment they looked toward us as if we were expected to formally announce our arrival, but when we failed, someone strummed a chord on a guitar and they all broke into an ecstatic version of "When It's Springtime in the Rockies," though the words got changed into "Wan da sprangtim indo rockies," repeated over and over.

The captain, who outranked me, went first through the line. He had done this before and knew just how to do it so he moved along briskly as if riding on an escalator, presumably saying all the proper things. A girl tried to hand him a *lei* but he didn't see it in his haste to get into the shade.

I started through the line trying hard to please, but forgot my instructions, and, to my surprise, heard myself saying *"wie gehts,"* hastily changing it to *"Bon jour, monsieur,* or no I mean *yokwe yok." "Hello-goombye,"* replied an islander looking perplexed as he gave my hand a limp, discouraged shake.

One of the men, a muscular little fellow, muttered "I who is John" so softly that it didn't attract my attention, and I realized only later that this must have been the magistrate who had figured so prominently in the fall-out catastrophe. A pretty girl handed me a *lei.* "Are you Jimaco?" I asked brightly, remembering a story that I had heard regarding a girl by that name who had handed a *lei* to a naval officer as he was evacuating the islanders after the 1954 fall-out, but she hid her face behind a companion, giggled wildly, then fled up the beach, leaving a trail of tinkling laughter among the pebbles.

Then, when I had shaken the last hand, the receiving line suddenly disappeared and we were left nearly alone on the beach.

"Hey there, ya in the weapons-carrier! Can ya drive that damn pile of junk," yelled Bill Bailey at a young GI who was sprawled out half-asleep on the front seat.

"Ya talkin' ta me? Sure I c'n drive this or anything else—that is, if ya'll start it fer me, an' if it'll keep agoin'"

"Well, Commander, I got a top-notch chauffeur for ya. He c'n take ya, an' the captain an' that other guy down ta the camp while Doc an' me finish up with the freight."

The captain showed the GI how to start the weapon's-carrier and we started off with a sudden lurch—backwards. Doc and Bill Bailey shouting obscenities as they jumped out of the way. We stopped. The captain and the GI discussed the possibilities of various gear shifts and we started forward very slowly, creeping through the village in low gear, the motor roaring wide-open.

"Always did like ta drive," said the GI leaning back contentedly. "Drove a tractor onc't in Arkansas," and he started to whistle a merry little tune, so heady was he with his assignment and the roar of the powerful motor.

We left the harbor area and its make-shift structures, and entered the official village of Rongelap. It was laid out along the lagoon as a string of military-conceived houses on each side of the jeep trail, and it gave the appearance of a discarded mock-up from a movie about the Navy, for the houses were painted battle-ship gray, and were as uniform as torpedo boats. Each one was a one-room, square box with a porch in front, standing high on sturdy stilts as in a dry dock. The windows were open with no glass nor screen but there were heavy shutters that could be closed. And beside each house was a cistern, a privy and a screened cook-house just as ordained by some joint-planning committee ("Our analysis shows beyond the shadow of a doubt that the modern family on Rongelap requires a house on stilts, a cistern, a cook-house and a privy, all painted battle-ship gray.") But the committee could hardly have foreseen the furious sense of occupancy or the flare for improvisation that Rongelap Islanders would bring with them; for here exposed to the tropical sun, snatched, as it were, from the context of committee-room discussions and sociological explanations, here in its final exposition lay the village, good naturedly converted into a pleasant slum and practically purified from theoretical considerations. Certainly there was over-crowding, for oftentimes—or so it seemed from the heads that protruded from windows and doors, that several families lived in any one house, while another lived underneath on the ground, air-conditioned, as it were, in the dense shade. When I commented on the under-house dwellers, the GI said, "Yes, those are the lucky ones. The tin roofs are hot as hell an' no one wants to live upstairs, so they just go walkin' around below, stoopin' an' knockin' their goddamn heads on the beams under the house an' thinkin' how they out-smarted the people upstairs."

And most assuredly the village was untidy, for beer cans and Coca-Cola cans—probably a complete tally of the cans consumed since repatriation—were scattered over the white coral gravel, filling in the depressions and banked against the cisterns like snow drifts.

Physically it was as drab as a West Virginia mining town, although actually it wasn't drab at all once

Severe irradiation of Rongelap in 1954 forced evacuation of every human being so there were none present to repair the usual recurrent storm damage to their palm-thatched homes. Consequently, all homes were destroyed. Before the Rongalapese could be returned to their island, it was necessary for the military, a few months before I arrived in 1958, to design and build the kind of houses it thought were proper: tin-roofed, slat-sided houses that were supported on four-foot stilts, painted battle-ship gray, and very hot.

one got the committee-complex out of one's mind, for there was a lushness in
the way men sprawled in the shade while they idled over their nets or looked
gently out at the lagoon, nodding solemnly to us as if they had already forgotten their splendid receiving-line introduction of a few minutes past; and there
was tenderness in the way mothers nursed their infants in the doorways and
smiled at us vaguely as we passed.

I wanted to make a favorable comment about the village, to find a
valid public health basis for my feeling of interest and delight in these people,
so I said, "Surely the privies and the cook houses must have brought new
concepts of sanitation to these people."

"That's a good one," said the GI. "They ain't brought nuthin' but a
few more flies. Not a damn one of them has used a privy for a privy. You
know what they use 'em for? They use 'em to store breadfruit and coconuts.
An' cook houses! My god, they use 'em to pen-up their chickens or pigs.
Sanitation—that's a laugh."

We moved slowly and triumphantly through the village, our motor's
roar preceding us like a brass band. Naked children hearing our commotion ran from the street and climbed palm trees or the high porch railings
to wave at us and scream 'halloo-goombye'. Scrawny old sows with their
pigs jumped up from wallows in the street, snorting in disbelief as they
waddled away.

"Lots of traffic," said the GI. "Ya gotta watch out when you drive
through here. The Sarge knocked down a palm tree the other day an' it cost
him twenty-five bucks. Sure do have ta be careful, all them kids an' sows an'
things, an onc't in a while a bicycle."

The jeep-trail left the village, dipped through a deep pool of muddy
water, U-turned several times to avoid palm trees, then headed down the
narrow island through its central tangle of underbrush and jungle. Palm
fronds hung low over us and shrubby trees walled us in, holding the heat
motionless and dripping about us, enfolding us in its moisture—almost
womb-like. The four hot sticky miles to the camp seemed incredibly long
as the GI wheeled us in low gear over the jagged coral trail. When we came
to a barren section of the island where the jungle had been bulldozed off to
one side in one long ridge of tree trunks and coral boulders, the captain
asked, "What's this?"

"I dunno," replied the GI, "the natives jabber something about it being radiation, whatever that is. They think everything on this island is radiation, even coconut crabs. They're spooky about it just like they're spooky
about ghosts."

"I guess the A.E.C. must have had to clean out a radio-active hot
spot," said the captain, summing it up.

After several miles we came to a clearing where there were four or five A.E.C.-constructed homes. "Jabwon Village," said the GI "Native by name of Nelson lords it over the rest of 'em, a sort of boss-man or king or chief or somethin."

There were several more minutes of humid jungle on the bull-dozer gashed road, then, just as the heat and the closeness and the insects and the jouncing were beginning to seem like the normal way of life on Rongelap, then, without warning we came to the end of the island and out onto the bare tip of white coral gravel where military camp buildings and tents clung to the beach.

The truck lurched out of the track it had been following and buried its front wheels in a bank of sand with an impact that sent us against the windshield, and the motor stalled. Temporarily the truck seemed to be stuck, but the GI, ignoring the mishap and hoping that we had not noticed it, said cheerily, "Well, this is it men. This is our happy home. Hop out an' make yourselves comfortable. It's almost chow time."

It was an orderly camp, immaculate enough to be disconcerting to one who could never keep his desk tidily arranged. There were three dormitory structures, two being tents and one a frame building made with plywood sides and a shining metal roof. There was a small radio shack, a large machine shed, and a water-tower, tall enough and impressive enough for a moderate-sized village. It was all planned and laid out precisely with little paths, that were outlined by dying transplanted seedling palm trees, connecting the buildings. Off to one side were many oil drums, carefully piled on one another so that they could almost have been mistaken for hedge rows in a formal garden. Then on the very point of the island, just beyond the buildings, I could see several large trucks bearing great radar antennae that pointed westward. And beside them were cameras on tripods, hooded like falcons, and also pointing westward across the South Pass.... The polarity of Rongelap, it was easy to see, was oriented to the west—even the trade winds blew steadily toward the west.

The GI led us into camp, disengaging himself from the intimacy of the truck-trip as we progressed, and by the time we reached the metal dormitory, he seemed to be a stranger who merely nodded to us in slight recognition, and left us at the door.

"I am Sergeant Bascomb," said an alert young airman who opened the door for us. "Sorry I couldn't meet the plane but some dispatches were coming in. Your quarters are in this building, Commander; in fact there are a lot of things in this building for we are quite crowded. Step in and I'll show you about."

We were standing in the small dining room which served also as a hallway to the other rooms and which were separated from it by partial partitions; thus, doors led from it to the decoding and weather charting rooms, the kitchen, a shower room and toilet, and to the dormitory. "It's crowded," he said, "but just in case you don't like to move around much you've got it made, and you won't have to go more than 12 feet in any direction from where we are standing to take care of everything. Now, if you had a periscope you could tell which cook is slamming the icebox door, who is shaving, and who is wasting water by running that shower full blast."

We went through a door into the dormitory that was crowded with eight beds. "Not much privacy here but it's all we got and it's better than in the tents. You'll have a hot locker to yourself and a little extra space up at this end for storing your equipment."

There was a certain gaiety about the dormitory for brightly colored handicraft—baskets, handbags, fans, place mats—were strung on wires over some of the beds; there were gleaming sea-shells lying on the window ledges; and *Playboy* magazine pin-ups covered the walls.

This was military headquarters on Rongelap where I lived and "officiated" as commander for four months of bomb testing.

Several men sat on their beds, yawning and scratching from a morning's nap, and the sergeant, ignoring their slight confusion, introduced us. One was a civilian— "He's working on a project that's so highly classified that I'm not even supposed to know that he's here," said the sergeant. I felt a momentary impulse to turn my head and pretend that I hadn't seen him but the civilian hastily reassured me, "Oh, it's O.K.—you won't get any secrets out of me since I haven't the remotest idea what I'm here for or what I'm doing. All I do is turn dials, read meters and make reports."

Then, on the other side of the partition, the cooks started a chant of 'Chow time, ya lazy bastards, chow time," and we went to dinner.

"We got the best god-damned food in the whole god-damned Test Area," every GI whom we met told us solemnly as if he were taking a loyalty oath. And perhaps each one was, for the cooks stood in the kitchen door, listening to each one's uniform comment and nodding eagerly; sometimes nodding and smiling in anticipation of the comment that was sure to follow.

There were thirty-some men in the camp: five Holmes and Narver maintenance men (Doc and Bill Bailey and three cooks), five GIs who operated and maintained the radio, three GIs who operated the weather station; and the rest were GI and civilian technicians who were assigned to various classified projects. They were a sun-burned, tattooed, rough-looking crew, dressed in the bare rudiments of military uniform, and with heavy concessions made toward nudity. They could have passed for a crew of construction workers, a camp of convicts or, say, for a group of university scientists on a National Geographic field trip. All were veterans of other foreign assignments—even the young GIs had spent time in Japan or Okinawa before coming—and the adventure of being stranded on a 'South Sea' island impressed them not at all.

"The sooner we c'n get off this god-damn, lousy island the better we'll like it," each GI told us as if reciting an article of faith.

"Our morale's bad," said a young GI speaking authoritatively.

"Yes," said another pushing his way eagerly toward us, "someone ought to do somethin' about our morale; that's our problem, an' no women or nothin'."

Suddenly we were in the middle of a mass meeting as GIs crowded about us, presenting us—enthusiastically, picturesquely, even imaginatively—their claims of boredom. "It's like this," said an undersized GI whose face was scarred with acne, "I came here from Japan, an' all I do is keep thinkin' about them wonderful whore houses back there—just a thinkin' an' dreamin' an' rememberin', an' feelin' sad 'cause I hear they're closin' them. It's real tough bein' here an' bein' young."

"We got movies at night," said another, 'but they don' seem ta help our morale as much as they oughta."

"No, an' volley ball don' help either," added an athletic-looking GI.

"Nor fishin'."

"Nor takin' the boat out."

"Nor playin' poker."

"We talk a lot about our morale," said a fat, sulky looking GI, "an' try ta decide what someone oughta do about it; gets real interestin' at times; but we don' dare gripe too much or they'll send us to Johnson Island, which is even worse."

"Guess it's about time we have another picnic for 'em," said Doc Farrington, looking embarrassed. "Food's about the only thing that seems ta pick 'em up."

For a moment I fondled the image of an efficient house mother bringing calm and peace—as house mothers do—to Rongelap. Later, when we were alone, the sergeant brought up the subject of morale. "It's funny, he said looking perplexed, "but after listening to those guys gripe like that, I get the feeling that their morale is pretty darned good in spite of what they say, and I go to bed or off to the other end of the island knowing that all my orders will be carried out. Actually we've got a pretty good camp here and not a single one of them has caused us any trouble. Of course I have to close my eyes to a lot of things such as their running around half naked and getting a little high on beer. No one ever salutes out here, but everyone means to be polite."

After lunch, while the technician worked on the radiological equipment and the GIs returned to work or went fishing, the captain and Sergeant Bascomb and I walked out to the point. As we approached it, a cloud passed over us casting a heavy shadow and turning the ocean into lead. We stood on the point and felt its gloomy excitement and its portents. Behind us were the radar antennae and the cameras, and in front of us was the startling turbulence of the South Pass, for here the great ocean swells, arching broadbacked, sullen as lead and heavy as concrete, struck head-on the rushing lagoon current, meeting in loud claps of thunder. Geyser-columns of water and foam shot into the air, then collapsed in downward sucking currents, whirlpools, back eddies, and small right angle waves that broke across the narrow reef to die at our feet, hissing in the sand.

Across the four-mile-wide Pass due west from us, was Arbar Island, low-lying like our own side of the atoll. The captain pointed in its direction and said, "There is Bikini," Of course I knew that he was pointing across Arbar Island on to the area 100 miles away where Bikini was actually located, but emotionally I confused the identification, and always believed subconsciously that this flat shadow, this threatening blur of fuzzed palm trees, just four miles away, was Bikini.

"You'll have a ring-side seat when the bombing starts," he continued enthusiastically, and I felt ill as I visualized Arbar Island vaporizing and crisping beneath a gigantic fireball that filled the western sky and scorched me as I tried to watch it and record the results. "You may get shaken up a little," he said, not noticing that I was already trembling and as shaken as I was apt to become. "You're certainly the lucky one. The other fellows are all envious of your being up front like this." I couldn't answer, for I was thinking of my wife and daughter and feeling guilty that I hadn't gotten some additional life insurance before coming.

A little while later the captain felt that my introduction to Rongelap Atoll was complete. He and the technician told me good-by and left for the plane. And I was left alone.

After supper I arranged a small desk beside my bed, placed some notes and the camp log on it and sat there leafing through the pages, making motions of study, learning little, hoping that no one would speak to me, but knowing in my nervousness, in the beat of my pulse, and the horror with which I contemplated my activities, that I shouldn't have come to Rongelap.

RONGELAP: FIRST DAY

When I awoke the morning was softly blue and white with a trace of sunrise still folded among its shadows. This was to be my first full day on Rongelap and from my bed I looked through the screened door at the lagoon, brimming at full tide and only a few yards away, its surface wrinkled by little waves and white caps, lively as it lapped almost to our door. The cooks were banging pans and singing in the kitchen, and the GIs joked with each other as they ran their electric razors and flushed the toilets in the next cubicle. I had slept well, my gloom of the previous evening had disappeared, and I felt eager to get started as I joined the GIs in their ritual of shaving and toilet flushing.

Breakfast was mid-western farm style with fruit, cereal, hot cakes, eggs, bacon, and lots of coffee. And we prolonged it with a sort of lonely-male comradeship and tenderness as we listened to news reports from the Kwajelein radio station or made sly little jokes about food and the joys of over-eating. One GI was depressed, and a little proud at the same time, as he recounted the fact that a casual girl-friend from the States had written that he had gotten her pregnant, and that he must do something about it… "By God, she must be as big as a house by now," he said, his eyes popping at the magnitude of his achievement. "But I'm just a young guy," he lamented, his mood suddenly changing, "an' it jus' ain't fair to happen so soon. It wasn't fun either cause she was a silly, cross-eyed little thing an' scared to death, an' I was half drunk an' couldn't feel nothin', an' we did it in a back alley on a pile of tin cans. It jus' ain't right ta make me marry her when it happened like that." So everyone joked him about shot-gun weddings, income tax deductions, and his manhood. This brightened him up so that he told the story over again several times in ways that emphasized his masculinity, and that dimly implied many other rich and varied affairs that, if believed and reconstructed chronologically, must surely have stretched back into infancy…It was a fine time of day to sit and talk and boast.

After breakfast I returned to the dormitory. The first-aid kit confronted me on the wall and insistently demanded that I inspect it. I had seen it the night before, had noted its questioning look but had put off its inspection. Now we were together and alone and I knew that we must come to an understanding. Reluctantly I opened its rusty door, fearful of the truth that must surely be revealed, for out of its contents I was to practice medicine and establish my reputation on Rongelap—that is until the supplies would arrive from Eniwetok. And there, staring me in the face in two neat, impoverished rows, was my pharmacopeia. There were band-aids, a bottle of iodine, a bottle of mercurochrome, a bottle of rhubarb and soda, a bottle of eye-wash, and some aspirin. And that was all. I felt a trace of panic, but hastily reassured myself that the GIs looked intensely healthy with their youth and their glowing suntans. Yet I wondered how I would treat a shark bite.

I had the contents of the kit spread out on a table, glowering at them resentfully, when I turned and found a handsome young islander watching me.

"Whatcha doin', whatcha doing'?" he asked. "Ver' interestin' whatcha doin'."

"Oh I'm looking at the first-aid kit."

"Tha's fine. Fine 'Merican medicine. Better'n Marshallese medicine. Dumb Marshallese don' have nuttin'."

"I am Dr. Peck. Who are you?"

"I Ahab. I translator. Ver' important translator for village. I get educate an' translate for dumb Marshallese. Everyone know Ahab smart. Everyone know Ahab good fellow."

"Well, I'm certainly glad to know you, and, no doubt, I'll be asking you to translate for me."

Ahab fondled the compliment and stood in silent bliss hoping for more. After a time he became interested in the first-aid kit, and handled each item with ostentatious respect, and, as I turned my back slightly, slipped two bandaids into his pocket. Then suddenly recalling the purpose of his visit he said, "Oh yes, what I come for. Sick man in village, ver' sick, goin' ta die. Everyone waitin' for ya ta come an' mak' 'im well. Village don' wan' im ta die."

"Yes, I'll be glad to see what I can do for him," I said, feeling helpless as I looked at the aspirin and eyewash.

"Great hurry," said Ahab, "very emergency. I tell Doc get weapons-carrier for ya in hurry." And he sauntered slowly out of the room pausing beside my bed to look at the pile of radiological equipment and to pocket a discarded battery.

As we roared past the Jabwoan houses, Ahab suddenly said, "Stop here."

"What the hell for?" demanded Doc. "Thought we was in a hurry."

"Big hurry all right. Gotta take peple. Peple gotta go see sick man. Marshallese custom, all in hurry, all excite."

"They'd better be faster than usual," grumped Doc as he leaned back in his seat pessimistically.

The houses were in a palm grove about half a block from the road, and we could see great activity about them. Occasionally a woman would run from one house to another, voices screamed at one another; once a woman carrying a basket and followed by three children started to run toward us, then turned and ran back into a house; two teen-age girls started to walk slowly toward us but stopped halfway and began to laugh so heartily that they sat down, their backs toward us, rocking in merriment. Doc honked the horn disgustedly.

"Everyone in big hurry," said Ahab as he assessed the excitement with approval.

Finally they came; several men in the lead, silent and unmoved, then the women carrying baskets and bundles and shouting harshly at the children who wavered behind them; the two laughing girls, like well-trained sheep dogs joining in behind to herd the children in the direction of the truck. Slowly they advanced, these proud, distracted nomads, going straight to the rear of the truck, scarcely acknowledging us, though Ahab kept calling attention to himself sitting with us in the front seat.

First, the men got onto the deck of the weapons-carrier, swinging themselves up easily like athletes and sat down, abstracting themselves from the activities of the others as they watched the sharp-cut horizon of the lagoon, or scratched their bare toes. Then the women tossed their burdens up on to the deck and climbed up after them, laughing and shouting gamely at their awkwardness, falling backwards and starting over again, pushing and pulling each other, sometimes helping and sometimes interfering. Then the children swarmed pirate-wise over the high sides of the weapons-carrier, looking pleased with themselves for having done it the hard way.

"They ver' fast," said Ahab with elation. "All wanna see man bafore he die. All set now! All aboard! Let's go fast!" And lowering his voice so the other islanders couldn't hear him, appearing shocked and proud as he stammered thinly, "Go fast, go fast like ...goddam ...pissin' hell!"

"Tell 'em ta hang on," growled Doc as he crouched behind the wheel. The loaded weapons-carrier crashed into top speed as through a sound barrier and Doc threaded it unerringly through the ruts, dodging large rocks and tree trunks. It jarred springlessly over the rough coral track, skidded about turns, bucked over small obstructions. I held on, bracing myself against the dashboard and clenching my teeth so I wouldn't bite my tongue. Once I looked back and saw our passengers hanging on to each other with delight, the baskets sliding wildly from side to side, and at each perilous turn there were screams of encouragement and thrill.

We slowed down when we entered the village, diminishing our speed progressively as sows and children increased in the roadway. Those in the back of the weapons-carrier waved and shouted to those who were sitting in the shade of their houses, and carried on a running banter with them, exploiting their momentary social ascent as truck passengers and associators of the new technology. Ahab nodded constantly to the right and to the left, pointing proudly at himself. Several times he shook my hand, and when conditions permitted, he made little speeches that sounded strangely political. Slowly the villagers left their houses and followed us, some of them carrying baskets of food or bouquets of worn-out paper flowers. Once two naked children ran toward us yelling, "Doc, Doc, halloo-goombye," and Doc stopped the weapons-carrier while they climbed up on his lap and grasped the steering wheel in pretense of driving.

"What are all these people doing? What's all this commotion?" I asked Ahab.

"Oh, dey wanna see ya cure sick man. Witch doctor, medicine man and health aid all give 'im up. But 'Merican medicine cure 'im fast. Dey know dat. Dey come to watch."

"Oh," I said, clutching my bottle of aspirin and dimly beginning to perceive the heroic role that I was expected to play.

In the center of the village was the public area. On the left of the road, next to the lagoon, was the burying ground that was ornamented with rough-hewn coral slabs and many rows of neatly-placed Coca-Cola cans; and on the right were the council house, the school house, and the dispensary—as attractive and compact a municipal center as one could desire, for here the palm trees towered with particular majesty and cast pleasant shade so that people lounged about the big village cistern as they drank water from coconut half-shells and waited for me.

"Jaruleij!" a woman called harshly as we stopped, and a barefoot man came out of the infirmary, waddling with the gait of one who has congenitally dislocated hips, smiling, his hand outstretched.

"I who is Jaruleij, health aide," he said. This was the man I would work with in the village, and I looked at him closely. He was dressed shabbily in faded blue jeans; his bare feet were short, broad and prehensile from clasping the trunks of palm trees; there was a heavy primitive coarseness about his face (My nurse, my hospital staff, my dream of efficient, missionary-trained attendants or bright corpsmen! My God!) But there was simplicity and strength and kindliness about him that made me think of Mother Earth, and I felt that I liked him.

"Man sick. Need doctah bad. Come." And he led the way, waddling through the dispensary door, shooing the flies and children out of the way as we advanced through a dirty little waiting room and office, through another door, and into the 'ward.' The ward had two beds in it. In the first one lay a young woman who hid her face with a sheet and groaned softly. "Dysmenorrhea," said Jaruleij (but later I found that she was aborting) and in the other bed, behind a curtain, lay the sick man.

He lay directly on the mattress, his trousers on, and a sheet partially covering him. Two women stood by him, one with a fan and the other with a bowl of soup. It was hot here behind the curtain. The low bed lay below the level of the window, and as I bent over the patient I felt the heat and moisture well-up from him and smelled the stagnant scent of sweat and spilled food, and the heavy fetor that is associated with death. He was a heavy-set man, about thirty-five years old, who lay there breathing heavily—so intent on his discomfort that he barely acknowledged my presence. Small, clear vesicles covered his skin and when I examined him I found that these extended onto the palms of his hands, the soles of his feet and throughout his mouth and pharynx. His skin seemed to burn my hand. ("Temperature 105," said Jaruleij). When I listened to his chest I heard the sounds of pneumonia in both lungs. He grunted with pain when he breathed.

This was my first patient on Rongelap, and I stood there in bewilderment. The villagers had crowded in behind me, others looked in at the window, all watching me expectantly. I could hear my actions being relayed, my apparent decisions and reactions interpreted to those who were further back. They were respectful, intent and a little bit impatient—like a crowd at Lourdes—as they waited for me to do what I was supposed to do and perform a miracle of modern medicine. I had never seen a patient like this before and with no laboratory, no reference library, no memory for similar conditions, I knew that I had little likelihood of making a diagnosis. Was this the first case in an epidemic? Would there be a dozen or two dozen such cases on my hands when the bombing started? How would I ever be able to evacuate the island if half of the people were like this? How could we go into the lagoon for protection from fall-out if we were overwhelmed by pneumonia? And more immediately pressing: how should I treat this man when I had no diagnosis, and worse, when I had only band-aids and aspirin and eye wash and rhubarb and soda in my medical kit?

"This will take a little thought," I said to Jaruleij, and I went into the office and sat down disconsolately at the desk. "Doctah thinkin'. Ver' impor-

tant ta let 'im think," said Jaruleij as he shooed the villagers back from my desk
a few feet, but children continued to break through his barrier; one experi-
mented with the hair on my legs and another climbed up into my lap. I was
scarcely aware of these intrusions as I sat at the desk, sweating nervously, doo-
dling on a piece of paper and blotching it with my sweaty hand as I tried to
make sense out of a forlorn situation. Obviously I should try to get this patient
off the island and to a hospital, and I started reviewing the medical facilities of
the Test Area, and possible ways for communicating with them.

But just then there was a miracle—not the curative miracle that the
islanders had been waiting for, and probably not a very significant miracle
as compared to those that have been 'documented' in the past, but nevertheless as bona fide a miracle as a distraught physician on Rongelap could
have wished for; for there was a sudden roar of a plane overhead, and a few
moments later a dark, amphibious plane was landing in the lagoon.

"What's this?" I asked Jaruleij.

"Navy plane," he said. " We not take chance on new doctah: we radio
Majuro last night."

"Radio?" I said, "Where in heavens did you get a radio?"

"Got one in Council House, crank 'im up an' talk to Majuro when we
want sumpin'."

A handsome young surgeon in nylon flight coveralls came ashore with
a nurse and a Marshallese interpreter. He was brisk and authoritative, and
seemed to be very well oriented as he looked about and spoke familiarly to
the islanders.

"I hope you are an expert on tropical diseases," I said.

"I'm afraid not," he replied, losing some of his composure. "This is
the first time I've been off Navy base."

I took him to the patient, and with the help of the translator he examined him. He found that the patient had presumably been seriously ill
with hepatitis a few months earlier when an epidemic had involved the
area, but otherwise he was baffled by this syndrome of peculiar skin erup-
tion, fever and pneumonia. "Never saw anything like it," he said. "What do
you make of it?"

"Well," I hesitated as I dipped deeply into my barrel of improbable
diagnoses, fumbling among the diseases that I knew only by name but had
never seen, "maybe it's pemphigus."

"Pemphigus, well it might be, but I doubt it. At least it's probably a
guess in the right direction. We'll take him back to the Navy Hospital at
Kwajelein and give the experts a chance to study him."

"Let me know what they think," I plead, "for I've got to know what
I'm faced with here on Rongelap. Practically every man, woman and child

has been exposed to him these last several hours, crawling over him and kissing him goodby."

The young surgeon gave him an injection of demerol for pain and four men carried him on a stretcher to the motor boat. Islanders followed without any appearance of emotion. I saw no farewells, no tears: there was a feeling of confidence that all would be well. And then the plane headed for Kwajelein, using rockets in a sudden, brief take-off.

Two days later a message came that the patient had died, and that the body was even then being returned for burial.

The plane came again, looking strangely dark and hearse-like as it settled slowly into the lagoon. The islanders came down to the water-front, dressed in their Sunday clothes, the men wearing shirts. Bill Bailey and four island men met the plane in a little motor boat and returned with the dead man wrapped in a blanket, the limp form twisting a little as they shifted its weight from the boat to their shoulders. And as they trudged through the sand one could see the unsupported head droop and roll from side to side. The villagers formed a procession behind the pall-bearers and shuffled through the sand, their heads bowed, silent and dry-eyed, accepting death solemnly and as a part of destiny: there was a stylization and an ancient mannerism in the control of their grief. Except for one. One young woman stayed apart from the others and leaned against a palm tree, crying silently, her shoulders jerking savagely as if in conflict, as she tried to smother her sobs, her wavy, black hair falling over her face and becoming wet. The procession moved only a few rods to a house close onto the beach. The men carried in the corpse and placed it on the floor in front of the door, while the women knelt in semicircle behind it, uncovering the face, fanning it, caressing it, swaying slowly as they established their dry-eyed vigil.

The men had their own kind of work to do, and without signaling to one another or giving any evidence of pre-arrangement, four of them went to their homes and returned with hammers and nails, saws, a couple of saw horses, and lengths of plywood. With matter-of-factness, as though possessing the transmitted knowledge that this was the way it was supposed to be done, they set up a wood-working shop in the dead man's yard, so close to the dead man as he lay before the open door that he might—if such a thing were possible—have been able to oversee their activities and make corrections here and there as they proceeded to construct his coffin. To make certain that the size would be correct one of the men measured a length of plywood against his own body and marked it accordingly. Then the sawing and hammering commenced.

I stood a few yards away in the jeep-trail where the sun beat down so fiercely, partially blinding me, that I had the illusion that there were no shadows nor perspective—only stark, superimposed lines, like cave drawings. A four-year-old girl joined me in the jeep-trail. She took hold of my hand, and the two of us, excluded from participation, stood there pondering the juxtaposition of carpenters, a corpse and the swaying mourners who seemed, somewhat abstractly, to be illustrating fundamental truths about death and tenderness and expediency. So I stood there peering into the lives and a death of these people, watching as if from another world, or through a microscope, or through the eyes of the little girl. Finally, still holding my hand to steady herself, the little girl squatted and urinated in the sand.

The crew of the plane had lunch with us. The pilot said, "These people make quite a ceremony of death. Of course they have real affection for each other and real grief when there is a death. But there's another sort of crises going on—they're ashamed of it and won't talk to us about it even though it's the thing that's worrying every last one of them this minute. This man died away from home; the question is, can his ghost be reconciled to return with the body and lie quietly down in the grave? These ghosts from the newly-dead are an unpredictable and high-spirited lot, like prima donnas. They are easily offended by imagined slights, and are so easily distracted by frivolities in the spirit world that they sometimes forget, or refuse, to come to their own funerals. And when this happens there is another roving, fretful ghost added to the effluvium over the atoll. Everything that goes wrong with Rongelap—that 1954 affair, for instance; when someone gets drowned; when the fishing is poor; everything they don't like—is due to some fouled-up ghost. So they're going to make damn sure this one gets taken care of properly. This is the reason we didn't wait for them to ask us to return the body. I guess some of the younger people are beginning to turn away from the ghost theory, but it is still the prevailing lore of their thinking, and it keeps the witch doctors in business."

The funeral was the next day, and it went on for many hours at the church. The islanders had sent word down to the camp inviting several of us to come, not to the funeral whose long hours they knew no American could sit through, but to the ceremony at the grave, and so Sergeant Bascomb, and I waited at the burying ground. Two men were digging the grave. The little burying ground seemed so crowded with graves that I wondered that there was room for one more occupant. And perhaps there wasn't for the two grave diggers were impassively tossing out broken pieces of femurs and skulls along with the blocks of coral as they excavated a new hallowed six-foot space. I remembered from my indoctrination that Marshallese regard their dead, especially the heads, wherein the ghosts lurk, with reverence and awe. And I recalled a story from the time of repatriation: The islanders had insisted on exhuming several corpses that had been buried on Majuro so they could be transported back to Rongelap with them. During this messy procedure, while laborers lifted one of the decomposed corpses from its grave, the head had fallen off. There was a shocked, sickening silence among the onlookers, a sudden foreboding and a turbulence in the ambient spirit world as offended ghosts gathered to express their indignation. All were aware of the crises of the moment, but then one of the Americans, thinking very quickly, said "Oh, the body fell off the head." This explanation seemed to satisfy or, perhaps to amuse the ghosts—who in spite of their pedantry and huffiness seem to have a sense of humor— and the exhuming proceeded according to schedule.

So it surprised me to see bones, still recognizably human, piled along with the coral clods. But in a way I liked the practical aspects of it: this unconscious dehumanizing, dehallowing of excess bones—bones that probably long since had become separated from their ghosts so that further reverence for them could not possibly influence fishing or the weather, or a man's fertility.

The funeral procession came slowly from the church. First came four men, stripped to the waist—for this was heavy work that made them sweat— carrying the corpse on its litter on their shoulders. There was a pandanus mat spread over the corpse and when the breeze lifted the corner of the mat I could see the dead man's dark head crowned with a lei of golden flowers, handsome in death. Then came the mourners, dry-eyed, talking quietly to one another, occasionally smiling faintly depending on the turn of their conversations, and carrying their hymn books and bibles.

The procession stopped at the grave, and the pallbearers lifted the corpse into the casket that had been waiting for it. Several women rushed up to inspect the placement of the corpse as they positioned it to their liking. The pandanus mat wouldn't fit snugly in the casket and a woman, fetching a pair of scissors from her house, cut off the excess width.

An old man climbed on top of a large coral tomb stone nearby and started a funeral oration, a fervid and dramatic harangue that seemed to be directed elsewhere—toward the sea or the trade-winds or, perhaps, a past memory — for no one listened. People clustered about the casket arguing about details, occasionally rearranging the pandanus mat, finally hammering on the lid. Only one stood apart, the tall girl with the wavy hair; she stood with her back to the casket crying, and no one noticed her.

No one had thought to make preparation for lowering the casket into the grave and now there was discussion and gesticulations that illustrated concern over this unexpected problem in engineering. Finally, John pulled a great string of keys from his pocket, twirled them importantly as if they were an insignia of his office, and strode off to open the warehouse so that he could fetch ropes and two planks. The coffin was placed on the planks over the grave, the ropes were looped under each end of the coffin in readiness for descent, and then, in the manner of a hanging, the planks were knocked out of position.

There was poor coordination between the rope-handlers at each end of the coffin so that one end dropped down too abruptly and became wedged in the coral crypt. Again there were arguments, the women, especially, pointing out to the men what they should do next. Finally the grave-diggers, by hacking at the walls of the crypt with their spades, succeeded in dislodging the coffin, and it descended to its final resting place with a light thud. Now there was more discussion and uncertainty. Finally a man walked back into the jungle and brought two palm fronds to lay over the coffin. Then the coral clods were shoveled into the grave and the burial was over.

That night a hog was slaughtered and the dead man's family gave a feast in his name to the village. And the next morning the burial ground had the appearance of a gigantic spider web for strings hung across it from side to side and at all angles supporting all manner of objects—handicraft, shells, discarded clothing—all gifts from the dead man to his friends. The feast and the gifts made his departure a sweetly, sad event, and the village resumed its routines with pleasant memories of the dead man…Death had not been gruesome nor unnaturally unkind.

Later, someone covered the grave with bone-white fragments of coral, out-lined it with partially buried Coca-Cola cans, placed a small white cross at its head. "This 'Merican way," John told me concerning the wooden cross. "No more old rockses," and he pointed with disdain at the lovely old rough-hewn coral headstones.

RONGELAP: SECOND DAY

John said to me, "It be John, da Magistrate of Rongelap, dat mus' hep ya."

It was my second day on Rongelap, and I was preparing to set up radiation monitoring stations. I was in the dormitory with a pile of equipment in front of me, probably looking a little perplexed at the Geiger-Mueller counters, the five-gallon demijohn for collecting rain water, the air pumps and filters and the film badges, when John came to return my official visit of the first day.

"Only da Magistrate, who be John, can hep ya, it bein' ol' Rongelap custom," he repeated quietly and almost reverently as if he were enunciating an ancient dictum that had controlled the use of Geiger-Mueller counters on Rongelap since the beginning of time. He stood before me in faded dungarees that were tattered up to mid-calf, barefoot and stripped to the waist; very erect and full of dignity as he looked up at me; young for such authority but with the poise of Moses; handsome as a legend, and profoundly anatomical. His muscles rippled under his brown skin like water in a dark pool, and his motions were gliding, quick and joyous. But his manners were the manners of Marshallese royalty (to which he bore lineage) for there was a firm restraint and discipline in his soft, nearly inaudible speech, in his almost womanly gentleness, in his concern for my feelings, and in the way he measured his careful statements—strange contradictions to his rich animal moods.

"Tell John wha' ya wan' an' he do it," he continued in third person.

"Well, first we must establish film badge stations about the populated areas of the island. I do wish that I had a map of the island so I could locate these positions and number them."

"Ya wanna map, mebbe?" he asked, grasping the one phrase that was intelligible to him. "John mak' ya fine map." And, taking a pencil and paper, he sketched one very rapidly—and with workable precision as I discovered later when I compared it with a navigational map—putting in the houses (his house appeared huge and gave the island a top-heavy appearance in that region) and the property lines, and an occasional palm tree, which, for some obscure reason, gave it distinction above the thousands of trees that he left out. He even placed a nondescript fish, a quarter the size of the island, alongside in the lagoon.

"Na we ready to do sometin' 'bout it, mebbe," he said, watching me expectantly to see what equipment I would pick up.

I collected the box of film badges, a ball of string, a notebook and a pencil, and we got into the jeep and started up the island. Jabwan village seemed to be almost deserted, at least no one came out of the houses, so we simply tied badges to several convenient trees and recorded their location on the map in the notebook. Rongelap village, though, appeared thoroughly occupied

John Anjain, the magistrate on Rongelap, who became my closest friend on the island. His oldest son who was heavily irradiated in 1954 developed cancer of his thyroid. This was successfully removed, but then he developed leukemia, also caused by radiation, and died— still a teenager.

and active. I got out of the jeep and started to stride from tree to tree look-ing for good sites for film-badge stations, John following my big strides at a dog trot, his arms full of film badges, the notebook, the map and pencils which kept dropping so that he had to stop and pick them up. But I hurried on for I was getting hot and my mind was on other things that I must do that morning.

"Doctah-commandah, Doctah-commandah," I finally heard him gasp. I waited. "Peple watch-watch. Mus' go in village lak Rongelap custom." And he took my hand, slowing me down to a formal, stately motion, com-posing his breathlessness as best he could as he guided me slowly—though firmly—through the center of the village. We became a sort of procession, the two of us, our hands sweatily clasped and with the tread of well-re-hearsed pallbearers, we made our entrance. We might, from all the dignity we achieved and from the wave of admiration that ascended about us, have been wearing striped trousers; although, a little crazily in the heat the im-age of Solomon and the Queen of Sheba kept flashing before me. People came out of their houses to ask John what we were up to. But he put them off with monosyllabic, and probably meaningless, replies while we surveyed their palm trees. Twice we walked the full length of the village while the villagers fell in behind us, watching us carefully; each home owner, as we passed his place, pointing out the advantages it possessed for whatever pur-pose he thought we had in mind. Each time I started toward a likely palm tree, John would hold me back, saying, "Not yet, nex' time, mebbe." The enthusiasm behind us increased; the chatter became shrill and imploring; there seemed to be competition for our attention. Once I said to John, "But won't someone steal—I mean remove—the badges?" "Not after dis'," he said and grinned a little bit sheepishly.

On the third trip through the village he let me put up one film badge, on the fourth trip I put up three more, and on the fifth trip I distributed them as freely as I liked. But each time I tied a badge to a tree there was a respectful silence and a thrill as if I were conferring knighthood on the coconut tree. It was a sort of heady experience, and when I was down to the last film badge, and feeling carried away by my own performance, I turned to John and tied it about his neck. There was a prolonged hush, several men removed their hats, and there was a polite flutter of applause. I knew then that John was assured reelection at the next voting, and that my film badges were safe.

Next I drove stakes as markers into spots at the camp, near Jabwon village, and in the center of Rongelap village. These were stations for tak-ing Geiger-Mueller counter readings, the idea being that one would hold the counter at exactly three-foot height above the markers while taking official readings. But why the three-foot height? And why regard it with such ceremony? Ah, because this, in the average male, is the critical level of genetic concern, the level of self-conscious preoccupation in a world fearful of radiation, the level of nervous tingle and somber speculation; it is the level that had been agreed on as a standard by radiation engineers who, of course, are all males. So after placing the stakes I took initial readings, holding the counter carefully three feet above the stake just as I had been instructed, but feeling self-conscious and a little tingly about it…I turned my back on John so he couldn't see what I was doing, and blushed.

Soon after that, the villagers being no longer with us, John lost interest and wandered away.

Back at the camp I got Doc to help me assemble the rainwater collector and place it on a platform of discarded crates over the demijohn. We constructed a small shed-enclosure for the air pumps, and I started the motor. But the roar of the electric motor was so dissipated by the surf sound, the immensity of the sky and the trade winds that I was struck with the puniness of my sampling efforts— "How can I impress my technology on such vastness, or on the bomb itself, with only a tiny roar that loses itself at twenty feet?"

I checked over the continuous, self-recording Geiger-Mueller counter, which had been installed by the technical sergeant who had come and gone on the plane of the previous day, and found that it was operating sagely and sanely as it steadily proclaimed normal background radiation and placidly recorded it—a little bored with such unexciting information, I thought; but there was an attitude of hopeful expectation about it that frightened me.

Then I sat down at my desk to confide my activities to the daily log, and to send a radio dispatch to the officials at Headquarters to inform them that Rongelap was in readiness, politically, technologically and genetically, for any devastations they might provoke.

MEDICAL EXAMINATION OF MEN

On the next day, my third on Rongelap, Jaruleij came to the camp early in the morning. He approached me in the toilet while my back was turned and I was brushing my teeth.

"Bein' Health Aid, being' Jaruleij, halloo-goodbye," he commenced, introducing himself as if to a stranger, perhaps on the assumption that no one would remember him for more than a few hours at a time.

"Oh good morning, Jaruleij, glad to see you again."

"Bein' Health Aid, being Jaruleij," he resumed his prepared, formal statement, slightly annoyed by my diversion, "halloo-goomby."

"Yes, Jaruleij, hello. It's nice to have you come down to the camp. Can I show you around the place? Will you have some coffee?"

"Importan' message. Importan' Jaruleij say it all. Importan' no interrupt." He took a new breath, settled himself firmly on his crippled hips and started out again, patiently. "Bein' Health Aid, bein' Jaruleij, halloo-goomby, and I need ya. Come dispensary now. Patients wan' doctah quick."

"I'll be glad to come. What seems to be the trouble?"

"Oh, many ache, many constipat', many here trouble, many there trouble, many weak back, oh many trouble."

"My goodness, it sounds like an epidemic," I said bracing myself for a catastrophe, but, with some perplexity, trying to fit the symptoms he had described into a single syndrome.

I dressed as rapidly as possible, not waiting to shave, and together we hurried to the weapons-carrier, Jaruleij waddling heavily behind with his bad hips through the sand but encouraging me on with little grunts of urgency—Jaruleij with the kind, heavy face of Mother Earth, look-

The dispensary on Rongelap. All of the available medications can be seen on the shelves. I am standing behind. The three men standing in front of me are, from left to right: the witch doctor, the health assistant (Jaruleij), and the translator.

ing as if he had given birth to the atoll, possibly a few millenniums back, or at least acted as mid-wife to its birthing, a sort of ancient symbol of creation with his labored waddle and grunting; Jaruleij with a primordial quality about him that made one think of swirling nebulae and of amphibians crawling out of rich, stagnant pools; Jaruleij shooing me on to perform my duties.

Most certainly the situation at the dispensary did appear alarming for the waiting room was filled with patients who overflowed out into the yard where they lay on the ground in the building's shade and the shade of neighboring pandanus trees. Curiously, all were men ("perhaps this is an occupational disorder or a peculiar, inbred, sex-linked disease," I made hasty clinical note);

and, even more curiously, all were smiling amiably, and there was an appearance of luxurious good health about them as they stretched their muscles and sprawled contentedly as though savoring some secret inner source of well-being.

"Wan' doctah, wan' doctah bad, all lak' new doctah, ver' importan' occasion," was Jaruleij's comment.

I knew the way through the waiting room and through the 'ward', and I hurried ahead, stepping over my waiting patients who lay on the floor not moving, but nodding relaxed welcomes up at me.

"Whatever is wrong with them," I thought, "it most certainly is not nervous tension."

Jaruleij pulled several keys from his pocket, tried one after another in the lock to the treatment room, found that none would fit and waddled back over the patients to bring another handful of rusted keys. Finally he found one that released the lock and we entered the sanctum of Aesculapius. It was hot, dark and sticky with little ventilation or light from its two windows. In the center of the room was a small operating table, the kind of flimsy affair which a patient must crawl up on squarely in the middle, balancing his weight carefully, or one end would fly up. It was partially draped with a torn, bloody sheet, and beside it, in a basin, were a few blood-stained instruments. Jaruleij grinned and said, "Catch baby las' night. Ol' cat have kittens all same time," and he pointed proudly to the corner where a scrawny cat was licking a nest full of mewling, rat-like creatures, still sleek from their obstetrical experience. There were shelves on the wall with a few bottles that contained medications. I looked at them closely and in wonder for never had I seen such grandeur in a shelf of drugs: aspirin, for instance, assumed a fetching quality I had not considered possible for it was in a bottle labeled Courvosier Brandy. There was a cough mixture in a bottle that was labeled Martini and Rossi Vermouth and a liniment in a bottle of Old Granddad.

"My goodness," I said. "Someone around here seems to have very good taste in liquor." But Jaruleij, missing my sarcasm, smiled proudly and said, "Pretty med'cine, pretty bottle, alles sen' ta us lak dat. Mak peple weller faster in pretty bottle." I could see that Jaruleij was proud of his dispensary and I tried to see it through his eyes. "Doctah, wanna wash han's now?" and he rushed me over to a tap from which he slowly dripped a trickle of cistern water into a small basin, produced a sliver of soap from his pocket and, after rummaging through a pile of unsorted laundry, found a huge beach towel on which the word 'aloha' was printed. "Doctah wash now an' Jaruleij bring in patients." This, I gathered, was a sort of ceremonial cleansing, more to purify me professionally than to improve my personal hygiene. So I washed with a flourish and returned the soap and towel singly to his waiting hands, being careful not to touch him as if I were preparing for surgery; and for a few brief moments, while the illusion of asepsis lingered, I had him hand me such things as a pencil and paper, and stethoscope, which I touched lightly by my finger tips. Things beyond my easy reach, that had to do with Jaruleij or the dispensary somehow were taboo until I conferred to them my special Pasteur-derived, special ceremonialized purity…Thus Jaruleij and I developed our bond of witchcraft.

There was a desk in one corner. I sat down at it, arranged my stethoscope and pad and pencil, cleared my throat and said that I was now prepared to see the first patient. In came an oldish, dignified man who stood before me smiling, and, I thought, glowing with health.

"What is wrong with you, sir?" I asked.

He knew no English so Jaruleij took over for him. "Oh, he ver' importan' man, very importan' man in village."

"Yes, I can see that. But does he have a pain somewhere?"

"Oh ya, ya. Ver' importan', ver' great pain. Pain in… in…oh ya, ver' great pain in belly." He jabbered rapidly in Marshallese, the patient looked perplexed but put his hand over his right lower quadrant, directly over the area of the appendix, and groaned.

"Is he constipated? Does he have anorexia?" I asked, becoming suddenly alert. And the old man nodded eager assent even before Jaruleij had completed his translation.

"Well, I guess I had better examine him," I said, a feeling of vague horror coming over me for I had not performed an appendectomy in twenty years.

Jaruleij whisked the torn, bloody sheet off the operating table and replaced it with a pandanus mat and helped the patient onto it, steadying the table so that it wouldn't fly up. Carefully I went over the abdomen, but it felt perfectly normal to me, the wall being flaccid, the palpable organs where they should be. But several times, as I approached the right lower quadrant, palpating deeply, the patient groaned and stirred with appropriate uneasiness, though at these times I suspected Jaruleij of giving him cues.

"To be entirely certain that this is not appendicitis," I said, " it will be necessary for me to make a rectal examination. Will he object?" I asked apprehensively, remembering the briefing at Eniwetok in which Rongelapese had been described as being excessively modest ("Their bodies are holy temples and your hands and your gaze must not profane them," the anthropologist had said so impressively and so lyrically that I had believed him).

"Oh, na na, he proud of fine rectal exam'ation," said Jaruleij as he stood the dignified old man up against the table, and dropped his pants. I put on a glove, lubricated it, felt carefully past the sphincter, over the prostate gland and seminal vesicles, and on up over the region of the appendix; but to my relief, found no tenderness, no bulging, no inflamed mass. And I breathed a little easier.

"Well, I don't think we need worry about an acute appendix, or anything else for that matter."

"Na, na, he all right," said Jaruleij, "all he need is pill. Which one shall we give 'im? What color ya lak best for ol' man?"

The patient pulled up his pants, swallowed a pink aspirin and shook my hand affectionately, giving me, for a moment, the feeling that I had, perhaps, saved his life.

The next two patients were about the same: one with pain in the left side of the abdomen and the other with a pain in the middle of the abdomen. I made careful, methodical rectal examinations on both of them, and sent each one away happily with a benadryl capsule. But the next patient, who had a pain in his shoulder, as soon as we had finished a few preliminary exchanges of conversation and before I had a chance to suggest what kind of examination might be needed, simply dropped his pants and leaned over the table in eager expectation of my curious, exploring finger. One patient, when he entered the room, walked directly to the table and dropped his pants, so that when I looked up from my desk, I saw only brown, shining buttocks waiting for me. This was my introduction to Jonah, a happy, ever-smiling man, who on this day had come to have a splinter removed from his finger.

"Jaruleij," I asked suspiciously, for I was beginning to suspect that these sick-calls were social events and that my rectal examinations were status symbols, "do you really think that these patients all have the pains they say they have?"

"Oh my goodness ya," he said with alarm and defensive fierceness, "My, my, all need doctah, wait many months for doctah. Oh, ver' great pains, oh ver', ver' importan' patients." I could see that I was stuck and each morning, for the rest of the week, I worked in the dispensary, examining male patient after male patient, sweating in the hot, little room so that I had to keep blotting paper under my hand as I made notes of my negative findings or recorded the list of pink or blue pills that I doled out. Slowly we worked our way backward through the age groups, for Jaruleij or the patients themselves had ranked them in precedence by age. John, the Magistrate, for instance, since he was relatively young, appeared on Thursday complaining of a pain in his knee.

At the end of the week Jaruleij said to me brightly, "Well dats all of da men." I breathed with relief.... "Nex' week we start da womans."

MEDICAL EXAMINATION OF WOMEN

Monday morning came. This time Jaruleij sent a messenger: young, shy Jeremiah who was the school teacher. In a singsong voice, as if he were reciting memorized instructions, eyes downcast from shyness, he said, "Need doctah at dispensary. Many sick womans. Place full of sick womans. All hurtin', groanin', shoutin'. Good 'n sick. All wanna see doctah. Jaruleij say come fas' lak runnin.'"

"Where is Jaruleij?" I asked a bit suspiciously.

"Jaruleij got hands full. Too many womans. All noise. Lak flies buzz-buzz all over place." This time I thought I detected a true note of urgency, and I headed for my jeep with Jeremiah trotting behind me.

The dispensary seemed like an animated thing as we approached it. Even before I could see it, as I parked the jeep behind the school house, I could hear the crackle and spit—like some diabolical machine preparing to detonate—of Marshallese consonants from dozens of women who seemed to be hurling insults and, perhaps working themselves into a state of mob hysteria. For a moment I visualized Jaruleij pinned to the floor of the dispensary, his head bloody and his eyes gouged. But then several people laughed and there was a cascade of laughter and happy grunts and exclamations. Someone started to strum a guitar and there was a snatch of a song. Then there began another slow build-up of sputtering consonants. When I turned the corner at the cistern and came into view of the dispensary I could see the crowd. Women were leaning out of the windows (or not so much leaning out as bulging out—and there was a queue of them at the door maneuvering for entrance. Others lay on pandanus mats on the gravel under the building and in its shade; all were busy with conversation or with handicraft, and were smiling. Even as they elbowed each other for position in the doorway they chatted in a relaxed, happy way, smiling gently at one another as they sputtered their difficult language…But there was a collective determination about them, and a possessiveness, so that I knew that Jaruleij and I no longer dominated the dispensary nor the healing arts.

They made way for me at the entrance and I stepped carefully among the women who were crouching or lying on the floor. Those of child-bearing age were either pregnant or were holding infants in their arms. "Here," I thought as I made my way among the ripeness of swollen abdomens, "is the womb of Rongelap. Here is the elemental strength and the ferment that controls a matriarchy. And here am I, a foolish, venturesome physician, engulfed in the womb's warmth, drowning, perhaps, in its humid interior, a victim to the forces of generation and my own curiosity.

I picked my way on through the waiting room and a sudden hush surrounded me as if I were a foreign object—a rejected spermatozoon, for instance—that must be sequestered in silence. The women looked up at me as I stepped over them and smiled distantly and Madonna-like. Then, as I entered the treatment room I heard the crackle of conversation and gossip fill the space behind me. The guitar picked up the chords it had neglected and continued.

"Jaruleij," I said, when he had worked his crippled way through the treatment room, looking flustered but proud of this production he had arranged, sweating and puffing as he made last minute, tidying gestures about the desk, "Jaruleij, I can't possibly examine all these women today. Why don't I see just the sick ones, and you send the rest of them home?"

Jaruleij looked hurt, "All need doctah, all wanna see doctah, all ver' sick. Come ever' day till ya see 'em. Lak to wait an' talk an' play guitah."

"Very well," I said but I felt uncomfortable in this role that I knew he had prepared for me as a professional entertainer, a sort of physician roadhouse performer.

"Womans up front need Jaruleij. Give ya Jeremiah, da school teacher, for translate," and he waddled out. Jeremiah came through the waiting room, a wave of titters following him, and he came in blushing. His blackgleaming shoes gave off the odor of shoe polish and seemed to pinch his feet, his trousers were neatly pressed—this young exponent of the educational process—but he wore no shirt, and his muscles were hardened into the bold, controlled curves of a wrestler. Somehow I expected him to be myopic in the manner of a book-worm athlete, but he wasn't for his eyes glistened with curiosity and with surprise for each thing that caught his quick attention. There was a healthy animal quality about him that I liked. He took his place timidly by my desk.

The first patient, a very old and nearly inarticulate woman, presented no problem. She had a pain in her back, or so she maintained, and went away happily with a couple of aspirin. But the next woman, slightly younger with a determined attitude and an eagerness to be understood, completely upset the well-ordered events of the morning.

"What is your trouble," I asked.

"Poor appetite and pain," Jeremiah translated.

"Where is the pain?"

There was an appearance of horrified embarrassment between the old lady and Jeremiah; the old lady seemed to be insisting on a point while

Jeremiah seemed to be denying it and retreating from it. Finally he said to me almost tearfully, "Pain somewhere we can't talk about ta womans. I call nex' patient an' sen' her home."

"Oh no, this may be important. Ask her," I said, trying for an acceptable approach, "if she has had any constipation or diarrhea."

Jeremiah blushed violently, drew himself up with great dignity and said, "Those ver' bad words, refuse translate to womans, resign now," and he rushed out of the room.

The old lady appeared relieved, she made a deprecating gesture at his retreating figure as if despising his maleness, and we laughed together. Then she pointed to her abdomen, and, without the slightest hesitation, said: "Los bijik."

When Jaruleij came in I asked, "What does 'los bijik' mean?" He looked startled and then whispered in my ear, "It mean constipate. Nevah say when womans listen. Ver' bad word. Worse 'n shit."

"But she told it to me," I protested foolishly as I tried to shift the blame for any indecency.

"Dat cause she know ya is doctah and not a man."

Thus was established the linguistic foundation for my meager Marshallese vocabulary that made medical practice possible on Rongelap. Before the day was over I had learned that "bijik" meant to defecate; that "maja" meant to urinate; that "botoktuk" meant menstruation; and that "jikin ninnin" referred to the uterus. These were words that I could use among the women in the examining room, but not beyond its portals, as I suspected at the time and soon learned for certain from a nightmarish bit of tongue-twisting. Here is how it occurred: Gradually, over a period of weeks as I gathered enough words together to attempt an occasional social foray of conversation, I became fearful that sometime, when struggling with a difficult problem of recall, I would grasp one of these first impure words in panic of forgetting and blurt it out; especially I was afraid that the word "bijik," the most obscene of them all, and which on the tongue has the feel of many other Marshallese words, would be the one to betray me. The more I thought about the far-fetched possibility the more certain I became of its inevitability. And finally it did happen, right at midday in front of the church after the morning service. It happened there in the chaste glare of an immaculate sky while I was reaching for an elusive word which would have explained to a little group of church-goers why I liked Rongelap. I felt it coming, felt it form uncertainly deep in my larynx, felt it stick momentarily cross-wise in the back of my throat, heard it reverberate unnaturally, gaining force and evil as I tried to hold it back with my teeth.

"Bijik," it roared into the Sabbath-serenity defiling the day and all who heard it.

There was a sudden hush. One man left the group. I thought I heard a sigh from the church shadows where the ghosts of missionaries were known to grieve and gossip and spy during the daytime (for missionary ghosts on Rongelap, unlike all others, lose interest and go to sleep at nightfall). The sunlight turned to blood and my incarnate soul fell to the ground in the form of a silent convulsion. I stood there alone, foreign and indecent and waiting to be despised. But then an old woman made a little joke, several people ventured very slight titters, and I knew that I had been forgiven...except that I heard a snort of disgust from the shadows of the church.

After Jeremiah had gone, I asked Jaruleij for another translator. He seemed perturbed that I had used up his translator so rapidly, and he scratched his head on how to replace him.

"Guess ya gotta haf womans for translator, but none talks English. Old Elsie know 'bout twenty words; maybe she do." So he brought in old Elsie. She perched herself on the top of a tall packing box, swinging her ancient, tiny frame that had borne fourteen children. Up on it with the skill of a pole vaulter, and sat there, feet dangling gaily and child-like, seemingly amused at herself. Her withered breasts dangled like tattered palm fronds behind the torn opening of her mother-hubbard, and the skin of her face hung in heavy rhinoceros-folds, almost concealing the sparkle in her eyes.

"Halloo...halloo-good-bye," she faltered, chuckling at the ridiculous-ness of her position. And we both laughed.

Together we got through the morning and most of the week, mostly using pantomime and the few anatomical names that we had succeeded in establishing as our common bilingual possession. As with the men, few of the women had any real symptoms and I knew that my examinations and interviews were really social events.

There were several ill patients among them who required antibiotics. When I told Jaruleij to give penicillin to one of them I found that he gave it in the upper arm.

"You must never give penicillin in the arm," I told him, "because of the danger of causing nerve damage. You must always give it in the hip."

He nodded agreement but each time I ordered penicillin I found that he continued to give it in the same area. When I took him to task he said, "Jaruleij be man, man on Rongelap. Not nice pull up woman's skirt on Rongelap. Won't do by Marshallese custom. Ya doctah. Ya not man on Rongelap. All right fo' ya to pull up skirt. Nex' time I give ya syringe an' ya give penicillin ta womans."

One day, late in the week when old Elsie was not present, Jaruleij presented me with a seventeen year old girl with symptoms that I thought required a pelvic examination. This was Sarah, a wavy-haired beauty, nubile and flirtatious, with a coy way of fluttering into shy excitement when spoken to, and of furiously combing her hair while her imagination—if one could judge from the sighs and animal sounds that escaped her then— seemed like a self-conscious and restless Lorelei.

"Girl goin' out in bushes too much at night," Jaruleij said admiringly, "too many men followin' her roun' at night." And a soft dreaminess came into his eyes.

"But," I objected vigorously, "this sort of thing doesn't happen here. They told me so at Headquarters. And that everyone is very pious and religious, and offended at the mere mention of sex. Didn't you see how sensitive Jeremiah was about women? Surely Jeremiah, for instance, wouldn't try to seduce a young girl like this!"

"Jeremiah go to bushes all right, almost more than anyone. Almost every man go to bushes. Everyone pious an' religious jus' lak missionaries teached,' an' don' lak bad words or pullin' up woman's dress," he said looking at me in bewilderment.

"But what about the missionaries who taught you about church and bad words and sin? Didn't they say to stay out of the bushes at night?"

"Na, missionaries went ta bed early. Nevah knowed about afta dark an' bushes." (Later, after I returned to the States, I learned from anthropologists that it is not exceptional, and certainly not hypocritical, for two sets of opposing moral values to operate together, one during the day and one at night.)

"Well, I will have to do a pelvic examination on this young lady," I said. "I will perform it with dignity and decorum and it should not be embarrassing to her. I must have an older woman with me while I am doing it." That seemed to amuse Jaruleij for he chuckled as he went out into the waiting room to make suitable arrangements.

He came back with Rebecca a twenty year old woman who carried a ukelele and giggled as she exchanged rapid comments with Sarah. Rebecca took her position—matron-like, I hoped—behind me, and I showed Jaruleij how to drape the patient, how to lay out the instruments and lubricating jelly; how to help me powder my hands and put on the gloves. Then, hastily turning his back, he left the room. Very carefully and with all the professional mannerisms at my command, I started the examination. I was proceeding in a methodical manner—carefully feeling the uterus, which was swollen in early pregnancy, noting its movability, its relationship to the Fallopian tubes and ovaries; thoroughly immersed in the anatomic verities of the female pelvis; lost for the moment in scientific wonder of the physiologic changes of procreation; feeling lecture-dry and academic about the whole matter and scarcely aware that another human being was participating in the event—when suddenly Sarah, spread-eagle in lithotomy position on the table before me, giggled happily and gave a Marshallese command. Rebecca strummed a chord on the ukelele and the two of them started singing a gay, dance rhythm, my patient swaying, as best she could, in time with the music. Blushing and embarrassed, I stepped back from the table, pulled off my gloves, and announced hoarsely that I was through as I sat down at the desk to make notes. But they kept on singing together obviously bored with my activities, and unconcerned whether I continued or stopped, whether I was in Rongelap or North Carolina; as disinterested as they could be that I had been subdued to a state of male-nothingness, where even being a physician did not save my pride. When I told Jaruleij about the pregnancy he seemed pleased:

"Nice ta have more baby on Rongelap. All peple wan' baby."

"But this baby will be illegitimate."

"What's dat?"

"It means it has no father."

"Oh it got plen'y fathers. Maybe half da men on Rongelap, an' Jeremiah most of all. All love baby. Now all know she get baby easy an' someone marry her."

Thus ended my week of examinations of the women of Rongelap.

CHURCHED

"Ya'd better be hidin' that lipstick your wife sent ya fer gifts," Doc said, "or better yet, throw it in the ocean with the garbage as the tide's goin' out, cause that's what the preacher's goin' ta preach agin' tomorry mornin', tomorry afternoon, hell, he's goin' ta take the whole goddamn day to preach agin' it an' the painted Jezebels who use the stuff."

"How can that be," I asked. "So far as I know there's never been any lipstick on this island, nor cosmetics of any kind, until my package arrived two days ago. My goodness, they wouldn't know a painted Jezebel from a Madonna."

"That's just it. No one uses it, couldn't buy it if they tried. So they can damn the Jezebels all they want an' not hurt anybody's feelin's. It's a safe thing ta preach agin' so they've made it their number one sin. Take it away, along with dancin', their number two sin which they've fergot how ta do anyway, an' smokin', their number three sin, an' they'd be pretty desperate.

Damn it, they'd be right down ta rock bottom fer sins ta attack, right down ta the things they love an' wouldn't give up fer nothin', like fornicatin' an' adultery, an' gittin' drunk, an' bein' lazy, or even usin' black magic on each other. But don't git me wrong an' think I'm makin' hypocrites out of 'em, 'cause they're serious about this religious business, dead serious, an' on Sunday, when things git kind of spooky an' all turned around, ya begin ta feel it yoreself. Shit, if one of these Sundays I see Christ come walkin' across the lagoon, I won't even blink. I'll jus' lean back in the shade an' wait fer him to change some water inta wine, an' maybe fix up that leper they keep hidden back in the jungle. An' the preacher an' Izikiel, an' all the rest of 'em git ta lookin' so goddam pious that I seem ta see 'em in Bible clothes an' with long, curly, black beards even though there's not an honest whisker amongst 'em, an' I know damn-well what most of 'em—leastways the lucky ones— was up ta the night bafore. Oh it gives ya the creeps. Ya'll see what I mean tomorry."

It was Saturday evening, just after sundown and Doc and I were walking slowly through the village, feeling a little tender about Rongelap and the way the night seemed to settle over it like a nesting bird. Each family was clustered about its tiny cooking hole, very quiet and intent and creche-like, scarcely noticing us as we passed. The trade winds reached down through the palm trees cooling us and bringing wisps of acrid smoke from the smoldering coconut husks in the cooking holes, and the fetor (though this may be the wrong word for it, for by this time such smells had become synonymous with village life and were almost pleasant) of unrefrigerated fish.

"I've never seen the village so quiet and orderly. What's going on?"

"Oh, it's always this way on Saturday night," said Doc. It's the Sabbath-spell comin' on, like as if they was preparin' fer a trance. Now they's cookin' up the Sunday food in those beat up ol' oil cans since no cookin's allowed tomorry—a little rice an' pandanus an' boiled fish that they'll eat cold an' mushy an' partly spoiled. Makes me think of the Jews an' their Passover, the way they's sittin' there waitin' fer somethin' that ain't goin' ta happen, an' fixin' no-good food. But don't let 'em fool ya, cause these people can't keep this up too long at a time, an' in a little while some of 'em'll git ta thinkin' things over n' decide it's better ta git drunk an' make a night of it in the bushes after all. This afternoon, when Izikiel was tryin' ta bum some powdered milk off'n me, he vowed he'd fix me up with one of them teenage gals tonight, one of them lush young things they's all tryin' out before they gits married—an' on Saturday night, mind ya, jus' when things is takin' a holy turn."

"You refused, I hope," I said, manfully trying to maintain the prestige of our Standard Operating Procedures on a point on which they were explicit: *Sexual relations or intent of sexual relations with a native is a serious offence and will subject the offender to court martial. The act need not be proven, suspicion of such an act being sufficient to invoke severe disciplinary action.*

"Oh, yeh, I turned him down on it alright, even though I let him have the powdered milk. Not that I'm against the idea, ya understand, it's jus' that I cain't stand the way they pick their noses. But if I stay here long enough I suppose I'll git over bein' so damn fussy."

We walked the length of the village, the night as it deepened, became velvet folds about us…. The surf breathed easily and spoke carelessly in parables…. The stars were lizard eyes.

"Times like this," said Doc, as if completing a thought, "I git ta thinkin' this mus' be Beulah Land. I shore like the way these people 've got things figgered out."

Sunday morning was a time for introspection as we looked into the white and blue glare of the sky and felt its early morning beat on our heads— the pulsation of its after image, its scouring of our souls— was like a call to worship. Doc stood over a wash basin behind the dormitory energetically scrubbing his dentures. As loose-jointed and slack-strung as a discarded puppet, he performed his purifying ablutions with especial care, his lank muscles moving like mechanical devices under gaudy tattooing which, in spite of the wicked-girlish figures, seemed vaguely ecclesiastical in the slit-eyed glare. He put on a white shirt several sizes too small that choked him so that his adam's-apple rode the collar as if it were learning to post, and he terminated his sentences, sometimes, with a gasp. Then looking conventionally uncomfortable, he started to sweat—easy-going, relaxed Doc, suddenly rendered indistinguishable from any other sinner preparing for repentance, a Salvation-army quality about him or he could have passed for a Southern foot-washing Baptist. I put on shoes instead of my usual zories, a clean shirt, and we headed for the jeep. The carnal qualities of a military enterprise, all military masculinity, all of our durable hormones, seemed to leave us as we waded through the sand, though Doc managed a final "Ah go ta hell, ya bastards," to several silent GIs who looked as if they might jeer at him.

The church stood on the barest elevation, six inches, perhaps, above other parts of the village, but it seemed as if it stood on a knoll as it strained slightly toward the sky: four-square and triumphant, a strident singer of hosannas, an implacable revealer of grace in grace, it seemed to me—this Holmes and Narver construction made of plywood, corrugated metal and chicken wire. But so effectively was it planned with its high, tented—no, cathedral—roof, its low, open sides (where chicken wire opposed entry of livestock) and its latticed ends (for added ventilation) that one forgot its utilitarian materials and marveled at its eloquence. It was battleship-gray like the other village structures but it gleamed gloriously this Sunday morning beside its single barren breadfruit tree and under its towering palm trees like a vision of John Bunyan...It stood there propounding arguments in favor of parthenogenesis that I could not answer, and advising amitotic division as a way of reproduction.

We stood at the entrance of the church, peering into its inner coolness. The floor was a solid cement slab ("Solid as a Rock," I thought), and the pews were stark, rigid benches, obviously constructed by people who were not used to sitting in chairs, though they contained a certain calculated intellectual quality like spikes must have for an Indian mystic. Exposed two-by-fours lofted the pitched ceiling far up, far up above everything else on Rongelap except for the palm trees, and there formed a special sanctuary of clotted darkness over the congregation, like a storage place for mysteries. The altar was a packing crate, painted gray and festooned with torn paper roses and ancient Christmas decorations. On the wall behind it were long sheets of wrapping paper covered with Michelangelo-scrawls in colored crayons: various representations of Christ, dark-faced, stiff and a little sinister, and, if one could judge from the awkward fit of his draperies, very muscular. There was a kind of bird which surely was meant to be a dove; and a great shaggy beetle with five legs which I think was intended for a lamb—all done in simple, charming purity. I made a mental note that the dark vault of the church was sufficiently spacious for a small cloud "like a man's hand" to be floated freely, or for a pillar of fire to appear if such needs should ever arise.

We were a few minutes early and we waited at the entrance feeling like a couple of pool-hall loiterers, Doc choking a little on his tight collar and drenching, his shirt limp with sweat; the villagers, heads bowed, struggling past us to take their segregated seats, the men on the left and the women on the right. Faceless, disembodied and unfamiliar they seemed to me in their crisp Sunday clothes which had been designed to conceal a maximum of brown skin and any lust that might be connected with it, though bare feet remained like roots securing them to their island-soil.

Then we saw John up front motioning to us, his face bright-beaded with sweat after recent scrubbing. We hesitated, feeling shy, suddenly a little defensive of our momentary ostracism, unsure that we really wanted to mingle our souls with anyone else's. John came toward us smiling encouragement, as self-assured and persuasive as a professional usher; and taking our hands, he led us—Doc pulling back a little—to the visitors' pew, a special hard bench up-front that squared-off at right angles with the pulpit in a critical sort-of-way as if it were for a tennis umpire or a jury. John sat down between us, encouraging us with soft gurgling sounds to settle ourselves as comfortably as possible in our exposed positions.

"Now I teach ya songs we sing," he said as he pulled a small hymn book out of his pocket and handed it to me for inspection. Thumbing it rapidly I found that missionaries had prepared it by applying Marshallese words to old New England hymn tunes, many of them unfamiliar to me, but—as I found later—worthy and stout, and with the verve of the Reformation.

"But I cain't read music," protested Doc as he looked with terror at the silent congregation in front of us.

"John hep ya, don' worry, but mak it sof' so no one hear," and he led us as best he could through the strange, dignified old hymn, trying conductor-like to indicate all four parts and their phrasing.

"Na, na, mus' hol' dat note four counts. Don' go cheatin' an' breathin' lak dat. Mak it purty, Mak it holy. God lissen, mebbe. Mebbe hummin' bass hisself." And he cast a momentary look of concern at the shadows over us. Doc bowed his head like a chastised choirboy and became intent on matters of breathing. Sometimes John stopped us to correct our pronunciation, but the missionary spelling was so wonderfully phonetic that approximate reading was fairly easy.

"Do all Marshallese read music?" I asked.

"Sho, jus' lak missionaries teached us an' whacked us. We know good an' alright."

There was a nice feeling of air moving through the church and our voices seemed strangely muted and held down to the visitors'

Church of Rongelap. In front of it is the young Lieutenant who had been assigned the duty of teaching me (a suddenly created Commander) the good military manners that my rank demanded.

pew. No one but John seemed to be listening to our struggle, and we rehearsed almost in privacy.

The church had gradually filled to its capacity. Old people quietly read their Bibles, holding them at normal distance, using no spectacles.

Every so often a woman would get off of a bench and find herself a comfortable cross-legged position in the aisle. And each time, the self-conscious warden, watching me for my reaction, would motion her with a stick back into her pew, or tap her head warningly. One woman, catching my amusement hid her head and refused to budge. Each time the warden tapped her head with his stick, she peered a twinkling, impish eye at me and glued herself more firmly to the floor, and remained there the entire service. Other women, keeping close check on the warden, slipped back to the floor when he became distracted with other matters. Children were allowed to sit on the floor in the space between the seats and the altar, a seething, ameboid mass with pseudopods that could not be wholly controlled.

Then with common accord, for I was unaware of any signal or direction, we were all standing and singing, singing the same hymn John had rehearsed with us. The women sopranos pitched it where they wanted it, which was about a fifth higher than the music indicated so that their tone came out baby-thin, squeaking and probably painful, though loud and bossy, and as challengingly matriarchal as bloomers. At first I thought it strange and funny, particularly the way all the other voices were thrown out of range so that they had to jump from octave to octave to find notes that could be sung in comfort. The basses boomed far below, full-throated and wayward as the surf, sometimes dropping down an unnecessary octave to give a pulsing organ tone, or grasping an ascending run, taking it like a team of well-coordinated athletes with mad, independent acceleration and roar. I sang with the tenors or altos, whichever, in their transposed ranges, seemed closest to my physical needs. Doc, not reading music, agonized on the melody line like a boy soprano in adolescence, contorting his face, trying to breath like John had told him, carried away by the fervor that increased with each verse; and slowly losing his voice with each succeeding hymn so that when we finally drove home he could communicate only in half-whispers and signs; and rub in dismay a nearly—or so he thought—disarticulated Adam's-apple. The choral tone, unquestionably, was odd so that at first I felt myself sniggering at it, but it wore well, especially its sincerity, and soon I was thinking that this was the only kind of tone that should be permitted on an atoll.

A very old man with pierced ears, the lobes so distorted that one could have passed lighted cigars or the thigh bones of infants through their holes, stood before us to preach. He was stooped, though lively, and there was a suppressed excitement about him which, at intervals of fervor, overflowed into wild chanting—rhythmical and singsong and indistinguishable, to one not understanding the language, from the heady, almost maniacal fight chants that the old women, after I learned to know them well, would perform for me secretly late at night. "This is heresy," I thought. "It is like eating the missionaries," and a kind of wickedness spread across the congregation as heads swayed momentarily in rhythm. But then he would drop back into a style of quiet pleading and assured blessedness—and Moses-serenity would fill the church again, as if it were a challis. Of course I couldn't understand a word he said, and it probably had to do only with the sin of lipstick, but I wanted to believe that here was a mystical experience, as tangible as a fragment of the Grail, and that I was being enticed—here, just one hundred miles from Bikini—into a dangerous sacrament; that in a moment I would be expected to perform an ancient, utterly elemental, absolutely essential rite, such as whirling like a dervish or peering at a liver; that soon I must accept cannibalism, and have my ears pierced.

When the old man had finished, we said the Lord's prayer together in Marshallese, Doc and I mouthing the cantankerous syllables behind John's guiding finger in the Bible. We sang another hymn and then the preacher, who had been sitting off to one side inconspicuously, made his first appearance. He was an humble man with a perpetually apologetic look, and he wore a white waiter's coat and pinching black shoes that made him limp, though, as I found later, this was only on Sundays, for on week days I saw him swinging along barefoot like a professional hiker when he walked the four-mile road between the village and camp. He was the only villager there with glasses, and they were held in place, askew and almost flat against his eyes, by a wrapping cord tied about his head. He had asthma and as he approached the altar he pounded on his chest to clear up the wheezing. There was professional polish and calculated oratorical boom in his delivery, and some of the magic went out of the service; that is, I was able to relax into a sort of post-hypnotic state, comfortably elated but capable of looking about while I lolled luxuriously in the long roll of his phrases. Hell-fire, for that was probably the substance of the sermon, seemed like a carefully controlled conflagration and pleasant to watch: a sort of safe spectators' sport.

A dog wandered slowly up the aisle, sniffed at my feet and lay down. The crude drawings of Christ, the lamb and the dove were becoming slightly animated, and seemed to be showing interest in the service. I looked through the chicken wire and saw pigs rooting a few yards away; unusually contemplative, they seemed, and willing to serve as animal sacrifices if things should take that turn. The mass of children on the floor seethed with inner tumult, mostly controlled, though, by monitoring older children. A two-year old girl, escaping from her clutching sister, climbed the frame of the altar itself, going higher and higher until she peered over the top, her face coming within inches of the orating preacher; but no one, except the twittering children and the frantic sister, seemed to notice. A three year-old boy achieved more spectacular and compelling success when, scrambling free from restraint, he planted himself daringly in the aisle in front of the altar and in full view of the congregation, unbuttoned the front of his pants and urinated man-wise, the thin stream arcing upward gracefully, silvered and shimmering as a fountain before the altar of the Lord: it was like an offering of the first fruits of manhood. There were a few mild exchanges of smiles, but no one was disturbed by it and the little boy gloated wickedly in his achievement...The palm trees made contented sounds above us in the trade winds and I could feel the soft thud of the far-off surf.

We sang once again, Doc barely squeaking, though his soprano counterparts were still as robust as ever. The preacher came toward us with extended hands. Doc and I both thought he was taking up the collection so we each handed him a dollar bill, but he was merely wanting to shake hands—though he took the money after a momentary display of embarrassment—and to tell us that the all-day service was at a point where we might find it convenient and graceful to leave. Since the preacher spoke no English, John handled the translations: "Preach tank ya fo' money, an' wan' ya come back nex' Sunday so he make fine gift ta ya." I told the preacher that I appreciated the singing and asked him if they ever sang any of their old pre-missionary music. John and he had a prolonged discussion about this, and we went away without getting an understandable answer to my question for John would do nothing more than grunt, "hard sayin', hard sayin', special tough," when I prodded him for a translation.

Though he could produce only a half-whispered, broken-harpsichord sound, Doc kept trying to talk to me as we drove home for he had become elated by the service, and, perhaps, by his own performance. "That'll keep up all day long," he croaked, his voice feathering, "except now things'll start gittin' hot an' personal. Now's when they start squealin' on each other, an' decidin' whose goin' ta git 'churched'. John, fer one, is on the docket; so we won' be seein' him on Wednesday afternoons fer a spell, fer he'll be mighty busy up there a prayin' an' repentin' an' vowin' he won't do it no more."

"My goodness! Surely the magistrate can do no harm! Whatever has he been up to?" I asked with some alarm, hastily reviewing my own record.

"Oh, he got too damn polite, that's all. Last Sunday, just after church, my man Bill Hanlon went up to the village ta take a message ta him. An' there they all was, jus' comin' outta church, an' dressed up like ya seen 'em now. An Bill with his shirt off an' nothin' but some ragged shorts on. He saw the dirty looks he was gittin' from the pious bastards so he asks John if he'd done somethin' wrong, cause all at once he felt full of sin."

"Oh no," John says, "'Merican never do nothin' wrong, an' pullin' his own shirt off, right there in front of the whole goddamn pack of 'em, he takes Bill's hand an' they goes walkin' like man an' wife back an' forth, conversin' about the message an' the weather an' so forth, Bill Hanlin feelin' comfortable an' thinkin' what a fine way ta live. But not the congregation what knows that on Sunday—when they's all pretendin' ta be Adam an' Eve—ya jus' don' go around showin' off yore navel. So John, magistrate or not, is probably gittin' it now, jus' like Jezebel did when we was lissenin'."

That was my first Sunday at church.

On the following Saturday night a message came from the preacher: "Be sho' an' come fo' church, sometin special fo' ya."

Seven men, dressed as nearly alike as Rongelap wardrobes would permit—white shirts, dark neckties, crisp trousers, polished shoes, hair laid low with coconut oil—sat together on the front row of the women's section. John, Izikiel and Jeremiah were among them. Some of their clothes were probably borrowed, for several of them limped painfully when they moved about: Jeremiah, the muscular one, the smoothly coordinated athlete, moved like an old Chinese woman with bound feet for both of his shoes were for the right foot. But there was a radiant look about them. A look of recent baptism and anointment, and also a kind of slyness as if they were involved in a holy conspiracy. Once when John limped over to me to make sure I had a hymnal, I asked, "What's up? What are you fellows planning to do to me?"

"Extra special surprise, no talk," and he hurried back to share his amusement with the others.

The church seemed gay this morning for across the front was strung a wire from which bric-a-brac swung: baskets woven from palm or pandanus and dyed the color of sunsets; mats, the size of place-mats, and complicated as far as a weaver's imagination could carry them by fenestration, fringes, tassels and intricate patterns of color and weave—all a-swing in the breeze.

The church service progressed as before up to the point of the sermon. The preacher rose, pounded his chest to clear its wheezing, but, instead of walking to the pulpit, he joined the seven men, signaled to them with a sound similar to that used by drill sergeants, and they rose and wheeled as a platoon-front to face the congregation. He sounded a pitch—choirmaster-like, making sure they all had it—and they broke into a wild, primitive song, part chant, part wild crescendos with flights through a limited scale of possibly five notes, but flashing with guttural snarls and animal yaps—belligerent and voluptuous at the same time, savage as a nightmare and as unnerving as a mob scene before the Bastille. It came like a salvo from the German Navy across our heads, and at first we were stunned and expressionless. But then, little by little, as the meaning of the primitive ballad began to unfold, as its punch lines caught fire and its recurring refrain emphasized their meaning, sly titters began to ripple across the church, and finally—for the preacher was in the center of things giving special dispensation to the riot with his big bass voice—roars of encouragement shook the congregation as the eight men belted out their wicked annals.

"That was terrific. What was it all about?" I asked John as he sat down beside me when they had finished. John, still puffing from his effort: "Oh, dat da ol' song lak you ask fo'. Preacha 'members ol' songs. Almost da only one what 'members. But he not let us sang 'em till he change Bible names fo' ol' idol names. Den he teached us ever' night las' week. Real funny. All 'bout Abraham getting all mixed up wid Queen a' Sheba in da bull rushes. Peple lak it cause it soun' lak Sat'day night. We sing more ol' songs fo' ya' soon as preacha change names aroun'. Ya come back ta church. Ya started sometin."

"Yes, like undoing a century of missionary work," I thought.

But that wasn't all of the church service that morning. At intermission, the preacher came to us as before to shake hands, and after we had given him our dollar donations, for this seemed like a precedent we couldn't withdraw from, he turned to the front of the church pointing to the baskets and mats, and said in Marshallese, "Gifts for you." And when Doc and I returned to camp, our jeep was piled high, rainbowed and riotous with some of the best basketry ever produced in the Pacific.

Communion day was a little different from the others. There were the usual hymns, the now-usual special wild anthem, but as time approached for the sacrament, a peculiar apprehension seemed to close in on us. Every so often a man, usually a fairly young one, would rise from his seat, looking uncomfortable with averted eyes, and wander out of the church—not to go home, but to stand in the shade of the breadfruit tree; until finally there were more men standing under the tree than there were in the church. Two women joined them, pretty, young-matron types, frisky-looking; all eyes following them curiously as they walked out swinging their hips. John was there under the tree, and Jeremiah…The congregation had developed a weighted look, being very heavy on the women's side of the aisle, so that if it had been a boat it would have capsized.

"What's going on?" I whispered to Doc.

"They's the ones that's been churched," said Doc, "mostly fer smokin'. Shore looks like they'll be havin' good attendance on Wednesdays fer a while."

We sang an especially sad hymn and, sneaking a quick glance at the sinners under the breadfruit tree, I saw that they looked despondent and that the two women were crying. They were like the Multitude of the Slothful in Purgatory.

The preacher and a couple of very old men brought the sacramental bread and wine to each of us who remained, starting with me. The bread consisted of large, torn segments of loaves from the ovens down on the beach, delicious, and I wished for more. The 'wine', served in paper cups, was 'Cool Aid', weak and lavender-colored—anemic as from one suffering from a blood-dyscrasia, and I drank it with mystical foreboding.

When the sacrament was brought before a seat-full of adolescent boys, a crises arose, a minor panic that started with the preacher, rippled across the women's section, and lapped against the sinners under the breadfruit tree so that they leaned forward with interest: for the boys refused to touch the bread or 'wine', lowering their heads obstinately, and refusing to heed the preacher's admonitions even though he stepped back a few paces so that he could squarely aim his voice and his gestures at them. Several women, presumably mothers, rushed to them full of tears and pleading and promises. Bewilderment seemed so sincere that I wondered if such a crises had ever occurred before. And the boys, sin-entranced, making a first decision in their young lives, eyes mesmerized by their own feet, stalked out to the breadfruit tree. I thought the sinners seemed rather proud of the boys' performance, and they greeted them as if they were men.

Izikiel told me later, "Preach's religion too ol' fashion. Izikiel goin' be lak Moses an' start new religion so we c'n do 'bout ever'tin we wants, lak' smoke an cook on Sunday, an' fish, an' not worry 'bout dat God-damn hell anymore, an' not get churched all time, an' say shit, an' talk lak GIs. We wanna be lak 'Mericans."

NUCLEAR DETONATIONS

Headquarters, fearing that I would become bored on Rongelap, twice sent me to Eniwetok for close-up viewing of bomb detonations.

First viewing on Eniwetok

One morning we had a pre-dawn shot. A truck with a siren woke me with a thin, impersonal wail that I preferred to interpret as a warning that didn't concern a sleepy man—such, for instance, as Headquarters burning down or someone making off with the secret records. But a little later a truck with public address equipment came to beat me with an aural stick and make me understand that I must dress and feel my way through the darkness down to the beach area on the lagoon, just five miles from where a large kiloton bomb, about twice the size of the Hiroshima bomb, was to be detonated.

I got there nine minutes prior to shot time and stumbled over people lying on the ground until I found a place where I could sit. We were all there. Everyone not performing an essential job at the moment was there by command (on my way down I noted that the barber was staying behind—no doubt on essential business) to watch the spectacle under the discipline of the countdown. Each minute the time was given on the second, and each minute, as the announcement was made, I settled myself a little more firmly on the sand. So there we sat, indistinguishable from a crowd waiting for a fireworks display at a county fair, yelling at those in front to sit down, while those in front yelled at us to stand up. At five minutes before shot time a siren wailed; again at one minute it wailed more menacingly and we put on our black goggles. In complete darkness and sudden silence we listened to the final count-down at 30 seconds, 25 seconds, 20 seconds, 10 seconds, 9, 8, 7, 6, (if I had been the announcer I would have gotten confused about here and counted in the wrong direction) 5, 4, 3, 2, 1...and then a sudden hot flash that seared my face, then a fireball on top of the water which extended with terrifying rapidity into a ghostly hemisphere covering much of the lagoon; then, with single pulse, it contracted.

The phenomenon thus far occupied no more than a second or two. I counted to ten, turned away, removed my goggles (a little more slowly than those around me who were more experienced), and looked into the heart of the bomb: a tortured carnival of orange and violet flame

Rongelap villagers relaxing between bombs.

churning its way upward while fragments, like sparklers, fell away into the water—until finally gaining enormous altitude, its knobby end caught suffusion from the invisible sun and formed a fragile sunrise of its own amidst twinkling stars.... As a mushroom it would have classified as a pink-tipped morel.

The shock wave came somewhere in the midst of these transformations. It came with a jolt like a slap on all sides at once—whole body jolt—

and with a crack like lightening striking your house. We had been bracing ourselves for this, and when it was past I felt exhilarated by the excitement and started for breakfast. But as I walked toward the mess hall I slowly lost my appetite, and began to believe that I had been man-handled a little too roughly there on the beach.

Second Viewing

Later, I made another trip to Eniwetok, this time to observe the detonation of a much larger bomb—a huge megaton bomb—from across the lagoon at a spot that was 15 miles away. It was a daytime detonation and it wasn't handled in the same theatrical manner as the nighttime one that I have just described. This time there were only several dozen of us casual spectators on the beach. The General's pleasure yacht was anchored in the harbor in front of us, and across the lagoon we could vaguely make out the rocky strip that had been selected for the blast. The count down came over a loud speaker and when it neared the detonation point we all put on our black glasses and lay down solidly on the sand with our shirts pulled over our heads, for we had been told that exposed skin might be burned. The loud speaker announced the count down, and at the moment of detonation I felt as if I were on fire—though still no sound and no shock of impact. I peered stealthily through my black glasses and saw a huge, dense, black cloud mass exploding upward from the rocky strip across the lagoon, and a moment later, the full shock wave hit us, stunning me for a moment and it would have knocked me down if I had been foolish enough to have been standing. I watched the black cloud mass contour itself into the shape of an enormous backyard mushroom, extending its flat top till it covered much of the lagoon like an umbrella. During this development, the surface of the lagoon became animated and sent a 'tidal wave' surging at us with such fury that we had to jump and run for higher ground. Then with an apologetic swish, the waves swept back, leaving the harbor almost bare and the General's yacht canting dangerously on the bottom. I, of course, was speechless with amazement, but several GIs who had been through so many similar detonations that they had become bored, took off their film badges and held them up toward the black cloud that spread over us, hoping that the badges would accumulate sufficient radiation to send them home.

VISITATIONS

Occasionally the clouds would part, a plane would settle with a mighty splash in the Rongelap lagoon, and a chaplain, ready and eager to perform a visitation, would come to our island. There was a nice feeling in having a chaplain arrive by air transport, for even at the relatively low cruising elevation of the transport plane, he seemed to pick up certain celestial perfumes which he continued to exude for the space of his short visit with us. Curiously this minor prodigy didn't apply to the crew members, or at least couldn't be detected, since they usually hurried away to go fishing.

Our first visitation was by a chubby, good-natured Protestant chaplain who created a bright spot in a routine day. He seemed to be consumed with genuine interest in our spiritual lives and in the activities of the islanders, but also in distributing bibles and tracts, with the possibility of obtaining the gift of a model canoe—all thoroughly understandable motivations, especially the last which he reminded me of, or, perhaps dunned me for, in three subsequent letters.

After the noon meal he offered to conduct church service. Since it was a hot day we decided to set up church outdoors on the volley ball court where the trade winds bore down with force across the white coral gravel. And there we sat, lined up on three rows of dining room chairs a few feet from the breakers, stiff and pious in the purity of the blistering brilliance that was still haunted by GI profanity from a thousand volley ball failures. We dutifully held our tracts, a Bible and a song book from the wind and squinted self-consciously at the chaplain. He stood in front of us, disarming and friendly, and squinted back at us while he tried to create some of the homily and holiness of the church at home. Though his voice was carried away by the wind and battered by the waves, it created such child-like yearnings in us, such nostalgia for far away places and times, that we began to avoid his eyes for fear of confiding intimacies to a stranger; and instead squinted furiously into the gravel. We sang a hymn in piping, unaccustomed voices, weaving uncertainly about his firm melody line—a lonely and unsatisfying arabesque around the Old Rugged Cross. But the surf sang on sublimely in a different key about an unknown deity, and I had a momentary feeling that we were profaning a holy place with our poor performance. The chaplain preached a sermon about being proud to be American and Christian as if the two were synonymous, and for a moment we thought they were, and I felt sorry for the 'natives'. He preached over-time, just like preachers at home, and delayed his plane's departure. We liked him, he seemed to like us, but somehow we never quite recovered from this sneak glimpse at the 'ledger', during this moment of ultimate humility, when we learned that our souls were priced at just one model canoe.

Our second visitation came two weeks later when a Catholic chaplain arrived. He stepped onto the island carrying a large cross in front of him in the manner of a Spanish conqueror. But this was misleading since the cross was a gift to the islanders' church from the Protestant chaplain, who in an accompanying letter strongly recommended that the bearer return to him, not empty-handed, but with a model canoe, and—perhaps following more mature assessment of our souls—a coconut doll.

In my eagerness to please the pleasant priest and to demonstrate my friendliness to the cloth, I assured him that many good Catholics were joyously awaiting him at camp. But when we got there, we found only two; and one of these, in his determination not to be taken alive, promptly took off for the other end of the island with three cans of beer. This left only one young GI of somewhat uncertain conviction and practice—and no joyousness at all—to support my enthusiastic claim. But I was proud of him for he did his best to create the illusion of a well-disciplined parish as he made arrangements for mass. Space and privacy were the problems. Wind velocity ruled out the volley ball court; various consultants and technicians, who were traveling on the same plane, were tying up all areas with their specific tasks which had to be completed before departure; a technician and I were working on Geiger-Mueller counters and their recording devices on one end of a ping-pong table; so the GI, with superb disregard for protocol, commandeered the other end for divine service, using my little desk (on which I write such profane comments as these) for an altar. Drapes were arranged; candles were lit; the technician and I hushed our voices and avoided controversial problems in repair; the priest put on a white and gold vestment which, out of the corner of my eye, I kept confusing with a mandarin gown; the room became excessively warm; we all broke out in sweat; and the service began. Low, intense, rapidly muttered Latin; the mystery of the Mass reenacted in a moment of transport, peace and dignity; the intimacy of a great religion—all suddenly exposed to my non-believer eyes on the other side of the ping pong net. I liked the sound of it, and as I listened dreamily and fingered batteries and read dials, I wondered at the vast hierarchy of church and saints, of dogma and ritual all converging for a moment on one lone, cooperative GI.

Then it was over. The priest went to the men's room to wash up, and the GI brought me a copy of "Our Lady of Fatima" to read.

CHECKED OUT

Four miles across the South Pass was Arbar Island, low-lying and fuzzed on the horizon by its scrubby shrubs and its few palm trees. When we stood on the point of Rongelap Island, there beside the camp, and looked westward in the direction of Bikini, thinking of bombs and where fall-out might come from, we were looking directly at Arbar Island and the mystery that it seemed to present.

Clouds had a habit of banking themselves behind it in mushroom configuration; and, at sunset—when, indeed, we were most apt to be standing there looking westward with the dread of the next day's bomb schedule in our heads—the clouds would discolor themselves with livid purple and orange like mammoth nuclear fireballs. The island seemed far away—a good 100 miles, the distance of Bikini, for instance—and beyond our control because the waters of the Pass were turbulent and often appeared catastrophic for any small boat that might foolishly try to cross it. Planes coming to us from Eniwetok and Bikini first appeared directly over Arbar Island, it being the landmark for their approach. We never actually said it to each other, yet each of us accepted Arbar Island as the landmark to watch, the one that was threatening us—the real Bikini. And oftentimes there was a GI or two standing on the point, presumably occupied with fishing, but eager to report the slightest happening on this deserted, waste island.

The weather boys were its most enterprising watchers, and when they were not tracking a weather balloon with their theodolite, they usually had its rather imperfect, salt-etched lenses trained across the Pass and on to Arbor Island. "It looks to me like that farthest palm tree lost a frond last night," one of them was apt to report at breakfast; or "There are more coconuts on the trees in the interior of the island than on those along the water's edge;" or he would construct a hypothetical problem and spring it on us, such as: "Who'd ever think of lookin' for a criminal or a spy or somethin' like that hidin' out there?" And his companion, whose observations carried a lot of weight with us because he also had access to the theodolite, would carry the proposition one step further: "Yeh, if that island wasn't in our way, we might—god, I'd even bet as how—we'd see that damn yacht that's tryin' t' get itself fried under the bomb, sneakin' in. Probably, that is! Or someone spyin' at us an' radioin' everything we do, every time we send up a balloon, or take a leak on the beach, just as if it was any of their business."

And one afternoon one of the weather boys came to me breathlessly, "There's somethin' movin' on the island just as we always thought, you know, on that island over there that we've been watchin'. It's movin' like a man slippin' along close to the surf so we won't be seein' him;' or a seal, maybe, but probably a man; or a funny way the surf's been breakin' this afternoon; or a log; or a naked savage, maybe; but I'm pretty sure it's a man, an' a mighty suspicious one. James Henry, he looked too, an' he says it's a man all right, maybe with a walkie-talkie on him; he couldn't tell for sure if he had clothes on or if was a savage; but we're pretty sure he's a spy. We couldn't tell if there's a ship on the other side of the island, or if there's a submarine stickin' its periscope up. But there might be. Or that goddamn yacht with the fryers on it."

"I must report this to Headquarters and see what they think we should do about it," I said. But by the time I had reached the radio shack and Sergeant Bascomb, who was taking his turn at the transmitter, the whole idea was beginning to seem so fantastic that I changed my mind.

Sergeant Bascomb said, "Let's go over and have a look at it ourselves before we go reportin' crazy things like that. I'm a good boatman. I've been checked out on small craft and won't have any trouble getting across. Hell, this is just what I've been waitin' for—for a good excuse to get over there."

"Well, I don't know a thing about boats. Are you sure our little motorboat is up to the Pass? It looks mighty rough out there to me."

"Nothin' to it, nothin' to it at all. I've been checked-out all the way on boats, how to handle them in rough water, how to handle them in the surf, how to take care of motors—grease 'em and so on; how to predict the weather, how to enter a busy harbor, an' how to navigate—least ways when you're in a river. Oh I'm dependable on boats, an' that's the reason they sent me here. Let's start first thing in the morning."

So we started planning our expedition. As we planned it, it took on increasing dimensions until six people became involved, including John, the magistrate who should have known better, but who apparently deferred all judgments, even in such matters where he was expert, to our white-man's omniscience; and Kenni, the medicine man, and two adventurous GIs. The weather boys, who had particular familiarity with the waves of the Pass, declined our invitation: "We had better stay an' watch you through our theodolite," they said.

And the next morning, promptly on schedule, for our planning had been precise, we left the village in our 12-foot boat, gunnels heavy in the water, the 10 horse-power motor puttering under its unusual load, the sergeant at the tiller looking confident and elated over his authorized sea voyage.

There was a large hamper of sandwiches and Coca-Cola, and a pervading air of happy outing. I felt pleasantly elated with being in command of the expedition, and of having at my beck and call such well checked-out technical assistance—command in depth, I believe, is a technical way for describing such a resource. The sun was bright and lit up our orange life preservers with the gaiety of a circus.

It was easy motoring down along the lagoon side of Rongelap Island, for the wind from our back caught us only glancingly and helped propel us. But as we started across the Pass, though we stayed well within the lagoon, choppy waves began to pile up behind us, pushing us nervously off our course. Sometimes we would slide diagonally into a wave trough, wallowing there for a moment as our little motor seemed to panic from the mishap, and each time this occurred Sergeant Bascomb would apologize for having made a foolish error, saying, "In a moment I'll be getting on to the hang of these waves." But each time the magistrate looked at him in a perplexed way.

The further we went the choppier the waves became, piling up behind us and urging us to speeds that our little boat could not comprehend. Prow-heavy and stern sensitive to the criticism of the waves, we yawed this way and that, until we must have looked like a hula dancer sashaying across the lagoon.

Several times as we approached the island the boat turned cross-wise in a deep trough— 'broaching to' I learned later, a very dangerous and entirely inappropriate mishap, that often terminates with capsizing or swamping—so that the waves, white-bearded and curious, leaned over our boat and looked down at us, plainly puzzled by our conduct, perhaps trying to remember snatches of the Odyssey. But the sergeant remained cool, saying, "I've been checked out thoroughly on these situations, and I'll have everything under control in a moment."

The Magistrate and Kenni crouched on their seat, mute and expressionless. I found it rather exciting, having no concept of the danger we were in; and I admired the way the sergeant always seemed to bring the boat back under control, back onto the crest of the next wave so that we would shoot forward like a surfboard into our next yaw.

The coast of Arbor Island consisted of coral boulders, and the surf sprang high in its impact against them. "We cannot possible beach our boat here," we agreed, so we slowly circled the island counter-clockwise, passing over a low point of the reef until we were on the ocean side of the island and in its calm lee. There we found a small area of sand, and we made our landing.

"First," we all said, for we were eager to forget what we had just gone through, and even more eager to delay the next decision, which was how to return to Rongelap Island, "let's eat."

So we brought out the picnic hamper and ate the sandwiches and drank the Coca-Cola, strewing the little beach for the first time in its millennial history with Coca-Cola cans and crumpled paper. Then we strolled off individually or in pairs, some looking for shells and others for the giant coconut crabs which were known to inhabit this particular island; and looking only incidentally for what we had come for: the mysterious human figure slinking behind the surf's spray.

The island consisted almost wholly of coral rubble on which low-growing shrubs and a few palm trees managed to survive. John found several nice cowry shells and the sergeant found a large Japanese fishing ball, intact, and still in its rope net. But none of us discovered evidence of human or subhuman habitation, other than that shown by our own strewn garbage.

After an hour or so we came together on the little beach, needing each other, for we could no longer defer the problem of our return trip. The wind seemed to be increasing and was coming at us from Rongelap Island, whipping low over the waves. Whitecaps stood out like signal lights against their slate-gray shadows.

"We could probably live here for several weeks off them there coconuts," a GI said hopefully, thus introducing the depressing subject; but added darkly, "We should've rationed them ham sandwiches."

"Yeh," said the other GI following the same subterranean channel of logic, "No sea plane'll ever be able to land over here cause it's too rough. Probably nothin', but a destroyer'll ever get to us." "My wife and kids are in Japan, an' waitin' for me," said the sergeant with no actual discontinuity in the train of thought.

"How tough do you think it will be going back against those waves?" I asked.

The sergeant turned pale as he mentally reviewed the information on which he had been checked-out, and John, the magistrate said, "Too much chop-chop."

"But what if we were to take to the ocean instead," I said with sudden inspiration, "Maybe the long rollers out there will be easier on us than the choppy lagoon waves."

From our quiet sand beach, there in the lee of the island, we could see the ocean waves, tall but peacefully contouring themselves like good productive Iowa farm land. In our perplexity the ocean had the quality of a pastoral idyll.

"Better than spendin' Christmas here," said the sergeant who was still thinking of his wife in Japan. John and Kenni made no comments, though they disappeared among the palm trees and reappeared a few moments later with armloads of drinking coconuts (roughly a week's supply of rationed fluid and food) saying, "Ready now," which was as far as their comments went during the entire expedition—these two, the only experienced boatmen in the group, deferring meekly to our 'captain authority'; but who should, no doubt, have mutinied long before, at least to the extent of putting me in chains and drowning the sergeant.

So long as we stayed in the lee of the island our going was smooth and gracious—up the long, sloping rollers and down them with hardly a splash. "This was a very good idea," said the sergeant...and it occurred to me that perhaps Captain Bligh didn't have such a rough time of it after all.

But when we passed the point of the island, entering the Pass beneath the dark clouds, it was as if the climate and all attitudes toward mankind had changed. The wind came steadily at us from across a thousand miles or so of open ocean; rollers loomed far above us, streaming icy pennants of spin drift from their crests, hissing savage encouragement to each other, soaking us instantly at each blast of wind and wave, and filling the boat with water. Like an irritable animal deity the Pass grasped us and pulled us in under its clouds, and slowly our overloaded little boat teetered and bucked and lurched and panicked its way across the Pass.

But it was after we had landed at the camp and dried off and changed our clothes that we spent hours recreating the ferocity of the waves and wind to impress the weather boys who had been watching us through the theodolite. But they needed no impressing for they had seen us appear at erratic intervals on the crest of waves, pausing there nearly lost in the geysers of surf we were creating, fight for another moment of survival—or so they had interpreted our plight—and then disappear as if forever as the water rolled over us. Once they had been on the verge of sending a radio message to officials at Headquarters advising them to notify our next of kin; and to utilize, as best they might, the information that we had just drowned two of the leading Marshallese citizens.

"Oh, for Christ's sake," one of the two GIs who had made the trip with us would say, "them waves was higher'n our barracks, probably as high as that old palm tree over there; and they kept coming at us like the Rocky Mountains, one damn peak after another. Every time we'd look up from bailin' there'd be Pike's Peak starin' at us and its glaciers astartin' ta slide, an' a blizzard blowin' in our fuggin' faces so we couldn't see nothin' at all but that we was gettin' swamped."

"Well, the waves were probably about 15 to 20 feet high," our more conservative sergeant would say, "Mighty big for a small boat, but fully covered by my checking-out instructions, and I knew we were never in any real danger."

John, the Magistrate, and Kenni who had sat stolidly on their bench throughout the return trip, downcast and essentially uninvolved (I don't recall that they ever helped bail even when it was most urgently needed), each told me later, with minor variations: "We extra awful frightful out dar. Don' know why we no capsize most of time—most every wave. Ya good cap'n an' lucky. Always do wrong t'ing an come out all right. Importan' ta have good cap'n."

But I didn't care about anyone else's explanation for I cared only to remember—and to make everyone understand—the long, slow way we had chugged to the top of each wave, barely pulling ourselves onto its narrow, breaking summit—a half-ton of water blasting our faces. And I remembered the giddiness, during that instant while we teetered there far above every landmark, knowing that now we must take off wild and uncontrolled down that horrible descent yawning before us…though when I had finally been convinced that our course was charmed and that no matter what happened we would not sink, I had begun to think, "This is like a Nantucket sleigh ride and maybe I should be enjoying it. Maybe I am not really suffering at all; for instance, if I were a tourist who could expect an enormous bill for this tour with all of its little, planned surprises and thrills, how memorable it would be and how exhilarating!" Or, "This is merely a wholesome wintry respite from too much tropical living, and I must overlook chilblains and such injuries as might come from skiing or from climbing Mt. Everest; and also how fortunate it is that I am engaged in a noble mission at this time, otherwise I should feel guilty for taking such chances, especially with other people's lives."

I thought, though, that in spite of the exhilaration of those of us who had made the trip, that I detected a mood of disappointment in those who had remained in camp, as if the diversion of watching us survive had ended too soon and maybe in the wrong way; and several of them, as they left us to go back to read comic books in bed or to drink beer, made such muttering comments as: "Oh well, only ten more days for me on this rock," or, "In a month, if I'm lucky, I'll be makin' the rounds of them places in Japan or even shackin' up, an' will I be forgettin' this place in a hurry!"

But one GI, with special friendliness, called me to look at a stonefish he had just speared: mud-colored, moss-entangled, with underslung jaw that was still moving up and down mechanically, gulping foolishly at the unusable air; grotesque as a caricature of a war-time enemy, (General Yamashita kept coming to my mind) and each time we prodded it, it lifted its 13 pure vermillion, polished, poison spines just as Lieutenant Commander Lanpheer, in Kwajelien, had told me it would do.

THE IDIOT

"That stupid fool, that idiot, he almost killed me. He tried to de-, de-, decapitate me. I come all the way to Rongelap to inspect you, endure all this heat, all the gaff I had to take from that Air Force pilot (who I'll report to his superior officers when I get back) and what happens? A goddamn, stupid corporal tries to cut my head off, and would've if I had not been too quick for him. I'm telling you, Commander, that man has never been checked out."

So spluttered the Navy Captain as he stepped onto the beach, ignoring my practiced salute and the smart way I kicked my left foot with my right one as I came to attention; and the fact that a chorus of villagers, with their pigeon version of "Happy Birthday" were howling themselves hoarse in his honor.

Several days before, a radiogram had arrived, whining in a high-pitched, top-secret code. When the sergeant had decoded it, we read: "Captain Roschmueller arriving Friday flight for inspection. Desires honor and rifle salute."

"What's an honor guard?" I asked Sergeant Bascomb.

"Oh, ya gotta get at least four guys what don't mind actin' like monkeys and have 'em fuss around a little with guns and flag. But we can't do it. What with men from the night shift asleep, the radio having to be covered, and others handling the boat, we ain't got four men to spare; least-ways, that can be our excuse. Besides there's not a damn gun on the island, nor a flag that can be carried.

"Well, he expects special treatment," I said, "and we had better see that he gets it or he'll never in this world overlook the sloppy way we're running this camp."

"How about having the villagers meet him an' sing for 'im?" Doc asked. Doc, who always happened in when secret messages were being decoded. "I can fix it up with the preacher to arrange somethin' real sprightly."

"Yes, I think he would appreciate that sort of graciousness," I said.

"Swell idea," said the Sergeant, "we can probably get-by not pressing' our shirts if they make it loud enough." So we planned our reception and our distractions.

Usually we had difficulty in determining the exact plane schedule so that we could organize our trip to the village, launch our small boat, sweep the lagoon free of floating objects, and arrange ourselves in a semblance of readiness for whatever might step from the plane. But not on this occasion. Every five minutes we received a message informing us minutely of the plane's progress. It made us a little nervous, like a flight of enemy bombers coming our way, and we were all on hand half-an-hour before plane time; Doc placing the village chorus in position and instructing them on their cues; the sergeant coaching the boat crew in protocol and their timing; and telling me, "When you salute him, don't say 'hello' or 'good morning' or 'nice t see you', cause he's a Navy man, an' he'll want you to say, "Welcome on board, sir': an try to say it as if you thought it made sense."

The seaplane zoomed in low over Arbar Island precisely on schedule, sloshed into the lagoon in a perfect landing, taxied to the buoy about half a mile from shore, and tied up, Our boat crew approached it warily, remembering their instructions, and came alongside the plane as the door opened, and waited there, bobbing gently. A man, presumably the Navy captain, appeared in the door, hesitated a moment and leapt heavily into the boat. We could see our crew making welcoming gestures to him and motioning him to a seat, but he remained standing, assuming a stance as if he were preparing to cross the Delaware. This we had not anticipated and had not prepared the boat crew to expect. A little befuddlement seemed to shake them.

And then it happened, happened there in the lagoon, at least the one for which we felt responsibility at the moment. The corporal should have cast-off from the plane and allowed the boat to drift with the current until it was clear of the plane, as far as possible from its low, partially-obstructing wing, before starting the motor. But in his confusion with the uniformed presence looming over him, he started the motor at once, fumbling with the controls which suddenly seemed like foreign, unknown devices in his hands, and which, for reasons that he later could never understand, went into 'forward' instead of 'reverse', and with sudden, headstrong determination gunned itself as if preparing to take-off with a skier in tow. Straight for the plane's wing the boat charged full-speed. "Low bridge," yelled the corporal which was all he could remember to say at the time, though he added 'sir' when they had recovered themselves half-a-block in front of the plane.

Having barely skimmed beneath the wing, the captain picked himself up off the floor of the boat, dripping bilge, perspiration, and profanity.

"That man has not been properly checked-out and is a disgrace to your outfit," the captain lectured me in the stern voice of a supreme court judge, as he disembarked. Great commotion was taking place on all sides. The village chorus singing at peak volume, singing 'Happy birthday, dear Captain' in their broken pigeon English, and smiling ornately at the Captain. The sergeant and Doc were frantically appearing and disappearing, contributing only to the confusion.

Helplessly I motioned to the corporal to come to my side. The captain glowered disdainfully at him. "See here corporal, you could be court-martialed for what you almost did to me. Where in hell were you checked-out on small boat handling, that is, if you were checked-out at all. Tell me right now with no excuses. "Where were you checked-out?"

"In Eniwetok, sir; by the Navy, sir; all of us were, sir."

The captain moved uncertainly, then turning on me fiercely. "Commander, this man has been checked-out thoroughly and properly. I don't understand why you are making such a complaint. This is the trouble with you civilians!"

He stopped for a moment, listening to the chorus and swaying briefly to the rhythm. "By the way, Commander, is that the Anvil Chorus the natives are singing? Let me compliment you on their performance. They have been well checked-out."

TUNA HO!

I drove the length of Rongelap Island from our camp to Rongelap Village, with no particular purpose in mind except to fill in the lax time of day between supper and the camp movie, and to say good evening to the Magistrate.

It didn't require much of a purpose since I liked to drive over this rough coral track that plunged through water holes and twisted on itself to avoid palm trees. Sometimes when I was in a hurry—for instance, when I was called to attend an injured islander and had some justification for recklessness—I would bounce my jeep in four-wheel drive as fast as I could over ruts, jerk it around curves, and gash the water holes into sheets of spray, all with an appearance of heroism and dedication, though really only as an outburst of exuberance.

This was particularly glorious when I had a jeep-load of islanders all squealing with delight at each hair-raising incident, and telling me in a mixture of English and Marshallese that I was a jet pilot, and a very good one, probably even better than the one who clipped off a palm frond when he buzzed their island.

But at other times, languid from a day of sun and wind and salt water, I would drive lazily up the island, quietly loving the comfort of the trade wind that blew in my face and swayed palm branches across my path, while I wondered at the improbability of any island being so long and narrow, and so constricted through its mid-section, that on one side of the road you could watch huge ocean swells labor and tear at the coral reef, sense their impact and hear them groan and sob; while on the other side, through a fringe of palm trees, you could see the lagoon shine placidly in the late afternoon sun.

If you had a large scale navigational map of the Marshall Islands in front of you—although few things are more unlikely—you would see a little more clearly what I mean. On it you would recognize familiar names of several of the atolls—Bikini, Eniwetok, Kwajelein. Mixed among them you would see the names of other atolls that have never meant much to statesiders except a few missionaries and traders, but have had intense and passionate meaning to the people who inhabit them. People who, even after a succession of disasters—typhoons, famines, wars, invasions, atomic bomb tests—maintain a fierce attachment to these stark rings of coral outcropping in the Western Pacific wastes.

Ailinginae Atoll possesses one of these unfamiliar names. No one lives there now, and it is pertinent only by way of a ridiculous legend which, however, explains all the geography and geology you need to know for making this jeep trip from the camp to Rongelap Village.

A very old woman, so wrinkled and bent, and so tattooed from ancient rites that no one could doubt her authority on legendary matters, told it to me as we crouched beside a lantern late at night. Partly in stylized prose, partly in solemn, heroic chant she narrated an epic of creation which, for our fragmentary purpose, commenced with a cowardly giant by name of Los who lived on Ailinginae when it stood alone in this part of the ocean.

One day a huge wooden bird (constructed and operated by magic songs) flew low over Ailinginae, panicking the giant so that he started running wildly across the Pacific. By the time he arrived in the area now occupied by Rongelap (30 miles east of Ailinginae), his stampede and confusion had reached such proportion that he could run only in a circle, thus building up a coral reef by a process of primordial accretion. But the bird would not let up. It kept darting at him, and, worst of all, kept chanting to him in a horrid monotone, until his terror exceeded the physiologic limits of his normally housebroken sphincters. In this way—embarrassing to us who love Rongelap—the islands were deposited on the atoll, and distributed along the reef at about the intervals of a giant's stride if you allow for an occasional hop, skip and jump. Rongelap Island, the largest and longest island on the atoll, was formed in a special manner. It was formed, or at least shaped, as the result of a skid just after Los leaped across the four-mile-wide South Pass and struggled in the precarious footing to make the next turn up the atoll.

On the navigational map this seems to be a very good explanation of the shape of Rongelap Island, for there on the map, clearly delineated beyond all doubt and certified by the United States Hydrographic Office, you can see that it is widened at the point of Los' landing, but narrowed and streamlined through the length of an enormous, panicky skid.

It is probably no coincidence that this narrow stretch, extending between the camp and the village, is exactly four miles long, the same as the width of the South Pass. It has often occurred to me that a nice problem in the forces of acceleration and deceleration could be developed from this observation...particularly, if one knew the mass and velocity of giants in those days.

In this manner, comfortably and safely contemplating the misery of Los and the creation of an atoll, I approached the village. After a double switch back in the road, a final dip through a puddle—fine testimonials, incidentally, to the operator of a bulldozer who knew that the US government would have to pay $20 for each palm tree he knocked down—up a little incline as the island broadened; and, suddenly, without sufficient warning, I was in the village and immersed in its sweet smell of copra, its havoc, its litter of beer cans, its taboos, and its welcome.

The village always confused me with its mannerisms of quaint piety, recently learned and awkward, ruling the day, and its traditions of ancient times cropping out after dark It was like a mishandled revelation, a partial great truth, a fossil from a purer time, a tender mirage. Nothing like it exists elsewhere. Oftentimes when I visited it, I noted with surprise, but with laudable clinical observation considering my disorder at those times, that my sense of gravity seemed to be precisely the same as elsewhere, and that the effort of respiration seemed no different than at the camp or at home eight thousand miles away. But these were the only common reference points I could cling to as the tumult of the village would break over me.

Although I had spent several hours in its tiny infirmary that morning, my arrival was like homecoming. Naked children set up a cry of 'halloo-good-bye', halloo-good-bye', and mobbed my jeep so that I had to slow to turtle-pace. Several of the quicker ones climbed on the rear and shouted triumphantly in Marshallese, "Now I'm a doctor, too."

Adults left their cooking pits and their sprawled comfort to come speak to me. One brought a drinking coconut and another brought a bright pandanus basket; and while they welcomed me with pleasant speeches and gifts, they would snatch up rocks to throw at the children, and shout "Jab! Jab!" at them to teach them good manners. It was always like this; always exciting, charming and improbable.

Midway through the village I had to stop when an old sow with her pigs blocked the road. I started to get out to shoo her away when John, the magistrate, suddenly came to do it for me. To him this was a serious incident and he approached me full of apologies for the behavior of Marshallese livestock. There was eagerness behind his concern, and once I had praised the independence of Marshallese sows, he had an activity to propose. He introduced it casually as if it had just come to mind, and not at all as if I had pushed him into it by my strong hints over a period of several weeks, and he said, "We gung tuna feeshung ba moonlit; come do lakwise." Ever since I had seen a camp movie on tuna fishing in Sardinia, I had been indicating my availability for such an expedition, and I was delighted now to find that he had understood me so well.

He suggested that I should return to camp and that they would pick me up as they came past in their sailboat. This was a good suggestion since I could have gotten warmer clothes and could have stocked up on dramamine. But it seemed a nuisance, and as I sat there in the jeep feeling excited about the trip, seasickness or discomfort of any kind seemed very remote possibilities. So I said no, I would leave with them; and parking the jeep at the infirmary, I walked to the beach with him, hand-in-hand as Marshallese do.

The village boat, a 28-foot ketch, lay at anchor sheltered by the contour of the island from the strong current that swept through the lagoon and from the wind. It was a graceful appearing craft that was important in the work and activities of the atoll. I knew that the islanders, after one of their few unanimous decisions, had purchased it with US $2,000 of common funds several years ago. It had no bunks as such, but there was space for sleeping on the framework under the deck and on the bags of ballast on the cabin floor.

When, for the sake of classification, I had tried to learn how many it would 'sleep', I had gotten a surprising variation of opinions running from six to thirty. Similarly I could never determine its passenger capacity for there was always room for one more Marshallese—just as there was in my jeep. Usually, when I saw the boat under sail, its deck seemed to pulsate with a type of Brownian movement as uncounted numbers of islanders struggled for space. Although they spoke proudly of its seaworthiness, its sails and rigging seemed appallingly threadbare and the possibility of a serious accident—at least in less experienced hands—impressed me mightily when I prepared to embark.

Many of the islanders had followed us down to the beach, and eleven of us paddled out to the ketch, one at a time — that is one man as passenger and one serving as boatman—in a tiny outrigger canoe which could hardly stay afloat with such a load...like two men riding an underprivileged burro, beating it. The last man aboard brought a 12-year old boy to paddle the canoe back to shore, and for his pains, gave him a baby sooty tern which had been sitting on a coil of rope. As the boy paddled back, we saw him ambushed for this mark of favoritism by a dozen five-or six-year olds who set on him with a barrage of rocks and insults. He tossed the baby tern to them, and they became distracted by the adventure of tearing it apart while he beached the canoe.

Most of the crew members were particular friends of mine, and I greeted each one with affection since I suspected that each had come as a favor to me. There was, for instance, the preacher, Ilswo, who had worked as seaman in a Japanese fishing fleet for many years. He composed music—

good sound choral music—to celebrate every occasion, drilling it painstakingly into his parishioners. It never occurred to him that he was being erudite, and my admiration surprised him.

There were others whose friendship I had won less signally by an exchange of smiles or by a successful excursion into my tiny Marshallese vocabulary. There was also the captain, an edentulous old man who had appeared so insignificant around the village that I knew him only vaguely. I suspected that he had been persuaded to come, not because this trip required a navigator's skill, but to give it special status.

Years ago, before copra boats started their scheduled rounds among the atolls, a captain was considered enormously important, for the islanders' survival depended on his uncanny knack for deciphering wave patterns and setting a true course across their barren expanse. Without him there could have been no aid during famines, no wars, no stealing of women, no legends of heroic deeds nor great sea adventures. But today this prestige is recalled only at times of story telling or when a stretch of rough water must be crossed. Now on shipboard, the captain assumed his traditional position of authority, and, to my landlubber eyes, suddenly appeared very important and wise. He checked over the sky and found it satisfactory, but shook his head sadly at the rigging. He gave the necessary orders and we headed for the South Pass with the wind behind us. Thus we began our expedition.

I was an inexperienced sailor, and I approached the adventure wide-eyed and infatuated with it: the motion of waves rocking us gently; the swish of foam alongside gradually changing into a half-mile-long wake; the quiet chatter of men working over trolling gear; the amazement of my being here at all and sharing this sea, this breeze, this rich laziness, these heavy smells with my friends; the whole 'South Seas' myth suddenly revealed with startling clarity, and with me at its very center—these things produced such a sense of transport and rapture that I stretched out on the deck too happy to talk, and greedily tried to preserve every moment.

John, misinterpreting my silence as boredom, rummaged through a pile of tackle, dried fish heads, rotten bait, torn comic books, broken shells, finally found what he was looking for and brought it to me to read: a paper bound copy of Stephen Spender's 'Poets of my Generation.' Feeling a bit self-conscious—something like Stanley meeting Livingston—I read the first paragraph but decided that for the moment I preferred my poetry raw, non-verbalized and undeniably authentic, and tossed Spender and his generation back among the fish heads, never once wondering how Spender had gotten there.

We were approaching the South Pass and the camp on the far tip of the island. The wind increased and we began to get a foretaste of the ocean swells. The slight uneasiness I felt from time to time was easily discounted. In fact, in my state of exultation it seemed unworthy of recognition, and I was fully occupied by imagining the amazement of the GIs on the beach when they would see me sail nonchalantly past them as a Marshallese seaman.

When we passed within half a block of the camp, they were all out on the beach, gathered in little groups to talk or fish and to watch the sunset. I waved to them and they waved back, one of them even did a little Indian dance, but no one recognized me no matter how vigorously I called attention to myself. (Later that night when I failed to return on schedule they became worried for fear I had an accident in the jeep, an event they often predicted.)

Then we passed the point and entered the turbulent water of the pass where ocean swells and lagoon currents meet. The horizon began to heave. At one moment we could look down on the camp, and the next moment we could see nothing but waves arching the sky above us and cresting like clouds over our heads.

The deck lurched wildly and I anchored myself in the rigging. Flying spray; flapping sails; wind whistling the jews-harp rigging; the sky suddenly flaming into sunset; the preacher at the tiller singing a Marshallese hymn with several of the crew adding gentle, note-perfect harmony; John and Gia letting out the trolling lines; the captain amusing the crew with anecdotes and considering them a success when I, without understanding a word, would laugh—these things continued to build my faith and excitement in our venture as we headed into the darkening pass.

The plan was simply to troll back and forth across the four-mile pass, aiming at Arbor Island on one tack and for the lights of the camp on the other. And this we settled down to do, the crew spelling each other in handling sheets, tiller and trolling lines.

The sunset faded, and suddenly the sunlight went out as if sloshed by a wave. The moon developed the steel-hard intensity of a searchlight, and great cumulus clouds scudded, white and startling, across its beam. The temperature dropped until the spray, instead of refreshing me, began to sting and chill, and I hugged the deck for the little warmth I could get out of it.

I must have looked unhappy at this turn of events, for John asked me if I would like to go below to sleep. I wanted to tell him that I must stay here to fondle each sensation, to experience each moment passionately and to sense its subtlest nuance, and to fix it by some stubborn act of will in my poor memory; that some bodily discomfort was, perhaps, even essential to such a hedonistic exercise. But I couldn't find words in pidgin English to say it, and besides I was beginning to have to swallow too frequently to permit involved sentences, so I simply shook my head and managed one care-free gesture of delight.

I think I was becoming a little befuddled for it began to seem that my nausea and chilliness were increasing independently and in competition with each other, each being intent on the honor of ruining me in its own way; for each distracted me just at the moment when the other was becoming unbearable…

The upshot of this bizarre conflict was victory for neither; instead there settled over me an overpowering weariness, an unwillingness to move, a nearly paralyzing fatigue as if I had been given curare.

My last effort at resistance came when I heard one of the men singing a plaintive melody which sounded aboriginal and wild. With flagging anthropological interest I crawled forward to ask him what it was. "Oh, it Chris'mus song. I tink ya call it somehow lak 'It cam on Midnight Clear.'" Crushed and profoundly tired, I crawled back, found an old rain coat, curled up under it, and without further pretense of being a well man, went to sleep.

Each time we tacked I had to wake up so I could change sides of the deck, otherwise I would have found my head awash; and each time I made the move it became more difficult and seemed a little more pointless. Sleepily I watched the men dash nimbly about the slanting deck at these tense moments, and I wondered if even impending disaster could induce me to such activity. The answer came a little later. Near disaster did come and did not move me to any effort at all, nor did it even interest me very much.

It came on our last tack over by Arbar Island when the rudder broke and the jib sail tore loose. I awoke believing that the spectacle before me—the ketch standing on edge and threatening to capsize, the men clinging to the deck and shouting wildly at each other—was just another manifestation of my motion sickness, and, like a wave of nausea, would pass by if I could think of something else. And so it did. Someone found a plank that he held over the side as a rudder, and brought the little craft under partial control. Then we began to beat our way inefficiently back toward the village, gaining very slowly as we tacked back and forth across the inlet.

This information I pieced together later for at the time I felt little interest in either the affairs of the world or of the ketch.

Of the elements of my misery, cold finally became the most demanding and I crawled through the hatch to lie under the deck on a framework that supported me a few inches above sloshing bilge water. The air was heavy with the sweet smell of copra and the stench of rotting fish—a combination that signified the Marshall Islands and that later was to evoke in my memory more pleasant than unpleasant associations. Passingly, it occurred to me that this was no place for a seasick person, but I was developing an attitude of fatalism, having noted with a remnant of clinical determination that my disability was advancing with nearly constant, straight-line progression without regard to change of position, or the distraction of an accident. I went back to sleep but had to awaken to change position at each tack, and each time I noted about the same progression of nausea I had learned to expect. Several times I pulled myself up to see that our camp lights were scarcely changing their position, but somehow even this was beginning to seem unimportant.

The last time I awoke I heard the anchor chain rattling. John leaned through the hatch to say that we would be unable to get to the village, and that we were anchoring offshore not far from the camp, and that they would shout to try to awaken Nicodemus who lived nearby, so that he could come out after us in a canoe. I went back to half-sleep but became aware that a new off-beat, unpredictable pitching of the ketch at anchor was up-stroking my curve of nausea.

Then someone seemed to say that Nicodemus had come; and, without my knowing how it happened, I was reeling on the deck, blinded by moonlight. The lagoon, the air and the sky were an amorphous glare of steel, horrid, unnatural and sickening. Distant voices, nearly lost in the glare, kept urging me to do impossible things like walk to camp after a truck, get into a canoe, stand up. Something below, probably waves, kept pushing up at me. Then I saw Nicodemus, very gay as usual, holding his tiny, bobbing canoe against the ketch while he motioned for me to get in. I lurched at him, somehow got seated, and we floated free.

When the first wave hit us, we sailed high in the air, and I managed a very sick 'whee.' When the second wave hit, we shot high again, and I vomited. Vomiting always has been a heroic procedure for me, with explosive sounds and range. Coming as a climax to such grand-scale preparations, I fancy that this must have been an unusually spectacular display.

Vaguely I can remember Nicodemus facing me in the tiny canoe: at one moment consoling me, then dodging wildly and paddling furiously for shore. He was dodging when the last wave hit but dodging the wrong way — so that he received my full impact square in the face, panicked, let the canoe swerve and we sank in four feet of water. I staggered onto the beach, lay there for a few moments exhausted and miserable, and then tottered off to camp. By the time I got there it was three o'clock in the morning, and I was beginning to feel pretty good. I got the truck, drove back to the landing, picked up the crew members and took them to the village.

John sat with me in the front seat shaking his head. It had been too rough for him, he said, and the smells on the boat had finally made him so sick that he had vomited. He felt terrible and showed it by holding his head in his hands, shaking, and concealing his face.

Glowing with sympathy and companionship, I forgot my humiliation, and nearly forgot a conversation I had with him a few days earlier when manfully he had asserted: "Marshallese men never get seasick. Only women get seasick."

The next day I canvassed the crew. Had John become seasick? The answer: No. And Nicodemus? No, also. And how could I make amends to him for my disgusting, unsanitary behavior? No problem, I was told, for he had simply denied that he had been there that night.

And the tuna which this report was supposed to deal with? We caught no tuna. Some said that it had been too rough, others that the moon wasn't right; some said that we had trolled too fast, and others that we had trolled too slowly: but all agreed that no one should have expected to catch any tuna that night.

SHARKS

Our Standard Operating Procedures—our standard of piety— called for exercise of the buddy system by those going near the water. But as I gained confidence in the reef, surviving each new venture, reaffirming, so it seemed, my comforting doctrine of indestructibility, I began to disregard it. Especially when there were no GIs near enough to be perverted by my poor example.

Across the island, on the ocean side, the waves crashed with unusual violence at the edge of the reef, and then poured in a flood of milk and swirling eddies over the honed, flat coral surface. Like the surface of the moon, it was pitted by small holes, and in these holes, small creatures hid, timing their cycles with the tides and the coming and going of predators; and here, a mile from camp under a sky as silent and wild as it was before Rongelap was inhabited, I used to go shelling at low tide, probing at the creatures in the small holes half-expectantly, half-reluctantly. I never found much, probably because I really wasn't interested in shells, but only in the mood of the place: the feel of the ocean coming at me; the way the horizon seemed to raise itself up on its elbows, very blurred as if trying to conceal some indecent activity; an impenetrable security device behind which stern generals, forgotten ancient chiefs, and creditable modern scientists were stirring vats of strontium. As the tide turned and the water came in dank, cold and boisterous and with a deep-ocean smell, there was always the sense of a storm brewing beyond the reef and of hovering danger; and sometimes I would dare myself to stay out there long after shelling had become impossible. Small manta rays wandering in with the tide could be startled into crazed, wild flapping; and strange schools of fish, not seen on the lagoon side, would flash past unexpectedly.

Once, two small sharks only a little over a foot-long appeared that had probably just been born (as a later 'obstetrical experience' with a shark suggested), and were now seeking shelter from a voracious cannibal mother. They were the color of sand, so classifying them as 'sand sharks' and of no significance. I started playing with them, herding them toward the shore, trying to stampede them into beaching themselves. They drove before me like a pair of matched ponies coordinating their movements obediently almost to the beach, but always slipping past me at the last moment. Again and again I herded them patiently almost to the beach and their destruction but so intent on infanticide was I that I watched nothing but the two babies while trying to gain their confidence and gentling them for the final kill. But then I saw the shadow behind me, my size or a little larger, moving as I moved, gentling me, and stalking me just as I was stalking her off-spring. I lost interest in the baby sharks and tried to move disinterestedly away from them, even humming a little tune as if I were there only by sheer coincidence. But the gray shadow moved with me. I waded faster, feeling a little panic as my muscles tightened and urged me on to faster and more effective motion through the waist-deep water that was trying to trip me with its heavy roils; and the shadow darted in closer with increasing interest. I stopped and it paused, though it continued to drift toward me.

My "military command" on Rongelap consisted of 30-some bored GIs who sought relief from island life by such distractions as catching sharks and playing with them.

The logic of the buddy system over-whelmed me for a moment (although why I should wish to have involved an innocent buddy in such an affair with a shark was not clear), and the mile from camp became an eternity of space. Seabirds flew overhead like wreckage from a bomb, and there was a sensation of rapidly advancing dissolution. I looked about for the baby sharks, hoping to evoke in this maternal gray shadow a cannibal longing for them, but they had disappeared, and there was only the mother shark and I facing each other as if preparing for our moment of truth in a bull ring. But then, without thinking it through, probably only a reverse form of panic actually, I was yelling, waving my arms, trying to look larger and hungrier than the shark, and charging as rapidly as I could through the waist-deep water. The maternal shadow hesitated a moment, turned tail and headed wildly for the edge of the reef, its dorsal fin slicing the water as spectacularly and as finally as if it had been planned just that way. I lost interest in the babies, whose lives I had probably saved from their cannibal mother, and hurried back to camp, telling no one about the encounter, though for a day or two I was a stern enforcer of our Standard Operating Procedures.

But somehow I never could feel unkindly about this shark 'attack', for it had begun to seem that the ocean was at last accepting me, in terms, though, of its own private ecology.

⊕   ⊕   ⊕

The GIs loved to fish for sharks off the beach beside the camp as the tide was flowing in. They did it by baiting a huge hook with a fish weighing several pounds, and tossing it as far as possible out onto the coral apron where the water was three or four feet deep, and where sharks kept careful surveillance of all the fish activities. But it was not simple, for the sharks were nervous and became panicky when shadows fell the wrong way or when a GI made a sudden motion or yelled in his excitement and impatience. I often felt a little stupid, as I watched these cowardly sharks, for having let one of them, on the other side of the island, herd me about and panic me. Suspiciously they would swim back and forth near the bait, trying to find a reason for not abandoning it, but sometimes an inexperienced shark would take the bait and get itself hauled onto the beach—a hundred or two hundred or even three hundred pounds of worthless shark meat—dangerous, no doubt, with its slashing teeth, but scarcely worth the sporting-time involved. Once a curious GI set about autopsying a shark, and when he had slashed open the tough belly, three small sharks leaped out—about the size of those I had chased—and flipped themselves into the water, two of them taking off like experts, the other requiring a few moments of floundering orientation in the new environment before following its mates. The GIs could easily have killed them, but they didn't, and they stood there watching them paternally.

STORY OF THE GREAT GRANDFATHER

"If ya lak ta hear 'bout old times," Izikiel told me, for he knew of my interest in Marshallese history, "'ya gutta get ol' women ta talk. Ol' women be story-tellers lak ya never heard, with flowers an' good smell an' blood an'screams; lak bein' back in ol' days ya self, but ol' womans no tell ta strangers. Tough! Ver' tough!" And he started to walk away. My curiosity was aroused, just as he knew it would be, and I hurried after him. "Look here, Izikiel," I said, "I'm not a stranger any more. I've been here four weeks. I know the names of many of the old women and have treated most of them for constipation. What more can I do to get them to talk?"

"Ver' tough, ver' tough problem. We gutta tink 'bout it hard, but prob'ly ol' womans jus' won' talk," he said provocatively for he liked palaver and prolonged, difficult conclusions. So we sat down on the sand together while he persuaded me over and over again in compelling surges of conviction that only through the performance of the old women could I know the enchantment and horror of the Pacific islands; that only through their worn memories could I possess, even passingly, the feel of valor and great deeds. "But," Izikiel would periodically puncture my determination, "Ol' womans won' talk, jus' won' talk, don' know how mak 'em talk." The sun beat down scorchingly on us and it wasn't until I began to stir somewhat uneasily from it that Izikiel, noting my agitation and fearful that he might lose my interest, said, "One ting ya try. Give ol' womans gifts, lak gifts, might talk after gifts. Don' mak no mistakes."

So I laid out my campaign craftily, trying to avoid all conceivable mistakes. Discreetly and with the appearance of spontaneous goodwill I distributed gifts among the very old women, and, while they cooed and gurgled happily over the remnants of brocade and gold lame that my wife had sent me for such purposes, I would make little speeches about my interest in old times. And they, like the natural orators they were, would make gracious little speeches back to me, thanking me for the gifts and lauding the glories of modern times. All except old Jera, the oldest of them all whom everyone believed to be more than one-hundred-and-twenty years old, maybe one-hundred-and-thirty or maybe one-hundred-and-forty years old; Jera whose small frame was bent until she seemed child-sized, but whose face was as noble and wrinkled and dew-lapped as a bloodhound's. She was like a thousand years of passions and heroics and odd genetic formulae contoured and locked in code. She was pampered by the entire village and preserved like a precious relic, possibly a profane one, for there was a feeble wildness and a smell of discarded history clinging to her. I knew, for instance, that those pious folds of her mother-hubbard covered tattooing across the belly that was as wildly imploring as any tattoo artist, living or dead, could execute. But old Jera would merely accept the gift I gave her and mumble a little curtly to the translator, "Make up a speech for him," and go back to inspecting the coral gravel she was sitting on, and digging little holes in it with her long, curved walking stick.

"Ya no get stories from 'em till Jera say so," Izikiel warned me. "She boss-woman 'roun' here."

"But why won't she cooperate? Is she no longer smart enough to understand what I want?"

"Shore, she plen'y smart, smart lak ol' times, can navigate all way ta Kwajelein. She know wot ya after, why ya give gifts, she jus' don' tink tellin' ya stories importan'."

"Did she ever ride in a jeep?" I asked, grasping for another approach.

"Na never did, good idea, better try it."

So one day I loaded her into the front seat of my jeep and drove her up and down Rongelap Island, at first in stately fashion as became her age and fragile bones, but then, when I saw that I was getting nowhere, I speeded up over the bumps and took a couple of turns a little crazily so that her watery old eyes sparkled and she squealed "whee, whee." But when I took her home to Jabwon village she merely turned to Izikiel and said, in Marshallese, of course, "Make up a speech for him," as she squatted in the gravel and resumed its inspection.

"Well," said Izikiel several days later for he disliked seeing a conspiracy falter. "'Bout las' ting ya gotta try on ol' woman is movie. Never saw movie. Bet ol' woman lak western movie ya gonna have tonight at camp."

"Can she see well enough?"

"Don' know, but she'd better or ya won' get 'em talk."

We had movies almost every night at the camp, as often as the air transport brought in new ones or the GIs could bear repetition of the old ones. We had them in the space behind the dormitory where we could sit in the coral gravel along the edge of the volley ball court, but where it was possible, when it rained, to crowd backwards under an awning that gave slight protection to the garbage cans and to the hardy GIs who were willing to sit there through a downpour. Just a few yards away the lagoon threw white tendrils of spray toward the flickering movie lights. And overhead at movie time there was the spectacle of tropical nights: the sky wet with stars, the massed clouds that seemed bolder and whiter than at high noon, the Southern Cross staring obliquely down from somewhere beyond the equator a little uncertainly as if unsure of its bearings in this hemisphere. On the far side of the volley ball court there was a good-sized movie screen that clung for support to the water tower, a brave screen that resisted the wear of the trade winds and salt spray, glaring and wondrously white for the GIs were always repainting it as a sort of act of devotion. It had only one defect: it was square. The projector was adjusted to its square dimensions but the films, coming directly from stateside movie palaces and designed for football-field shaped screens, were not. The result of this unnatural combination was a remarkable compression of the images from side to side that gave Lincolnesque nobility to all of the characters, and disproportionate height to everything; thus, a valley among gentle hills became a frightening chasm, and Wall Street became sickening in its wild, curving plunges to unimaginable street level depths. The islanders never complained of this distortion, for to them it wasn't distortion: it was merely the way things are supposed to look in America.

So that night I brought old Jera to the camp movie in the jeep, placed her on a pandanus mat squarely in front of the screen, with Izikiel on one side of her and me on the other, bags of potato chips and peanuts, and an ice bucketful of Coca-Cola within easy reach; all carefully planned in advance as a roue might plan a seduction. Every grunt she made, every uninhibited belch seemed dire and laden with meaning that somehow required immediate action from me… "This is it," I kept telling myself, "this is my last chance. There must be no flaws."

Suddenly Doc's hoarse voice rasped from behind the movie projector, "Sorry men, this film ain't no western. It's some goddamn thing about a guy called Jimmy Walker. Probably a damn kid's picture. Well, here we go fer better or probably fer worse." The GIs, lounging about us in the gravel or squatting on makeshift stools, snorted

Yes, very hot. The lucky ones chose not to live in the houses, but under them. Here is a picture of a happy family living in this cool space. This was the space in which I relaxed on those nights when I listened to the "Story of the Great Grandfather" and other accounts of ancestral times in Rongelap.

obscenities and several of them left in disgust. The islanders, sitting beyond them on the outskirts of the group, muttered in perplexity, unable to decide whether they approved or disapproved the change.

But I had seen the movie before and knew what to expect: Jimmy Walker, reprobate mayor of New York City, falling about in a drunken daze, a chorus-line of speakeasy nudes sashaying and kicking and wriggling with the bouncing vulgarity of the Twenties. And I should have brought this nice old lady, partial product of the Boston missionaries, to see it and to win her confidence!

The image burst on the screen in flares of overdone, compressed color, and, a little later after Doc fiddled with the mechanism of the projector, the voices, shouting at peek volume and very low fidelity, hurled from the loudspeaker that was placed half-way between us and the screen. The old lady jumped in alarm, studied the situation for a moment, then asked Izikiel, half in disgust, half in curiosity, "What's that fool box doing up there trying to talk?" …We were off to a poor start.

Then Jimmy Walker, appearing much taller and thinner than in life, and after a few preliminary statements about an unhappy home-life, became promptly drunk. I watched old Jera with alarm, expecting to see her recoil in horror, this kindly old convert to missionary preachments who must know (if any precepts had taken root) that drunkenness is a sin and that this was a particularly outrageous example of it. But she was laughing. Each lurch that poor, skinny Jimmy Walker made, each downward step that he took in his depravity brought another guffaw until finally she held onto my arm, shaking and weak from laughing.

But the nightclub scene, what about it? What about that flaunted nudity? And how does nudity appear to one who is wearing a mother-hubbard? "Inconceivable," I thought, "that this film has been sent to us." My Bible-belt conscience revolting just as it had when I had seen it before, but now being given new force by the missionary interdictions that seemed to hover like an ambient vengeance over the Pacific. I looked at her, ready to throw my own scrawny body between her and the screen as a token of respectability, feeling sick like the time I learned the meaning of a dirty joke that I had innocently told my grandmother. But she was clapping time to their furious gyrations, nodding with eager approval at each particularly effective grind—like a connoisseur of grinds—swaying in broken rhythm for the tempo was too fast for her; and softly saying over and over, almost as a fervent chant, "emmanlok, emmanlok, emmanlok;" which means "it is excellent" in Marshallese.

Suddenly I understood—it came to me like one of those instantaneous revelations that establishes a relationship between two apparently disparate events or objects (space is really in the shape of a curve, for instance) that this old lady with her roots in savagery, understood the roaring twenties better, and with surer affinity, than I. I looked about at the younger

Marshallese: they sat straight-faced and dour, perhaps not comprehending, perhaps being offended at the doings of the mayor of New York…At least they knew now that they would have preferred a western. But I was beginning to feel grateful to Jimmy Walker as to one who had given me the proper credentials for a difficult journey.

After the show I drove the old lady and Izikiel back to Jabwon village. As we parted, instead of the curt "makeup a speech for him," old Jera actually did make a little speech which Izikiel translated to me as: "We did it better in the old days. Come tomorrow night, late after bed-time and we will tell you about it."

Frequently after that, as frequently as I could get away from the camp, I came at night like Nicodemus, over to Jabwon village to one of the gray buildings that stood a little apart from the others, the one that the old women regarded as their special sanctuary. Each session would start in the same way. I would lie stretched out on a pandanus mat, looking dreamily into the flame of a smoking kerosene lantern; the old women and Izikiel lying or sitting about me, and several sleepy children playing quietly just beyond the circle of yellow light, but leaning into it as the story-telling got underway, partly to hear better, partly for the protection that a flame— even a smoky one from a poorly trimmed wick—would give them at that hour of the night. The doors and shutters were closed against prowling ghosts, for several ill-tempered ones were known to be leaving the burying grounds those nights, and the air enclosed us in a warm ointment of palm-oiled bodies and the stink of the lantern—not unpleasantly, though, for we were thinking about the days of unwashed savagery and a little pungency helped the illusion.

Old Jera would sit cross-legged and humped on the other side of the lantern looking into its light unblinkingly—a sort of grotesque South Seas carving that should have featured hanging, withered breasts, a caved-in belly with skin slabbed in leather pleats, and scrawny-shanked thighs, but, through some perversity or mismanagement, had gotten itself swathed in a mother-hubbard.

This was the moment of expectation before story-telling that stirred me like the movement of clock-hands turned slowly backward, like the uneasiness of a missed heart beat, or the moment of hesitation and hasty repentance when contemplating an unnatural act. This was when the old women clustered a little closer to Jera, ready to support or defend her, or lead her on to the next event, eager as marauders in a war party to cross over into forbidden times. They were the enemy beyond the river lined up under the palm trees, spears at the ready, waving their painted shields and daring me to approach…. It was like a seance with a trace of deviltry.

Slowly old Jera would begin to mumble indecisively and incoherently to herself, detaching herself by degrees from the present, jabbing slowly and persistently at her memory; faint smiles, looks of triumph and pain flitting across her furrowed face while she fondled old rhythms and old deeds. Sometimes Izikiel would say, "She's gung backnow, but no' far 'nough."

"Go back ta young girl-time, gran'moder, on back, way back, back bafore missionaries, back bafore sin, back ta edge of forgettin'," and she would mumble a little faster and a little more intently. It was as if she were trying to cross over a reef into an ocean of bright, bold waves. Sometimes Izikiel would drum his knuckles on the floor with gradually increasing cadence to help her along. Once, when she appeared to be getting herself organized toward a steady flow of recital, the old ladies began to titter and exchange sly glances, but Izikiel interrupted her a little harshly to say, "No, no, not that 'un, gran'moder, chil'ren lis'en, too many bad tings. Try anoder…Oh yea, tell 'bout ma great gran'fader, da 'un called Jekkar. Doctah wan' ta know about great gran'fader. Ver' great man." Suddenly her recital took on a new turn and new excitement, and she spoke so rapidly and with such determination that Izikiel had difficulty interposing a sketchy translation. It was a story that all the old women knew for they leaned forward in anticipation and, at times, joined in its recitation, word for word, in the sing-song torrent of a partial epic that had transpired within some of their memories

I could understand the grandeur and wonder of the story for these were in the tom-tom beat of the narrative that sometimes became a wild chant, and in the crescendos that sprang savagely into shrieks, in the ecstasy of the old women whose eyes were moons to the lantern, and in the intensity that settled over all of us and held us, almost hypnotically, peering into the flame. But I grasped only fragmentary details at this first hearing, and I had to ask many questions later, fill in background information gotten from similar later sessions; interpret the pantomime; flesh in the gaps, and then see it all, as nearly as I could, through old Jera's unreconstructed faith in a worn-out chivalry. Here is the way I understood the "Story of the Great Grand Father"…Its integrity is not in its anthropological precision—which, if it has any, is coincidental and unimportant—but in the emotional (almost mystical) transport of those evenings that I am trying to preserve.

> You men of weak backs and few children
> You weaklings
> You men who fear to leave the lagoon
> Or fight an enemy

Listen to this story we tell of mighty days
And of a mighty man
Man among men
Man among many women
    Father of uncountable children
    O mighty Jekkar
Cringe, you cowards, and beg for manhood
Shout to the sky
Dance in furious circles
Beat the ground
Liftgreat weights
Fight anyone who dares
Kick the burning logs and send the sparks flying
So that his spirit may fill your bodies with its strength.

Slowly it comes at first
Now faster and faster
Still faster until it is like a wind raging
Roaring in anger and joy and destruction
Entering you, killing you, maddening you
O glorious is the strength of Jekkar!

It comes—
It comes
It comes—
The spirit of the mighty one
Filling our livers.

We see you, Jekkar, we see you slowly gaining substance in the heavy
shadows beyond our lantern light, awful as a god, divine as a spook, O
most efficient killer. And we see you at all times in your life from the time
you left your mother's ruddy cleft to the time of death when the ghost-
world carried you, protesting and defiant away from us. But let us mark the
time your manhood broke its bounds, climbed the highest palm tree, as it
were. Let us sing of your most valorous moment, of the blood-bathed feast
that inspires our men and frightens our children. O let us praise the cunning of your brave right arm as it swung the great war club through the
protective spell of the Yap woman, as it spattered the brains of the Yap
woman, and freed the great fleet from sorcery. And with uplifted voices, let
us sing of that glorious, blood-bathed feast of Yap liver that marked you
forever godlike; and let us sing, but slowly with a sob and tenderness that

shows our understanding of the event, and of the subsequent sad feast of bitter bile, when war canoes bobbed high and low on the lonely swelling ocean ...and your great heart expanded.

O noble murderer, sweet murderer whose manly beauty brings tears to our eyes and dance movements to our old bodies; O step back to those years before the first killings; ah, to those years when maidens first enticed you to the gentle wrestle of loins in the bushes; lean back in time, stern, O most unrelenting ghost, so that we may thirst lovelorn—we barren, old women—in the deep pools of your youth: Ah, your eyes were for the search of far-places beyond the horizons, like the eyes of a seabird; your ears were for hearing the talk of warriors; your arms for the throwing of spears; your hips for the great leaps of the war dance and the tumble of sports; your thighs for the sure strokes of one who is fearless among sharks; and your ways were for modesty and obedience like those of a highborn woman—O gentle boy, creature of destiny, lovely shrub before its incredible flowering.

Carefully they coached you, the old men and the warriors, carefully they nourished your rages and cruelties, your greeds and your loyalties until your fame spread over all the ocean. In Utirik they praised the sadness you caused on Ailinglaplap. In Ujelang they chuckled at the despair you left on Pingelap. Your rape of ten women—though some said it was only three—on Kusai amused the gossips on Jaluit; and your fight with a giant on an island so distant that no one recalls its name—though all know that the giant was tall as a palm tree, with a voice as big as thunder, that you killed him in a fair fight, and then, as was fitting in those days, ate a piece of his liver, thereby considerably increasing your strength and possibly your height—yes, this fight brought your name to every watch fire, even to the watch fire of the great Iroij in Kwajelein to whom all Marshallese gave allegiance. Truly, Jekkar, you had become a warrior, But:

> What good is a canoe without an ocean
> A fisherman without fish
> A story-teller without a tale?
>
> What good is a reef without its encircling sea
> A watch-fire without Coconut husks to keep it going?
> Or food without hunger
> Or palm wine without a celebration
> Or fertility without children?
>
> What good is bravery that is hidden
> Or hatred that is controlled?

O, good things are for using
And for warriors there must be war

You were ready when the omens told of war: the way the seabirds swept in from the south, the unseasonable appearance of certain fish roe, the unnatural lingering of lights on the southern horizon after sundown, the restlessness of palm trees when there was no wind, and innumerable signs that could be seen and understood only by seers. The great Iroij in Kwajelein knew these signs and his seers knew them. They knew that powerful people from the south were coming in a fleet so huge and so overpowering that it would reach like white caps from horizon to horizon. Never such excitement! Never such eagerness to defend! Never such passion among our warriors to display their valor as night after night they danced the mighty war dance, scratching themselves until blood splattered the ground, shrieking their vengeance at the night-clouds! O the pleading of the women: their songs of ancient prowess, their taunts of deficient manhood, and their chanting which, in those days started slowly and quickened to a mighty roar so that no man, not even a coward, could stand against it, and all became fearless and numb to pain. O the screams, the wounds, the dancing into exhaustion as the women prepared their men for war.

And you, Jekkar, you were the first on Rongelap to ready your canoe and head it for Kwajelein. Others followed, their canoes loaded with warriors and wives and children, but you were first and fleetest.

In Kwajelein you saw the great fleet assembling in the broad lagoon: canoes from Majuro, Rongerik, Bikini, Ujelang, Ailinglaplap, and even from friendly islands in the Carolines; all in varied colors and shapes according to the islands from which they came, all freshly feathered with plumage of seabirds to give them speed and grace, all proud in their new-woven pandanus sails and fresh-cut outriggers…and, like white caps, reaching almost from horizon to horizon. And there, with the homage that was due, you offered yourself to the great Iroij, lowering your voice nearly to a whisper, bending your head in fealty, but so manly in your demeanor, so stalwart, so like a young prince, that the Iroij selected you above all other warriors to be always at his side.

Such was his affection for you that whoever would win the great Iroij's favor first brought gifts to you, as was fitting. You placed your sleeping mat on the broad deck of his war canoe, there among his family, his favorite warriors and his hostages, there among the fifty or more people that the great canoe carried, but your mat was in the place of honor: across the entrance to the hut wherein the Iroij slept, for you were like a son to him.

Now we must consider the Yap woman whose destiny is at the very root of this tale. What of this "villain" woman whose evil sorcery, rather than your own heroics, O great Jekkar—begging your pardon for having such thoughts in our heads—gives this tale its greatness above all other tales, for, after all, we have many other heroes just as hardy and handsome as you, with the same bulging muscles, the same graceful movements and gentle ways but there are no other villains, absolutely no other such villains as the Yap woman! Ah, we see her squatting on the deck of her high-prowed canoe; we see her, the huge Yap woman, fat and billowing, larger than any man, and as vigorous as an island in creation. O her arms were tree trunks, her breasts were full moons and as firm as a man's buttocks, her voice was thunder, her smell the sweet death smell and as overpowering as drowning. Such was the magic of her presence that even strong men—including yourself, Jekkar—felt their limbs grow weak, their thoughts twist to her bidding, and—amazing to them and so humiliating that they tried to conceal the event by some artifice such as stumbling and falling into the lagoon—an unavoidable tendency to spill urine as they approached her. Nor could the elements act against her will, for clouds crumpled when she fixed them in her stare, and great rollers smoothed obediently before her canoe. Some said she had ao, the wondrous virtue that winsomely wins all persons, but you knew her for what she was: a sorceress of evil charged with the malignity that lurks in the mountains of Yap.

At her breast she sometimes held a scrawny infant, letting it nurse ravenously for a few moments, even fondling it, then, in sudden disgust as her mind moved to other matters, pulling it away from the nipple to toss it squalling on the deck.

There were many Yappese warriors among you who, because their ways were strange and no one trusted them, had been dispersed through-out the fleet. But they took their commands only from the woman, as si-lently they listened to the boom of her voice, moving obediently whenever she gave a command. Two of her sons, strong mountain-grown men with a wild look about them, were kept as hostages by the Iroij. They lay on their mats never speaking to you when you passed them, never seeing you, for their eyes were turned inward in obedience to their enchantment.

And when the fleet was assembled and organized it departed from the lagoon, sailing southward in search of the enemy.

> O the great fleet is speeding through oceans of light
>   like a flight of spears
> Piercing the cresting waves as if they were clouds
> Passing southward

Ever southward
Into strange oceans where influences are unknown
    and the temper of guarding spirits must be
    anticipated and dealt with.
O the joy of birds flying and the loneliness of stars!
Listen to the murmur of the rigging as the wind rises in it
    until it is like a small boy whistling
Listen to the grunt of the mast as it leans against its moorings
Listen to the cry of the white clouds.
O you men in each canoe make ready for the precision
    of the tack, when all of you with common accord,
    each knowing his appointed task, will unloose the
    rigging and heave the heavy sail from prow to stern,
    securing it in its new position so that the ends of the
    canoe are reversed, all with the speed of willing it,
    while the canoe teeters perilously on the crest of a wave
    but without a flaw or struggle or flick of indecision.
Watch the unfolding pattern of waves under your prow
For these tell you how the winds will shift,
Feel the lift of the great sail
Your rise and descent through the troughs of the ocean.

And delight, O warriors, delight while you may
    in the joys of seafaring
For they, like your horizons
are transient.

(But, Jekkar, ghost of Jekkar, here in this little room as we recite your story, do not press so closely upon us; but yield as a ghost should to the lantern's light. Agch, the gore that clings about your eyes and the gaping hole in your skull frightens us and turns our stomachs. Take your old-man ghost back a respectable distance or we will tell how at the age of eighty-eight you earned your death through philandering, or a certain bawdiness that passed for philandering. Our little room is stuffy enough without you breathing down our backs. Give us space so we may concentrate wholly on the sweetness of your youth as it passed through the sad events that we must now lament).

The fleet sped on as the seers directed but to no end for the enemy had become elusive and remained just out of sight beyond the horizon and was never actually seen. But its magic was powerful and led our fleet further and further across the hungry ocean. And as food ran low and water had to be rationed, evil muttering was heard. And foremost among those leading the discontent was the Yap woman.

"Maybe there is no enemy," she would say.

"Maybe these omens are being misinterpreted. Perhaps they really mean that fishing is very good back in the lagoons, that the rain is falling on our islands and that the taro needs be tended."

"Oh, these seers simply do not know what they are doing. Surely they are leading us to our deaths."

"If we follow their foolish advice seaweed will soon be growing in our hair."

"In Yap such seers would be discredited and eaten without delay."

"Oh, how hungry and thin we are all becoming! Only the seers remain fat and well-fed."

Sometimes she would start a chant in her deep voice that carried over the fleet like a throw net, slowly and tentatively and carelessly at first, as if it was just a means of passing the time, so that one scarcely noticed what she was up to; but craftily increasing the tempo and the power until all men became caught in its magic and felt their wills weaken and their minds go foolish. But then, suddenly, she would break off the chant, laugh tauntingly at the havoc she had created, for oftentimes canoes were out of control by that time and sailing in all directions or even ramming into one another—and she would go back to grumbling: "Oh," she would say, "I think there is no enemy…"

The Iroij knew that his authority in the fleet was weakening and he held frequent council with his seers and his most trusted advisers. Some wavered and advised turning back but you, Jekkar, in the fullness of your faith, urged him to continue.

Hunger and thirst were normal accompaniments of sea voyages in those days and our people expected them, but how could they endure them when doubts and enchantment and foolishness clouded their minds.

Then one day, when hunger and thirst and doubts were at their peak, the chanting did not stop. She kept right on—the Yap woman—she kept right on hurling her mighty voice at the clouds, building such savagery in the blood, to such frenzy in the head, such power in the liver, that you felt that you would burst. You sat there with great strength surging through your limbs, yet you were unable to move for you were paralyzed and foolish in enchantment. And as you watched her, seeing nothing but her, she came to occupy the entire sky. O your eyeballs were filled by the Yap woman, and you saw red suns flash from her eyes, heard the crash of thunder in her bellowing chant, and smelled her sweating body above all ocean smells. There was the infant dangling as she held it by the legs and thrashed it about in the excitement of the chant. It wailed, or you thought it wailed for it had grown weak from hunger, and the roar of the chant was all you had ears for. O she waved the infant like a torch, whirling it about her head in a mad dance and snapping it back and forth until it may have died. But suddenly she stopped, suddenly she stood still in dreadful silence, holding the infant aloft as if presenting it to a god; reverently, sweetly she stood there as with a priceless gift. O the horror of such a mother's act—certainly no Marshallese mother would have done such a thing even in those days— she raised a clam-shell sword and with one motion cut the infant into two pieces.

"Kill," she screamed, "Kill, kill." Blood ran in a little whirlpool down her arm. Great foolishness seized the sun and all the world, and cracked the sky, so to speak, so that rivers of emptiness ran through your head, for you and all the Marshallese lay quietly like clams dying under the sun while the Yappese warriors flung themselves about killing. You saw her sons, the Yappese hostages, bash in the head of the Iroij's wife, stab his son and daughter, kill many warriors, but you could not move. O your great muscles could only tug feebly at your bones, and you lay there in foolishness and enchantment. You saw the evil sons go at the Iroij who lay paralyzed before them; you saw them raise their clubs and strike, missing him in their eagerness. And then it happened. Then, Jekkar, then you broke your enchantment. With the speed of an eel striking, with the sureness of a seabird's descent, faster even than thought, Jekkar, even while the heavy clubs were in mid-air seeking the kingly skull to crush, even then you acted. O you pushed the mighty Iroij—for this was the only way to save him—into the ocean, and with a hero's ferocity you turned on the two murderers, challenging them, baiting them. O you led them a merry chase about the canoe, over dead bodies, dodging behind the mast, all the time shouting insults at them: "Your mother is a rotting porpoise," or "Your mother farts to make wind for the sail," until in their anger, they forgot discretion. Then, with one sure fling of the sails' boom, you knocked them into the ocean; and while they were still spluttering, "Our mother most certainly is not a rotting porpoise, and she farts only to improve her digestion," you bashed in their heads with your club. O it was a good beginning, but the Yap woman still maintained her enchantment and the slaughter of our warriors continued. So by yourself, for you were the only Marshallese warrior free from the sorcery, you swam to her canoe. Stealthily as a thief at night you climbed on board; stealthily you stalked her. O you were a barracuda that day as you approached her from behind for you knew that her eyes must not find you with the sear of their red suns' flames. But even so, even as you raised your club, you felt the enchantment. Her smell, like sleep, nearly overcame you and your arm would not act. There was terror in your bowels and you could not contain your urine as you stood there wavering in enchantment. But then, Jekkar, your mighty will overpowered her: O it broke the circle of enchantment and the club came crashing through. And it splattered the evil woman's brains over the entire canoe, over the entire ocean, for the waves turned gray and the spray became like torn storm clouds. And sharks came and drank eagerly of the gray milk (though others, as you will hear, said the ocean turned red). It was a mighty event, Jekkar, and it quelled the mutiny.

All eyes were on you, Jekkar, and you knew what to do. Like a true hero who speaks with the gods—for no one else was permitted to do it— you knelt beside her as she lay on her back, belly up like a dead fish, her eyes no longer flashing suns for they were turned inward; and you slit her open. O the smell of the sorceress' bowels nearly overpowered you! And you took a piece of her liver, a tiny piece for you were near to vomiting. It was the proper ceremony of those times, and it had nothing to do with the fact that you were on short rations and nearly starved, and most certainly it was not cannibalism for we Marshallese have always been disdainful of cannibalism, fishing being so good about our islands. So you took the piece of the liver, mouthing it reverently, saying a sweet prayer to the gods; and as you did so, you felt a fire kindle in your belly in the region of your liver, a fine tingle go through your entire body and into your muscles, and a wonderful slyness slink into the shadows of your skull. All watching you knew from the signs that a mystery had been enacted.

This was the glorious feast of the great mutiny.

But there was sadness, too, in the fleet for the young prince had been savagely wounded, and from his belly there poured a yellow liquid mixed with blood. And the Iroij, knowing of the mystery, sent for you, Jekkar, and propounded these questions:

"Will my son recover?"

Remembering the stories from the old people and, perhaps hoping to utilize your new canniness, you knelt over the suffering boy, placed your tongue in the wound. Then answered: "The taste is bitter and the boy will die." This was the feast of bitter bile of which we have spoken.

Then the Iroij propounded his second question: "Perhaps, Jekkar, you are now a sorcerer. If so, can you save him from certain death?" And you placed your hand in the wound even though the boy struggled and grew faint, and recited this prayer:

O Etao
Rascal among gods

To whom we turn when we must circumvent nature
O Etao
See the joke in restoring this boy to health
This boy whom the Yappese have killed
O imagine their chagrin when he becomes a warrior
Come play jokes with us, Etao
For we know this is the only way we can interest you.
But nothing happened.

You tried to repeat a chant, but not very effectively since the woman's chants had all been in Yappese and you could make only the few coarse, nonsense sounds that you remembered. You pretended to cradle an infant in your arms, even letting it nurse. You pretended to swing it about by the heels, slashing at it with an imaginary sword, saying " ha" or "agch") whenever the imaginary infant and the imaginary sword met in mid-air. You made your eyes into red suns so that all were afraid to look you in the face.

But nothing happened.

O you did everything that could be expected of a sorcerer, but nothing happened because you did not become a sorcerer even though you tried.

But you were kind to the boy as he lay dying, like a mother, and the Iroij and all his people marveled that a hero might be so gentle. And those people from the southern Marshalls composed a song of gratitude for you which they still sing:

The Thunderer from the north
called Jekkar
From the dry, harsh atoll where weaklings die
Comes
With the radiance of sheet-lightening filling the sky
With the sureness of a sea-bird over the wave-tracked ocean
With the cold wind of lament from
Fallen warriors
Destroyed villages
And stolen women.
See him standing there against the sail of his swift canoe
Muscles taut with eagerness
Loins trim with youth and overcome with yearning
Agch!
Like a god
In the fierce sweetness of his manhood.

O cherish the hero and his beauty
For he is a young girl in his modesty
A bird in his gentle grace
A mother in his tenderness
A son in his courtesy
But a shark, lean and swift and terrible in destruction
Cunning is he and deceitful
As he seeks the strength of great adversaries
And the precious moment of their undoing
For the Thunderer eats the liver of his enemies
Gaining their strength.

Listen to his story
How his mighty strength saved us and the great Iroij

Listen
For its telling is in the sun that pierces our backs like spears
In the thunder that breaks the dry season
In the grace of dancers
In the mouths of our story-tellers.
Listen and sing with us
How he sipped the yellow fluid that seeped from
        the belly wound and, from its bitterness
        foretold the death of the Iroij's son.
Agch!
How also he killed in revenge, this Thunderer,
Killed the Yap woman, child-butcherer
Killed all those who obeyed her evil spell,
Gloriously,
With shouts that shook the heavy clouds,
Killed the mutinous Yappese to the last
        whimpering coward
So that none
No, not one—on that day of the great sea battle
Lived to boast of their crime and their dishonor

Agch!
The Thunderer from Rongelap.

CONCLUSION FOR BOMB TESTING

At this point I shall terminate the details of my bomb testing experience in the Marshall Islands…Those were experiences that are now best forgotten, and I shall move away from them hastily. But not from the essential ingredients of Marshallese character that steadied and gave purpose and insight to island lives over many troubled centuries, and that reached superb heights (or so it seemed to me) in the months of bomb testing that I shared with them. Marshallese comprehended matters of Life and Death more objectively, faithfully, and even philosophically than those of us who have sought to impose our western moral and social standards on them. Their attitude toward suicide illustrates how an act that is disgraceful in the world at large, can be transformed in a small island community into a social benefit—the equivalent of confession or of sacrifice. How else can one explain the death poem that was found pinned to the dress of a prominent Marshallese lady who, during the Japanese Administration, had hanged herself to protect her prominent Japanese physician husband and her children from her leprosy. I love this poem for it, better than anything I can write, expresses the intense loyalty of island people. She wrote it, of course, in Marshallese and, in my translation, I have tried to preserve the elegance of her style and the intensity of her emotion… I should mention that two of her thus-protected sons became physicians, one of whom I knew and worked with.

Her suicide was in Jaluit, the Japanese capitol of the Marshall Islands, and it was shocking to those in the upper levels of government, but the people, themselves, regarded the act of suicide itself as a stalwart and noble act that affirmed a great tradition, and they gave it honor by massive attendance at a funeral ceremony which the missionaries had hoped could be accomplished without much notice. Here is the poem addressed to her husband. You will note that the letters of her name (Isoda) introduce each verse.

Isoda (ISHODA)

(I)   I, wife grown old untimely
               Bequeath thee
               Soul   body   failed strength
               And love beyond comprehension
                             Nothing is left over
                             Nothing   Nothing

(S)   Save soul's eyesight
        SOUL'S eyesight shall follow thee
                        Tenderly   faithfully   forever
        And know with thee
        Suffer with thee
                        Each anxiety
                        Each hope

(O)   O   my love
        Lest my resolve weakens
        Lest my thoughts lose clarity
        Lest cowardice overcomes me
        Hold fast with me to that injunction
        That proves Death's impotence
                        'O Death, thy Victory is wasted
                        Thy Sting is pointless.'
        Tears   unquenchable

(D)   DRAIN my eyes dry
        AND are best forgotten
        Your words arguments consolations
                        Stay in my heart
                        Sing in my heart
        Sweetly as a hymn and forever
        But must not be heeded

(A)   Anguish, my anguish
        Agony,   momentary and discountable...
        But time's run out
        And my sun sets behind a cloud
                        Never to rise
                        Long night's chill's already come
        And my thoughts   Love   are of you
                        Tender beautiful
                        Tender respectful

    As a footnote I append the following commentary on Marshallese suicides that I recorded from many conversations with a close Marshallese friend of mine.

WHEN HONOR'S AT STAKE

He climbs the island's tallest coconut palm that stands over a pile of rocks and flings himself headfirst toward the rocks in silence, and with the reverence of a religious rite. Thus does he accomplish *tu-bar* the second most honored means of suicide in the Marshall Islands—justified by antecedents that reach to the very beginning of time when people first learned to live successfully together on very small atolls. The most honored form of suicide, however, is *tu-in-kier*, and it is appropriate for those whose nonconformity severely endangers the harmony of lives around them. By *to-in-kier* the miscreants make reparation to the very ocean itself and thereby cleanse their evil behavior from fact and memory. And they do this nobly and almost off-hand by diving so deeply into the ocean that air in their lungs cannot possibly support their return to the surface. Those moments of failing breath are thought to be moments of supreme insight and self-knowledge that give absolution and, who knows, perhaps a few seconds of abiding peace; and that erase the enormity of whatever act required such expiation. Or as a variation these same offenders might elect to dive more shallowly into the lagoon as if intending to spear fish, but tie themselves securely to coral outcroppings by knots that cannot be undone in moment of weakness or panic, and wait there as air fails them and remorse and repentance clear their souls, as well as the reputations of their clan members of responsibility and blemish.

Then there are other modes of suicide as varied as means and imagination permit (short, though, of using a weapon for a weapon is an evil instrument of destruction and murder, and should not be turned on oneself); and of these, hanging is the most common…But in any event the impulse to traditional suicide, whether for disease or asocial conduct, was an impulse built into atoll living itself to protect its fragile, complex way of survival and its body politic, by removing those influences that could harm it, and probably would—it was like a cleansing biological phenomenon.

⊕ ⊕ ⊕

The deserted island of Bikini. Nothing
left but a Japanese fishing ball, my own
tracks in the sand, and a destroyed
building.

CHAPTER THREE

ROUTE TO BIKINI

INTRODUCTION

Emotionally, and perhaps spiritually, the *Route to Bikini* belongs with the account of bomb testing in the Marshalls, and that is the reason I am inserting it into the manuscript at this point. But rationally and time-wise this is incorrect since this trip to Bikini did not occur until a decade after bomb testing had ceased. And then, instead of being the glorification of a noble cause, the trip had become an expedition for Washington and Trust Territory sinners to confess and plead repentance. As you will see, my conscience finally overcame me and I never completed this chapter.

RETURN TO THE BOMB TESTING SITE

In 1968, when I was the Commissioner of Health Services for the Trust Territory, an official sea trip, sponsored by Washington, was made to Bikini Atoll to determine if the level of residual radiation from many nuclear tests had decreased sufficiently to permit rehabilitation by its islanders who had been forced to live on another island ever since 1946. Politically this was an important trip for the situation had attracted international condemnation and many officials who had been involved in the Bikini scandal were grasping at this trip as an opportunity to redeem their bomb-damaged reputations. So, in addition to the engineers and technicians who were to measure and assess the radiation, the list of notables included the High Commissioner of the Trust Territory and supporters from his office, Wash-

As Commissioner of Health Services,
I am "debarking" on damaged,
deserted Bikini island. No sound
except for the surf.

ington representatives of the discredited bomb testing establishment, several high ranking military officers, several Washington bureaucrats, and even one Peace Corps volunteer. And since the trip had attracted so much attention there were newspaper reporters and photographers all over the ship. I was included in the ship's roster, mostly, I think, to act as ship's physician, but also, perhaps, as an opportunity to atone for my having participated in the last bomb tests.

Here is my account of the trip…a wasted trip, for our engineers and technicians found no evidence of dangerous residual radiation and recommended prompt rehabilitation, but they were soon contradicted and discredited by better qualified scientists who found unacceptable levels of radiation still lingering in such places as the subsoil, and the trip was thereafter written off as a political disgrace…A political disgrace, yes, but it was an honorable and exciting attempt to right a wrong, even though everything went wrong during the effort. Here is the way I have recorded the Trust Territory's and Washington's attempt to correct a historic wrong.

⊕ ⊕ ⊕

Bikini…Bikini Atoll with its scant rosary of bony coral islands, and a sky that won't fit because it's much too large and bright and beautiful… historic, notorious, scandalous Bikini…Bikini in the United Nations… Bikini on the national conscience…Bikini and a witch by name of Libokra! I am having difficulty keeping it in focus with its present squalor; its recent memories of the most devastating detonations ever conceived by mankind; and three Bikini men (ancient, dispossessed nobles of the atoll) seeing it for the first time in twenty-two years, standing on the remnants of an island near the site of one of the most powerful hydrogen bomb detonation (*Bravo* by name, which cleanly removed three islands from the face of the earth), crying softly now and pointing to three orphan sea birds shuddering at their feet: "See, they are crying with us for they, too, are sorrowful that this island we shared with them is nothing but a broken reef!"—though later someone assured me that the men had broken the squabs wings as routine procedure for keeping them immobile and tame until time for roasting…And this race of little brown people reminding each other of their ancestors' millennia of power and glory on these few, flat, dry, god-forsaken islands (no, that's wrong for God never possessed these islands until recently, the men of Bikini being the last of the missionary hold-outs in the Marshall Islands: the *kakin-met* those from the bottom of the sea, below the light, the out-back people, those beyond the beyond) when their name and nakedness were shame to their godly neighbors, their sorcery above the sorcery of all others, their navigators keener than those of Magellan, their story-tellers and poets capable of exciting warriors to frenzy and incredible valor, or soothing them with lyricism worthy of the Greeks. Witness this poem, doubly translated in my presence; first from ancient Bikini Marshallese (Chaucerian in age, perhaps, and complexity) to modern, slightly tainted Marshallese, and then to English.

> Stranger from the far island
> Drink this coconut we offer.
> Since thou be lonely
> > Know that little fish
> Little flying fish from thine own side of the atoll
> Are rapidly flying
> Flying with the speed of kind thoughts
> To enter thy heart
> > Deep, O deep, in the caverns of thy heart
> > Deep in thy heart's bitterest brine
> > Where loneliness is causing a great storm
> To bring thee calm
> And heartsease
> And a message that new friends
> Become old friends
> > Drink from the sweet coconut, thou stranger
> > Deeply...
> > Its friendly juice.

I never met a person from Bikini until October 1968 when I, acting in my capacity as Commissioner for Health Services of the Trust Territory of the Pacific Islands (and also as a sort of ship's physician and first-aid man) accompanied a ship-load of dignitaries and journalists and nine Bikini men back to this deserted atoll to determine the feasibility of resettlement—which is what this report is actually meant to deal with. But I have known Bikini Atoll, in very different context, for I lived in its 'shadow' (a sort of biblical way of speaking, for it's islands are only six-feet high and incapable of casting shade on anything but coconut crabs and fish that nuzzle their pock-marked bony shores and reefs. This by way of saying that during the 1958 bomb tests, I lived on Rongelap Atoll (the one that was irradiated four years earlier when Bikini's hydrogen bomb, *Bravo*, spewed its fallout in life-threatening dosage). There, just one hundred miles downwind from Bikini, I learned the terror of waiting for the next detonation, the uncertainty of planning what I should do at each possible level of catastrophe, the sinking feeling whenever the name 'Bikini' appeared in coded message—though secretly I learned to enjoy the deep, bone-marrow grinding sensation of the blasts themselves.

Slowly, as I learned more about Bikini, it began a strange and wonderful metamorphosis. From a simple, neighboring atoll it became a brooding giant that lay just over the horizon: cunning, savage and hungry, as symbolic of absolute evil as murder, as eternal and chaste as an Einstein equation. To utter its name was to shudder and wish for absolution. Given a little more time I might have constructed a new religion out of the idea: "Lamb of the gamma ray/ leukemic blood of Nagasaki, contused but immaculate brain of God/ glance of the beast," I once wrote in my diary as a starter.

Yet, when I flew over it, which I did several times on my way back and forth between Rongelap and Eniwetok, during the 1958 bomb tests, it was difficult to reconcile such a fantasy with this friendly, smiling atoll that I saw: A turquoise lagoon (20 miles long and 15 miles wide) outlined by a thin, childish scrawl of reef that supported several dozen scattered islands, most of which were barren and skeletal and uninteresting from the air. (The fact that they represented slaughtered and dying landscape did not occur to me then.) Only the two largest islands—well off to one end of the lagoon's rim, Bikini and Eneu, I

Trip of Washington officials to Bikini, with the High Commissioner of the Trust Territory with nine Bikini islanders and me to determine the feasibility of all Bikini islanders being returned to their traditional island. The trip was a failure because Bikini had remained radioactive. The High Commissioner is at the far right. I am next to him.

suppose—had any evidence of human habitation, and here there were peaceful, New England-appearing villages with neat houses for the bomb testers, and neat roads and a 'church with a steeple', at least that was my interpretation of a structure that I saw there. I could see no factories nor 'engines of destruction', and I can't remember seeing the great bomb assembly hall nor the observation towers nor block houses (though now I know they were there); no stoked fires nor smoking reactors; no mad scientists; no marching troops. In fact, I can't remember seeing people. . . .

It was like dreaming a Debussy dream of sunken villages and engulfed cathedrals, reassuring and sweet as long as sleep lasted; or like being a voyeur who finds that no one ever undresses anymore; or, more harshly, like trying to pray when all one can remember are four-letter words; or like seeing the Sacred and the Profane walk down the street together comparing parables, arms linked.

Such is my introduction to the Bikini story, but let us go back to the beginning.

It was on a Sunday morning, February 10, 1946, just after church, that Bikini became an international event, for it was then that Commodore Ben Wyatt, USN, Governor of the Marshall-Gilberts Subares, dropped down from the clouds in an amphibious plane, gathered the Bikini elders together and, in these approximate words, said:

> "My people, you have been chosen by the Lord, just like the Children of Israel, to save the world. Of all the islands and lands in the world, Bikini has been chosen as the site for developing a bomb which will end all wars, all strife among human beings. Like Children of Israel, even in their journeying through the desert, even in their trials and tribulations in Babylon, even in their eventual triumph at Jericho, you are chosen to sacrifice your atoll for the welfare of all mankind."

It was like the Annunciation: little Bikini being told that it was about to conceive in its coral womb a bomb which would save the world. And right after church. And to a 'congregation' of elders with Biblical names, with Bethlehem still shining in their eyes, and with missionary translated Bibles and Boston hymnals in their hands. So they squatted in the shade on the cool coral and heard 'Archangel' Ben Wyatt, U.S.N. issue words of wonder and prophecy…the sky from which he had just descended, stretching behind him hierarchically. It seemed almost impious for Judah, the Bikini leader, to say, "We tak' one hour ta tink an' tell ya."…(Imagine the Virgin Mary showing an hour's hesitation at such a disclosure!)…One hour later Judah said, "Council say yes, say we mak' sacrifice, say we save mankind," though apparently none of them believed that saving mankind would take more than a few weeks.

At first there was a feeling of adventure about it like the beginning of a crusade, or a grand tour, or a holy odyssey, or an escape from bondage; and the people set to weaving hundreds of sweet smelling pandanus mats to be used as thatching for their new homes ("Lak chil'ren of Israel we're makin' bricks, but out of straw," one of them joked.); dismantling the church and town meeting house for reassemblage in the new location, collecting cast-off military iron sheeting to be used for water catchment, selecting fifteen of the best outrigger canoes, wrapping their personal belongings into a few tiny bundles, trimming their lanterns which they must take with them to ward off evil spirits at night—and they were ready to go. But where? Which atoll should they select as the 'promised land'? No one could decide. Most of the atolls were already over-populated, though their inhabitants, when queried, usually invited them to come share their poverty. Lae Atoll, which was seriously considered, seemed unfavorable because it was known to be dominated by the spirit of Witch Lomkien (a cannibal woman who, after a natural death, thrice rose from her grave, thrice rose from the ocean where in desperation her sons tried to sink her, the last time with coral rocks about her neck, pleading, "Honored mother, honored mother, please stay down for we must get back to our atoll before dark," but she rose as soon as they were out of sight and had remained peevish ever since); Ujae Atoll presented navigational problems—rival feudal chieftains in far-off Majuro quarreled over apportionment of this dismantled fiefdom. No pillar of flame appeared, no convincing visions, no sudden lemming urge, so the Navy mundanely flew eleven Bikini elders from atoll to atoll to lonely island and back again several times without success...until they came to Rongerik Atoll. "Perfect," said the Navy men as they surveyed its lagoon full of fish, its reasonably lush coconut groves, and its 30-mile proximity to Rongelap Atoll. "Perfect, especially because it is uninhabited; it is almost as if we have discovered it!" The Bikini elders agreed since they could think of no rational nor Christian way for objecting, though they knew that here was Libokra, evilist of all Marshallese witches, witch-demons, poisoner of grand scale, thief (she had once dragged Rongerik from Christian southern Marshalls to this, her own forlorn, secret place), and that when she died and was thrown into the lagoon, those fish that nibbled her temporal body, they and their descendants, became and remained deadly poisonous—even red-snappers and skipjacks and eels which were sweet and wholesome on Bikini (and still are even after the bombing). But how could they explain things like these to men in Navy uniforms who spoke with the tongues of archangels?

On March 7th, 1946 the Bikini people departed their atoll in a Navy LST, chugged past Rongelap, and arrived on Rongerik on March 8th, where a Seabee pre-fabricated village awaited them, still smelling of fresh-cut ply-wood and new canvas. Almost at once, as if by atavism derived from a thousand generations of nomadic living across the Pacific (for it is probable they got to Bikini by island-hopping from Malaysia), the women started making neat coral paths through the village, chanting, so the Navy chronicle reads, "We will build a better land than our old one on Bikini." An awkward line to chant, at least if you try it in English). But it was an empty chant for they were already sensing the malignity of Libokra in the silence of the atoll, in the strange store-bought village smell, in the way the lagoon changed color: amber or indigo one moment and turquoise the next. "Don' eat fish from the lagoon," they told each other, and "the water is probably also poison." And on subsequent days: "The breadfruit trees are withering, the arrowroot has ceased to grow, and see how the coconuts are getting smaller and smaller…This is old Libokra's holy place, her tabernacle, and she says 'Bikini people get out'." Once a fire broke out that destroyed thirty percent of the coconut trees. Work on the coral paths stopped; no one tried to make copra or weave mats or baskets, or to fish. The supply of C-rations and bags of flour declined rapidly. At night they closed the prefabricated shutter-windows and kept their lanterns burning, the only defense they could think of against Libokra.

After detonation of Bomb Able—the much-photographed one that was used to demolish a huge target fleet—the Navy flew Judah back to Bikini, hoping to impress him with the magnitude of the operation and the impossibility of return; but his comment was: "Now ya got bomb, ver' big bomb, big 'nough ta save da world. Now ya gotta kept promise an' tak us back ta Bikini. Bikini fish look healthy, an' da many new houses are fine." In desperation the Navy flew the nobles to Kili, Ujae, Wotho and Ujelang. There was no longer talk about a 'promised land'—just any old island that would get Bikini out of their minds, and that had no witch.

EXCERPTS FROM A NAVY CHRONICLE
26 August, 1947

Gentlemen: We the council have held a meeting to fiend (sic) the best place to go. We have been to some other places to inspect and have considered them. In moving we fiend (sic) it quite a problem. The place we all agreed to stay on is Rongerik Atoll.

We, the Council

Officer: Judah, I have tried to impress on you to forget Bikini...Is
  there much hunger here?
Answer: We are very hungry.
Officer: Jebat, how long has it been since you have eaten?
Answer: One small fish since yesterday.
Officer: Why don't you want to move to a better island?
Answer: Bikini is close.

On February 3, 1948 a visiting Navy physician found that the Bikini
people were sick from starvation and that some of them looked like inmates of
a concentration camp. With emergency speed they were moved to a temporary tent village on Kwajelein Atoll for medical care and physical rehabilitatio
It took about a month to get them over their 'Dachau-look'.

Kwajelein Atoll had become converted into a military base and was
inappropriate for a permanent Marshallese settlement. Of all the places to
live, only Wotho and Kili now seemed reasonable alternatives. So once
again an indefatigable Navy flew some of the Bikinians to both areas so
they could compare them. Dry, parched Wotho, which they had inspected
and rejected in 1947, looked just as dry and parched as before, and its thirty
one scrawny inhabitants reminded them so personally of Rongerik that
they asked to leave at once. But unoccupied Kili was different. Kili, almost
on the equator, drenched with rain and Eden-green. Its soil, primeval deep
loam, bible-black and springing with arrowroot and herbs, seemed strange
and wonderful to men who were just recovering from starvation. (It looked
that way to me, too, from the deck of the *MV Cook*, twenty years later,
though I had just finished a ship's good breakfast. It was Everyman's dream
of tropical paradise; ethereal and emerald and languorous in mist, and so
loaded with palm trees that they leaned over the ocean weeping night's dew
into its surf that broke lightly on coral rocks below. A tender scene it seemed
to me, and I said to myself, "How can anyone want to leave this place, this
is where I shall retire.") So strange and wonderful did it seem to the Bikini
men at that time that Judah and ten others remained there for two weeks
reveling in its lush abundance; taro, for instance, which wouldn't grow on
dry Bikini. And bananas and breadfruit sweeter than they had ever known.

Yet when time came for a plebiscite the people sent word to the civil
administrator that he must make the decision for them since all they could
agree on was to return to Bikini; and it took a week to bring them to cast
their secret ballots. Kili 54, Wotho 22 was the way it turned out—though
they always accused the administrator of miscounting the votes.

Why this reluctance to accept paradise—paradise on a platter—and a good sized paradise at that. The reason: there was no lagoon. "Sometimes we get tired and restless and then we take our canoes and go sailing on the lagoon, and when we return a few hours later we feel good again; it's like praying," they said. Moreover, long, narrow, canoe-shaped Kili was so placed that for six months of the year, six-foot, ten-foot, twenty-foot waves—driven by trade winds—fought and clawed impartially at both sides of the island, rolled coral boulders about like bowling balls so that no channel could be kept open, filled the air with salt and thunder, and ruled on matters of life and death like a divinity. "We won't be able to launch our canoes; they will be wrecked, and when we can't fish, we starve," said these non-agrarians who had never planted a seed nor harvested a mango crop in their sea-faring lives.

On September 25, 1948 work crews were landed to construct a village and a few weeks later 184 Bikini people fought their way through a surf to become the first 'Kili people' (in historic times, at least). They were like our founding pilgrim Fathers, and they celebrated the event (a few months later) by eating the brood-stock of hogs that had been sent with them. A young Marshallese school teacher from a neighboring island tried to show them the simple agricultural practices of his island, but they said he was too young to know anything, and besides, he was a 'foreigner' and ought not be listened to. Storms came, wrecked their canoes as predicted, and also a 60 foot sea-going 'Kili boat' that had been built for them by the Navy. Apparently the island had no intention of feeding them indefinitely off its bounty. How then were they to survive? Simple: by joining the capitalist system; by making copra from coconuts and handicraft from pandanus leaves, and selling them to traders, and then buying back from the same traders their meager supplies of spam, canned fish from Norway, sugar, rice, and of course, kerosene (at a dollar a gallon) for their lanterns' nighttime vigils. Field trip ships, bearing traders from Kwajelein and Majuro came fairly frequently. Here are notes concerning these trading adventures through one period.

October 27, 1949, ship arrived but surf too heavy to permit loading of copra. Next field trip ship came on February 4, 1950 but surf too heavy for landing. Ship returned February 10th but sea still too rough. On February 21st a field trip party succeeded in landing with supplies of rice, flour, sugar which were soaked with sea water. Copra could not be loaded, and was beginning to rot in the warehouse. Unable to pay for supplies and every one was in debt. People said they were hungry and children were chanting Kili e nana (kili is bad), and the most popular song on the island went something like this:

Lament from Kili
>   The world's gone crazy, and I'm left out.
>   Dreaming don't help much
>   For Bikini's all I dream about
>   And it's awful waking up
>
>   On Kili.
>   My sleeping mat stays wet with spray
>   And rotting breadfruit
>   Simply stinks.
>
>   Jail house, jail house Kili!
>   There's nothing here
>   Just tears, shame, hunger, storms....
>   I can't stand it anymore.

⊕   ⊕   ⊕

The *MV James Cook* was a former army supply ship, recently turned over to the Trust Territory for field trip use. She was trim and petite (176 feet long), as white and bright as a cloud, and tidy by field-trip standards—which, of course, do not concern themselves with such things as cockroaches and bed linen; and steady in the waves, though at times, when swan-like she rose and dipped through great Pacific rollers, spin drift would hurtle at us through the dining room portholes, salting our soup and scuttling the tame cockroaches off the tables.

Because I had several bags of medicines and bandages and enough instruments and sterile packs for minor surgery (to my embarrassment I forgot band-aids, these being almost the only actual surgical necessities for the entire trip), I rated one of the few tiny cabins which I shared with a Washington official—the cabin so small that I passed out dramamine and aspirin in the dining room, consulted on deck, and administered penicillin in the toilet (Officer's Head, proclaimed the proud, gold Gothic lettering, though I was really using it to treat a prominent journalist's gonorrhea), leaning the patient over the bowl while I sat on the toilet seat to steady myself against the ship's roll. Newsmen and photographers, even those with lofty credentials, and several Peace Corps Volunteers lived in a makeshift dormitory under a tarpaulin; Bikini men (who joined us at Kili) were tucked into spare places throughout the ship. The crew was Micronesian and Babel-like for they had been hastily assembled from several districts and spoke different languages. The captain was a roly-poly Mokilese, so shy on shore that he said 'yes' to every question, but master of us all on board, when more often than not he said 'no.' And when out of an empty sea an island appeared, it was always dead-ahead, just as islands, for the last millennium, have been in the habit of appearing before Micronesian captains…

I had the feeling we were in an ark, and that the fauna that had been accumulated to save and replenish the earth, were mostly newspaper men, photographers, Washington officials, a High Commissioner, Peace Corps Volunteers, an extra colonel or two, and a couple of AEC officials with their Geiger counters. The crew, the captain, the Bikini men and I counted merely as observers of this motley cargo.

We boarded the ship at Majuro, the District Center for the Marshall Islands District, and promptly went through a fire drill. Those of us who had gotten our life jackets on backwards or upside down feeling belligerent about such foolishness, while the crew fought furiously to get kinks out of seldom-used fire hoses so they could tend an imaginary catastrophe…And then we headed for Kili over a sea that was as smooth as satin.

Kili in the next morning's early light was just like I have described it during its moments of good behavior: reassuring in an amniotic sea (an attack of doldrums, actually), and as secure and warm as a fetus in its womb. And there it was, this little trouble spot that had been shaking Washington, and the Security Council of the United Nations, looking as innocent of dissent as Eden before the Fall.

We came to anchor a quarter of a mile off-shore but could see no evidence of activity among its tiny tin-roofed houses, only a large sign which was too far-off to be read; and we asked each other guiltily, "Are they refusing to meet us, does the sign really say "Yankee go home?" But no, a little boat was coming out to meet us, and in it, the president of the Kili Women's Club and the Magistrate's wife, matronly as club women and 'first ladies' should be, and as floral in their bright muumuus as tropical islands are supposed to be…but aren't. Nimble as young sailors, they climbed the ship's ladder ("I'll bet they spend their time shinnying up coconut trees when they're not being club women," I told myself), placed leis on the High Commissioner's head, smiled happily at the rest of us…And the sign really said "Welcome to the High Commissioner"….Thus our arrival on Kili.

Actually we had not quite arrived for there was the minor but important matter of getting the dignitaries safe and dry through the surf. Even though the surf was nearly dead that day, getting boats through its coral rubble and slight heaving seemed treacherous, and Bikini men dressed in their Sunday clothes, jumped into the water to guide and steady each boatload of approaching grave-faced, worried, landlubber men.

We went to a grove of palm trees and sat down in its sweating shade, the dignitaries in front at a long, improvised table in a sort of Last Supper arrangement, and I (having left my status behind on the ship with my medical bags and syringes) sat on the white coral gravel with the Bikini people (the weathered, spare, stark, dark Bikini people, who, at a similar meeting twenty years before had encountered an archangel; they had the look, I fancied, of people who have come out of the desert—the look of Job, the look of people who have seen God and found that he was different than they had expected), and waited for the speeches. A Bikini leader made the first speech which, on translation, welcomed the High Commissioner in words like these: "We have waited very long for this occasion. Some of us have died and many children have been born. We have been promised many things with nothing happening and we have become cynical. We didn't believe you when you said you would come to Kili, but now that you are here we have seen you with our eyes and have gently touched your hand,

The High Commissioner addressing Bikini residents on Kili, trying to reassure them that someday they might be returned to Bikini. The Bikini people are listening attentively but without belief. There were grounds for mistrust.

some of our doubts are quieted. We await your statement with great interest and respect."

The photographers (who were soon to reveal the fruit of their activities in *Life Magazine*, *Look Magazine*, *The London Times* and other prominent publications) were dashing through the audience, hopping over babies and out-stretched legs, indignantly motioning those who didn't fit their interest or composition out of the way (I must have had to move at least six times to get my white skin out of camera range). One photographer climbed the pole of a radio transmitter and clung there, lemur-like while his camera clicked hysterically. Others were taking light-meter readings of the speaker's face, the High Commissioner's face, Washington bureaucrats' faces, (never my face).

Then the High Commissioner, handsome and avuncular (though his head-leis unfairly made him look exactly like Nero), rose and spoke with young Chuji, the Marshallese translator, repeating it after him in the vernacular: "Two of the islands in Bikini Lagoon are now safe" (click, click, as photographers dashed forward to get a close-up of his face) "to live on. But many preparations must be (click) made first. We must replant (click, click) your coconut (click) trees so you will have food to eat and copra to sell (click, click), houses must be built, and it will be several years before all this can be done." The photographers turned their cameras on the Bikini people to register their disappointment for, apparently, they had all expected to climb onto the *MV James Cook* with us and go straight back to Bikini. Now they sensed that several years might mean the seven or eight years that it takes a coconut tree to bear. "We will take nine of your most honored people with us now," he continued, 'so they can report back to you what the islands are like, and so you can all help us plan the re-establishment of your ancestral home. We will employ your men for much of the work."

A Bikini man expressed their partial gratitude, and the women brought handicraft for gifts, enough for everyone, even those unimportant ones who had been sitting on the gravel with them. And the High Commissioner, in true Marshallese fashion, gave them many bags of rice in exchange.

We departed several hours later, taking with us nine Bikini men, and a Peace Corps Volunteer who had been assigned to Kili as an agriculture specialist. Wan, languid, bespectacled, be-pimpled, more under-privileged looking than anyone on the island, he said many times: "I planted three gardens, just like they told me to do in training, but nothing ever grew. I don't know why. I'm a psychology major and I don't know about nematodes and trace elements and things like that."…It sounded like a verse that should be added to the *Kili Lament*, and I wondered how it would sound set to music.

Judah, who through the years had become known as King Judah—though this was contrary to all Marshallese custom—did not go with us, for he had died of lung cancer a year before: "Because he saw the great bomb," some of the people kept saying.

Kwajelein Atoll, the largest atoll in the world, is a giant catcher's MIT whose sole function (now that its population has been moved out of the way) is to receive missiles aimed at it from Vandenberg Air Force Base in California; and it was to Kwajelein Atoll that we headed for our first stop. Coming onto it from Kili, is like seeing a mirage in the sky. From its flat, almost ocean-level surface, buildings rear up mightily for two, sometimes three full stories, and a parachute-drop loft seems to be reaching for the clouds. Bewildering one-track meanings are everywhere: giant radar antennae, their pious mechanical eyes turned heaven-ward, are thinking wild thoughts of wars and sneak attacks and how to catch the next missile safely in the center of the lagoon (Kwajelein's 'mid-corridor', a term so controversial to displaced Marshallese as to be unmentionable in their presence); laboratories hug secret data and equations to their bosoms and hide behind the paraphernalia of a tight security system; sheltering bunkers lie in strategic pattern just in case a missile misses the 'MIT'. Yet there, in the center of Kwajelein is Macy's Department Store with stateside housewives in resort shorts carrying out their parcels and chattering about bargains and the last shipment of monkey-pod bowls. And just beyond is Suburbia itself; neat houses for scientists and technicians, with lawns primly squared off and manicured, and full of children and children's toys. There are tennis courts, bowling alleys, a marina, six movies, a hospital, a beauty shop, buses, club houses, showers of flowers in all the hedges, and a soft salt sea breeze. It is like a display of 20th Century culture (probably selected by the staff of an underground Free Press) to be preserved in a cornerstone for future (after the holocaust) unbelieving generations to admire…or denounce. It is like the disjointed sequences of a dream.

We were guests of Kwajelein; and the Commanding Officer, Colonel Milar, took all of us to the Officers' Club for dinner. I watched the nine Bikini men who, twenty years before, had lived there for a few months to recuperate from starvation. Tentatively they looked about for familiar landmarks, but seemed lost among its new-sprung splendors. But as we approached the Officers' Club, and finally leaned against the bar ordering cocktails, they were as casual and carefree as any of us. "They have gone through a time-machine and mastered all the intricacies," I thought as I heard them order frozen daiquiris or manhattans, and make easy conversation (as best language barriers would permit) with the colonels. I even thought their English had improved in the interval of time it had taken to get from the ship to the bar.

On sudden impulse the High Commissioner asked our host, Colonel Milar, to accompany us to Bikini; and, on just as sudden impulse, he accepted (who could have resisted? for our expedition was developing the headiness of a crusade, of the Eternal Quest, of Grails, and of far marches), and he dashed off to get several changes of clothes and his scuba diving gear. Then we were off again, questing Bikini...I sat on deck reading "The Journal" of Albion Moonlight which seemed almost to be charting our course. Such being the case, unknown hazards and warnings should be expected—and so they materialized. A warning came the first night. Chuji, the translator, told me about it. He was sleeping on deck comfortably in the light breeze and secure until one of the Bikini men said, "Here you must not sleep in the open night and the dark. Every Marshallese, even if he speaks English like you, should know that. We are near Lae Atoll. This is Witch Lomkien's country. Her cannibal appetite has never diminished, and you will surely be devoured before morning. That breeze you feel is her presence." And Chuji, fresh from a church college in Ohio and with a degree in sociology in his pocket, told himself stoutly, "This is merely old peoples' superstition," but, since he was shaking uncontrollably, he obediently got up and finished the night, sweating and miserable, somewhere in the deep interior of the ship.

Early morning and we were all up forward on deck, trying to look over the horizon, to catch the first glimpse of Bikini. The first thing we saw was the top of a tower, barely visible over the ocean's curvature, and flickering and fading in the heat's shimmer so that we argued about it. Gradually the tower lengthened and gained definition until it was like the end of a cat-gut suture protruding from a ragged wound. Then we saw another and another until there were four of them. We stood there transfixed and silent in the diesel motor's throb, scalding our eyes, sweating out our shirts, cursing our poor distant vision, until finally the fuzz of low islands appeared here and there beneath the towers. The Bikini men had crowded together at the prow of the ship, a few feet closer to Bikini than the rest of us, as was their right. Old Ahab, patriarch to them all, started a rhythmic, wild Marshallese chant, soft at first but with a crescendo that ended in savage shouts, the others listening gravely. Edging up to them I asked Nathan, who spoke English, what he was saying "Oh, nothing, nothing at all," he replied as he concentrated on looking at a cloud. I moved away feeling awkward, uninvited and profane. "Perhaps it was a purification ritual, a Trust Territory anthropologist suggested. Many months later, and after many conversation with many Bikini people I was able to get enough fragments to reconstruct it. Here it is:

Incantation Concerning Demons

I will start where?   I will start in the ocean
            God of demons   O god of demons
Look around   look around   eat those demons on that island
                                 on that reef   in that tree
            God of demons   O god of demons
Look around   look around   eat all demons circling the sky
            God of demons   O god of demons
Look around   look around   eat those demons in the ocean
                                 before they destroy us

            Sandpiper of the pandanus leaf
            Sandpiper of the dry palm leaf
            Sandpiper one and two
            Fly from distant ocean roadways
            Fly   fly   hastily fly
            And demolish the influence
                    Of those demons in the ocean
            O little creatures who can't sing
                    Sons of She-who-sings
            Chirp warnings
            Chirp effective incantations
                    And make benign magic that will save us
            Sandpiper of the pandanus leaf
            Sandpiper of the dry palm leaf
                    Sandpiper one and two
            Chirp warnings
            Chirp incantations
            Make magic
                    O incessantly
            Make magic
                    Don't sleep

            Shark eat them
            Quickly, shark, quickly
            Shark eat those terrible demons
                    Those demons in the ocean
            For they are delicious
            Shark is chasing them now
                    The demons in the ocean
            How sweetly they groan   like caught box fish

The demons in the ocean
They die slowly   screaming and repenting
        On rocks in the ocean
We are pleased   we are saved
        From demons in the ocean

⊕ ⊕ ⊕

At this point I have ceased writing about this trip to Bikini. But before leaving it, I must include a footnote concerning our Marshallese translator, Chuji, which, I think, reveals insight into Marshallese character and courage.

This is the remanent of a war-time
observation tower on deserted Bikini.

CHUJI

It is not necessary for you to understand Chuji since he participates in these events only as a translator, but you will be better equipped to understand the total complexity of Bikini and the Marshall Islands if you do. And you won't be able to understand him unless you know how he got to Heidelberg University in Ohio. Here it is in Chuji's words:

"I got to Columbus, Ohio late at night and got off at the bus station. There was another hundred miles to go and I had only three dollars in my pocket. It was raining. The bus station attendants apologized and closed the station and I was alone in the dark. No train, no taxi (even if I had the money for one), no more buses. I sat down on the curb soaking wet and cried. Then, suddenly (it came to me all at once like a great white light) I knew what to do: I knew that I should call the Governor of Ohio. I got him out of bed and said, 'This is Chuji. I'm from the Marshall Islands and I'm lost. 'Where's the Marshall Islands?' he asked suspiciously and sleepily over the phone So I told him all about them, and how they are different from Columbus, Ohio, and how I would know to take an outrigger canoe if I were there. Suddenly he said, 'Don't move, stay right where you are.' And a little later the policeman came with sirens and spotlights and all, and took me to the best hotel in town. I think they thought I was an ambassador or something. And before I knew it, someone was knocking at the door and giving me a check for fifty dollars. That's the way I got to college."

And that's the way a typical Marshallese reacts to catastrophe, be it bomb testing or just getting to college.

⊕ ⊕ ⊕

This is the Guam house in Merizo that
my wife and I lived in. Note the tall trees
standing over it, which, during
Typohoon *Karen*, fell on its roof thus
securing it. It was the only house in
Merizo that was so lucky.

CHAPTER FOUR

GUAM

INTRODUCTION

After four months of living with Rongelapese during bomb testing, and developing an almost fierce respect for their gentle, confident manners, return to established state-side life seemed deadly; and I spent my spare time writing the many chapters you have just read, and searching for an escape route that would take me back to the 'islands.' And as soon as I had finished my professional contract, my wife and my daughter and I headed for Guam in the Western Pacific where I became Director of Public Health Services for the next four and one-half years. We arrived there December 22, 1959, and once I had 'reconstructed' Guam to my liking it became precisely what I was looking for. 'Reconstruction' of Guam required that we should abandon a rather elegant house that was assigned to us next the hospital and move 30 miles south to neglected, wonderfully primitive Merizo where I became a weekend boatman and a nighttime diver, and wrote my second poem, which was the first one I ever sent to a publisher. Here it is as it appeared in *Harper's* Magazine, December, 1964. ("Virginia fences" as cited in the poem, refers to an earlier time in our lives when we were ardent fox hunters.) And following it are two articles I wrote while in Guam: *Typhoon*, which describes a typhoon with the highest wind velocity ever recorded up to that time, and *Beatrice* describes my nighttime diving experience.

POEM
Pacific Love Song

Gratitude to the brave little boat that brings us back to our village
And a kind of love for its chugging, evil-smelling motor
    that will cause me to pat it, and remove with care
    any sea-weed from its propeller, and rinse it with fresh-
    water as I put it away for the night
Never losing a stroke and measuring time like a good heart
O little boat, homing us with the certainty that your spark plugs permit!
O I know that there must be a spark-gap of exactly twenty-five
    thousandths of an inch, and that a slight erosion or crusting
    would stop you dead
And that Pacific currents would carry us steadily at four knots per hour
Southward   Defeated
Hour after hour and day after day
    Toward Yap
           Koror

                  Or may be Kapingimarangi
While search planes would comb each mile of ocean
Searching for wreckage
A floating gasoline can or a life preserver
And the Admiral smoking a cigar on Nimitz Hill
    called Nimitz Hill through the conceit of admirals, for Chamorros
    who knew the names of hills before admirals were invented, call it
        Libugon
              would issue a memorandum
"Civilian boatmen must be more careful and always carry a whistle
    and an extra anchor"
Or some such nonsense which would have nothing to do with your spark
plugs, or the fact that we would be headed for
    Yap
        Koror
            or Kapingimarangi
This morning in dark mist we left our Guam village and its
    encircling mother-armed mountains
Felt the slow-breathing, night-breathing ocean raise your keel
And the deep-ocean's strength come at you increasingly
Until the waves mounted about us like Virginia fences
Towering

Snow encrusted—
You bolting a little from panic, sun fishing, and twisting
        so I thought you might lie down and roll over
But learning
Until there was nothing to it.
And when the birds filled the sky in frantic joy
Pointing in duplicity the tuna run
O how you throttled up
Slamming into the waves with wonderful abandon, and
Throwing my wife
        —it was you not I that did this; it was your
        uncontrollable eagerness—
                to the deck in a tangle of lines and
        trolling gear so that she cried at me;
        "You don't love me. No man should treat
        a woman like that." But she forgot her pique
        for she must get up and let out feathered jigs,
        and brace her self for the fury of a strike
        and the sing of carried-out line.

O little boat
Bring us safely back to our village
That we
may attend San Dimas' Fiesta tomorrow.

BEATRICE

> Thou art not on the earth as thou believest"
> —Dante Alighieri, *Divine Comedy*

   Last night on Guam I spearfished and skin dived until midnight with four Filipino friends and my good Chamorro neighbor, Isidro Manalisay who acted as our boatman; fished out beyond the reef near Cocos Island until two of the Filipinos became sick from fatigue and vomited, and I felt claustrophobia from the sharks that were making little forays at us to get the fish that the Filipinos had all over the place: on their spears (skewered four or five deep), on stringers, snuggled in the waistbands of their trunks— hundreds of them, giving a wonderful fishy, bloody tang, no doubt, to our part of the ocean.
   The sharks had an ethereal quality about them, the way they would materialize from the merest shadow, buoyant on a beam of light like some-

thing seen in the clouds. They also had the quality of a fixation or a tick that couldn't be controlled, or a shudder. And they were as spare as an Einstein formula: not one excess part, no futile axones nor dendrites grasping at complexities more complex, certainly, than the principles of levitation or physical perfection or of their own species-survival.

The trouble was that they couldn't tell which of us had the fish, and were as likely to come at me, who didn't catch a fish all night, as at the real fishermen.

Once a six-foot shark came so close to one of the Filipinos that he kicked it, and then chased it beyond the light of our flashlights, saying later, "I would have shot it if it had really wanted to eat me." But another of the Filipinos said, "That one scared me."

Sometimes when the sharks became particularly menacing we would all come together on a little coral outcropping, submerged except for our snorkels and looking (as nearly as I could imagine our silhouettes in our flashlights' glow) like the marines on top of Iwo Jima as we hoisted our spears in the direction of the closest, most impatient shark.

It was peculiar seeing those scrawny little guys face-up to the big sharks, but then I guess they were raised where they went hungry when they didn't catch fish—whereas the Guamanians buy their fish at the market.

We got a moray eel as long as I am, and a squid the size of a large octopus. I did poorly because I lost the tip of my spear, and also because I couldn't get used to the sharks being so close—like overly concerned kibitzers making me feel nervous and inadequate—and I spent a lot of time tracking them with my flashlight instead of tending to the business of diving into the caves.

But I wasn't actually afraid and I aimed my spear as steadily as anyone whenever a large shark bore in on me, and dived at him, menacing him, just as if I knew what I was doing... "Although my aptitudes may be those of a fish-buyer," I kept explaining to myself, "my spirit is hungry, fierce, carnivorous and greedy—though atrophied at the moment. Ah."

When you are diving at night you are always following an endless tunnel of flashlight beam. The coral corridors, which under noontime sunshafts flame with the arrogance of an azalea garden prepared for a festival, turn ashen and as drab as the catacombs: no wonderland at night, no 'mine eyes have seen the glory' sort of thing...Yet if ever I see God or think I see Him, it will most certainly be at night, in deep water.

There is a symbolic quality about night-diving as if you are a character in an allegory: the dimly lit tunnel leading you down, a feeling of dust and betrayal and destiny, a feeling of ancient things: of Druids, maybe of

Gethsemane. ("Oh God, someone is kneeling before a coral altar down there on the bottom, purple-robed, and here am I suffocating in my mask!")

It's like that and I don't know how to explain it. But when I reach the cave and flash my bright light inside on a big fish, the fish seems to have been waiting for me, perhaps for many years, maybe all of my life, and seems about to say, "I am Beatrice."

Of course it doesn't say a thing, especially anything as nonsensical as "I am Beatrice," so I shoot at it, usually miss, and spend the rest of my breath wrenching the spear out of the coral.

And the lights from the other divers are like distant stars from which someone may be signaling. My goodness! All this, all these things, all metaphysically so confusing!....And so habit forming. Maybe I'll go again tomorrow night.

But I dived 40 feet this afternoon, or so Faustino estimated, to shoot at my private school of young barracuda (adolescents, still swimming in gangs, not quite ready for the swift solitary attacks they will soon learn) and created in Faustino, who saw the school for the first time (having been an unbeliever in its existence up to then) the same passion that I have for spearing these myriad's of maturing man-eaters.

Just as every other time I have dived for them, I lost something (once it was a partial denture): my good spear which came untied, but I was able to dive again, hardly waiting to recover my breath, and find it; though the 40 feet back up seemed incredibly far and I wondered about reaching the surface.

And there, when we got back home, was Patrolman Mangauta working away patiently at fiber glassing my boat's hull; and Mr. Quichocho cooking dinner for the whole bunch of us, sending beer down to the dock by way of invitation. Even the Commissioner, the smiling Mr. Tainatongo, somehow got into the act and was eating with us, shedding fellowship even with Mr. Quichocho who is his bitter political enemy at campaign time.

And we are going out again tonight after tataga. Such lushness! Though, perhaps, one could develop some of the same feelings around a fireplace, back home, using chestnuts instead of fish....Faustino is calling me and I must get out on the lagoon for it is getting dark.

Pretty good fishing. We got a 50 pound parrot fish or atuhoong (bent my spear when I miss-shot and hit a rock), and tataga and a variety of other fish. I ate barracuda kelaguen (a local way for preparing raw fish—somehow sinister and sin-enchanted, like a memory of cannibalism) mixed with fresh onions. Very good. One of the better kelaguens.

Such a fight and tussle a big fish can give a man when he's under 25 feet of black water, and the odds, I suppose, are about the same as for a matador. I am still a little breathless. But it was Faustino, the squat, bow-legged, 'fish punching,' intense little Filipino—who ended up getting it. I caught them in the glare of my flashlight from time to time. Faustino riding the fish as if it were a bronco, his mask getting knocked off, his face taut from the torture of holding his breath—Faustino who said later, "I worry maybe someday I die in bed. It must not be in bed. It must be with big fish, like *atuhoong*, and very, very deep."

The next big fish is supposed to be mine to kill and boat, though I differ in the essential philosophy.

TYPHOON

These are the Christmas holidays, and work is a little slack for the first time since the typhoon which occurred on the nights of November 11 and 12, 1962, devastating our little Pacific island. This is the first time I've had time to collect my blurred impressions of those hectic hours, and to try to unravel their meaning, if any.

Three events—quiet, pallid events—stand out as if in relief against the violence. On the morning of November 12, the front of the hospital gone, while the spangled, early light, cool and immaculate as if it had been scrubbed, gave us a sort of two-dimensional Gothic look there in the ex-posed hallway where nurses had gathered together a few dry bandages and a few intact instruments for setting up a first-aid station on a couple of tables that we had pulled from the debris and propped so they could stand on their broken legs. While we stood there still feeling unnaturally exhila-rated from the excitement of the night before, we exchanged poor jokes about the fine ventilation and view, though deeper down we were stunned and unaccustomed to the idea that we were still alive this morning; and we watched patients—dark-skinned, light-skinned, all shades of the Guama-nian spectrum—wander in almost nonchalantly from broken villages to get their nail puncture wounds and their bashed heads and hands and backs treated; then the first event occurred.

The husband and wife came together. At first they acted as if they would take their place in the waiting line, but finally pushing ahead, diffi-dently and gently so as to give no offense to those whom they were displac-ing, they came directly to me. The wife carried the three-year old girl wrapped in a sheet, and the husband stood just behind her, approving but mute, a sort of supporting public opinion like a loyal audience of television viewers. She placed the child on one of the tables so matter-of-factly that I was taken in and exclaimed stupidly as I uncovered the face. "Oh, the child is dead.". The face was pale and bloodless as a Spanish face.

"Yes, she died last night at 11:20 p.m." she said without a trace of emotion, her voice sweet and courteous, with the precision one uses with a second language. "We knew you would need to know the exact time so we checked it with a flashlight. Do you need to have an autopsy?"

"Well, maybe details will suffice," I said knowing full well that the morgue and the autopsy facilities were a shambles, "Can you tell me more?"

"She couldn't speak after the wall fell on her, which I think must have been about 10:20 p.m., though we failed to check our watch at that time. She couldn't speak and her breath came hard, and frothy blood blew out of her mouth. We tried to help her but we didn't know what to do for the typhoon was coming straight at us through the house, and it was dark. All we could do was shelter her a little with a mattress. We tried to remember these things as they happened so we could tell you. Then she stopped breathing at exactly 11:20 p.m. just as I said. You do believe me, don't you, doctor? My story is reliable isn't it?—though we are willing to sign for an autopsy if there are any discrepancies."

Nurses moved about, handing me a stethoscope, getting out sodden forms for filling in the death certificate and the burial permit. Patients on either side, who were receiving tetanus toxoid for minor wounds, watched the proceedings without much interest. It was the first death I had come on after the typhoon and it seemed to have the quality of a fugue.

"Yes, I believe you." Then, "You parents ...I'm so very sorry ...you are very brave." I felt awkward and compulsively sentimental as I put my arm consolingly on the woman's shoulder.

"It's all right, doctor, don't be upset. We know these things must happen to us. When you have lived a long time on Guam you will understand this."

That was the first episode, not the first in time, but the first in the scattered impressions that I grasp now in an effort to make the violence of that night understandable.

Then I remember my wife's story.

"Of course I won't go to the hospital with you. I want to make sure things are all right here. I can take care of myself as you damn well ought to know by this time, and besides the typhoon will pass over the other end of the island, or maybe miles north of it." So I left her alone in our native, tin-roofed house, 27 miles from the hospital, right where the eye of the typhoon was to pass, and didn't hear from her for three days after the typhoon. Then she told me:

"When I looked up through the rafters I saw the moon shining. There was a thin veil of mist over it like a bride's veil. It was calm, and if there had been any twigs or leaves left, they wouldn't have been stirring.... The moon looked like a holy wafer or the way I think a holy wafer ought to look. 'This must be the eye of the typhoon,' I thought, and I called to people who were beginning to move from our hiding places in this poor, destroyed schoolhouse shelter, 'and it will be worse than ever in a few minutes.' Mrs. Quichocho, the school principal who was under the same table with me, said 'If we are still alive tomorrow, it will be fun to talk about this,' and grinned impishly for she was probably already planning her exaggerations; and Rosa and Isabella recited the rosary again, very fast, almost menacingly as if it were a weapon to be hurled at typhoons, never quite in phase with one another. But it was cold for we were sitting in several inches of water, and I decided that the typhoon was lasting too long." ...So did my wife recreate for me this uneventful, pale moment.

The third event was a little different. It can be best introduced by repeating a citation from the Sixth Guam Legislature, one of many citations forwarded to most governmental offices. It was inscribed on very handsome vellum and signed by all the proper dignitaries:

BE IT RESOLVED BY THE LEGISLATURE OF THE TERRITORY OF GUAM:

WHEREAS, medical personnel and staff of the Guam Memorial Hospital and the private physicians, unselfishly carried through their tremendous responsibilities during the Typhoon Karen disaster, giving aid and help to the sick, treating those who were injured, and otherwise making themselves available and rendering assistance and comfort to patients at Guam Memorial Hospital, when such help was urgently needed and welcomed; and

WHEREAS, Guam Memorial Hospital doctors and staff and private physicians, in their performance of their duties, went on duty for hours without rest or sleep, and such exemplary

action on the part of these people merits the commendation
of the people of Guam; now therefore be it resolved. . . .

A fine, flowing, impeccably phrased statement, but of only partial
truth, for I remember the pale faces of two physicians, who, having hidden
in a closet through most of the typhoon until the closet itself seemed threatened and then took refuge behind a pregnant woman and her clustered
brood of children in a semi-hallway (the men's toilet just behind them as a
place for final retreat), said, as I passed them, "We think that we will be
safe here!"

And another who said, "Sorry, but I'm off duty this evening. And
another who said to the pharmacist, "Give me two tranquilizers or I'll hit
that God-damn Peck, for he's trying to make me work when I'm off duty."

And still another who said (the next day, however): "Oh, I forgot all
about the babies."

But there were also acts of heroism that I shall speak of in a more
leisurely manner as I get into the narrative, and away from the consuming
power of these static events. Early Sunday morning, soon after midnight, a
Civil Defense worker called me by telephone at my home in Merizo which
is at the southern tip of the island, 34 miles from the hospital. "This is Civil
Defense speaking, Doctor, we thought we ought to tell you that we are
now in Typhoon Condition Two . . . " he began somewhat ceremoniously
in his precise Guamanian voice.

"Do you have your crash helmet on yet?" I interrupted challengingly
for I enjoyed teasing the eager, too-serious kids who worked in Civil Defense.

"Why yes, I do. My goodness, how could you tell?" . . . there being a
note of pride in his voice such as I might have had as an intern if someone
had asked me if I had a stethoscope around my neck.

"It's the unusual resonance in your voice," I said, "sort of like a Rus-
sian basso." He continued, apparently intrigued with the idea for his voice
assumed the quality of one speaking into a rain barrel, "We understand
that you are in charge of the hospital while the director is off-island, is that
correct?"

"Well, yes, I guess it is," I conceded reluctantly and suddenly on the
defensive, for, being a public health physician, I had no stomach, nor competence either, for this assignment.

"Then, according to our Disaster Regulations you are required to go
to the hospital until the alert is removed. We hope you don't mind."

"Sure, I'll go, but tell me what you know about this typhoon, or any
typhoon for that matter. You know I've never been in one; much less in a

position where I am supposed to save forty-thousand people and a three-hundred bed hospital from one."

"This is just a precaution that is being taken, strictly routine up to now; looks like this storm will go from Truk (Chuuk) to Saipan and miss Guam entirely. Center winds aren't so very high—not even up to typhoon velocity yet—so we probably have nothing to worry about. Let me see now what it says you are supposed to do. Just see that the auxiliary generator is ready to go, and that essential personnel—you know, like doctors and nurses—are on the job. That's all it says here. I'm kind of new on the job, too. Say, these crash helmets are hot, aren't they. Sure thought you was smart to know I had one on. Oh, yes, one other thing, the name of this tropical storm is: *Karen*."

Hastily my wife and I pounded several pieces of plywood over our most exposed windows. There was a smell of the sky in the calm air as we strained to lift the heavy sections into position, and, in the darkness, tried to pound nails without hitting our thumbs; and the surf, two miles across the lagoon, snored loudly on its barrier reef under a foam of stars. The old Spanish village about us, Merizo, our favorite Guam village, really a Chamorro-Spanish village that had somehow gotten left behind when the new quonset-way-of-life swept over the island, was still asleep: The Tyquincos, the Aguiguis, the Chargualafs and Charfaurouses, the Acfalles, the Champacos, the Nangautas, the Manalisays, the Reyeses and the Torreses were still unaware of the warning…though they may have turned restlessly in their sleep for hammering in the night on Guam has an ominous ring to it.

Then I took off for the hospital, fifty minutes away over mountain roads that were bright and friendly in the full moonlight. "Oh, so incredibly lush," I thought as I always thought whenever I drove along these familiar roads, for pandanus leaves waxed the jungle to high sheen and palm fronds and ferns bent down graciously to frame the road ahead and the sea below in its fold of bays. I remember it well for the next time I drove these roads, the jungle was barren and branchless and as reproachful as an amputee showing his stumps.

The hospital slept on its cliff there at Oka-Tamuning, massively concrete and bone-white, six stories high at one end and sort of undetermined in its height elsewhere for architects had joined structures together, or built new additions from time to time in momentary inspirations, depending more on plane schedules and length of their stop-over in Guam than on ultimate design. Like a coral atoll it had grown by accretion into this monstrous, moonlit creature whose aseptic magnificence dominated the village of rusted quonsets and smelly latrines that was Tamuning—Tamuning before the typhoon. In the moonlight it was like the Taj Mahal. Far below, in the dark the surf thundered in the bay which extended three miles across to the crags of Amante's Point, filling the bay with mist as in a cloud chamber, for great rollers were beginning to tell of the turbulence that was to come. The coral cliff shook a little, at each impact, as a church shakes from its organ tones. The air lay heavy with night perfumes and the sweetish-fetid smell of disturbed coral growths. And there was a watchful calm about the hospital like a sleeping maternal presence; a sort of nocturne of stars, white walls, asepsis and fresh afterbirth—a nocturne, though, that was tightly sequestered to the cliff's edge for I knew that juke boxes were still belting out Tennessee rhythms down on Marine Drive in downtown Tamuning a few blocks out of earshot.

Work crews were already on the job wiring down the glass-louvered windows, the cantankerous mechanisms that should have controlled their closure having given way, to the incessant erosion of salt spray. The improvised wire fastenings appeared unsubstantial to me for I found that I could break them loose without much effort; and for the first time I began to doubt the durability of our kindly giantess, and thought: "Perhaps she foundered as she grew, and her bones and joints are too poor for anything but sleeping in the moonlight," and I asked the work crews to use heavier wires.

The housekeeper, Mr. Innocencio Carbullido, fat, comfort-adoring, patient, slow-acting (y-na-dankulon-taitao-kulan-cara bao, *he who has the size and temperament of a carabao*) came and started filling with water the steel drums that he had distributed to each ward on the previous afternoon when the first warnings had come of an emerging tropical storm to the southeast of us. This, indeed, was a far-sighted, good precaution, but the water was never used—even though desperately needed—for the ceilings and their layering loads of dust and asbestos were to fall, filling the barrels with their trash, and leaving the water stinking and unusable. But Mr. Innocencio Carbullido, the comfort-lover, ignoring comfort, worked all through the typhoon, mopping, carrying blankets, carrying mattresses, carrying patients—worked like a carabao, and during this time his house, which was only a couple of blocks from the hospital, was blowing to splintered bits. "But that is what I was supposed to do," he would have said, if anyone had bothered to ask him why.

At daybreak the cooks started preparing sandwiches so that in event of power failure none would go hungry: "Come what may we can feed everyone for a week," said the dietitian whose Navy husband was at that moment steaming out to sea with his destroyer to ride out the typhoon.

"No, I won't worry about him," she said when I expressed concern, "This happens all the time and I never worry. He's a good sailor, though he hates it and gets seasick."

A fortress air of expectancy began to engage us, and I walked from kitchen to laundry, from morgue to operating suite, from ward to ward, my impractical, unaccustomed eye trying to guess the danger spots. A nurse said, "The pediatric ward is too exposed and its windows are bad. If any ward is destroyed, it will be the one," I agreed, for it jutted like a glass jaw into the void above the cliff, right where the first winds would probably hit. "Very well," I said, "we will evacuate the children to physiotherapy on the ground floor any time we hear that the typhoon is actually veering in our direction." And so we made plans for this and that contingency as they came to mind—plans that came to little in the mad improvisations that were eventually forced on us when we raced patients just minutes or seconds, ahead of blown-in or blown-out windows, collapsing walls and falling ceilings. Yet a general pattern for mobility and rapid decisions was evoked in our minds.

I sent for ten delinquent boys, our legal charges, who were kept locked up out of mischief, and out of sight, in a rickety, old quonset miles away on a lonely hilltop, (Delinquent boys, perhaps, but most certainly resourceful ones, for once, escaping their guardians, they trudged ten miles to a high school, broke into a second-story office, and with the sort of creativity that erected the great stone figures on Easter Island and built the pyramids, made off with a half-ton safe.) They came in through a severe rain squall, dripping-wet and exhilarated, clean-cut as Eagle Scouts and just as eager to show their good manners. There was the intensity of a small typhoon about them and the feeling of lively, reliable hormones.

"Good morning, doctor."

"It's a nice day, sir."

"We wan' ta take care of yore patients, doctor."

"Ya got lots of patients here, sir, maybe th' crazy kind?"

"We hope there'll be a typhoon, sir."

"Yes, th' kind that blows everytin' down, sir."

"Whammy! Oh boy, wham, wham, down goes th' ol' quonset, I hope!"

"We'll behave, sir, an' be real polite ta ya, sir, at least if there's a terrible typhoon, an' we getta chance ta do things like carry out th' wounded."

"Hay, put out that cigarette back there when ya're talkin' ta th' doctor. An' take off yore hat. An' ya, I'm talkin' ta ya, stupid, stop blowin' yore nose on yore fingers."

"Stop hittin' me. It ain't allowed here. Hay doctor, ya don' allow no fightin' in this hospital da' ya?"

We put them in the sixth floor recreation room adjoining the psychiatric ward, and told them to play pool until we could think up some work for them; and, as they picked up their cues, chalking them expertly, they said:

"Thank ya, sir."

"We like it here, sir."

It had never occurred to me before that managing a typhoon could be so complex . . . nor so engaging.

I think it was a little after noon that we heard that the typhoon had changed its course so that it could be expected to hit Guam, and that central winds had increased close to 200 miles per hour. That was when we knew that we were in for a disaster. The winds about us had increased to nearly gale force and there was realism in these announcements. I called my wife in Merizo: "Beg, borrow or steal some more plywood, and get a neighbor boy to help cover up the rest of the windows; cover up the harpsichord with plastic sheeting and move it away from the window. Don't stay in our house for I am sure it will be flattened, especially if the mango tree falls on it. The schoolhouse is the official shelter for Merizo and you should spend the night in it."

"Don't try to panic me," she said with boredom in her voice for she had been through several typhoon alerts which had yielded nothing but minor wind squalls and cramps from sleeping in makeshift typhoon shelters—once she slept on a pool table. "I don't think anything is going to happen. The sun is shining down here and there's scarcely any wind. Don't worry, though, for I know the routines and I'll go through with them even though I think you are being hysterical." When I tried to call again an hour later the phones were out.

Several of the physicians were refusing to come to the hospital: "My first responsibility is to my family and I will stay at home," or "I was not employed to fight typhoons," or "This is scarcely within the scope of my specialty," they said in a colloquy of innuendoes and foreign accents. Hippocrates turned slowly in his grave while I pondered the situation and changed my tack: "Hell, if that's the way it is and you're thinking of your personal safety, just take a look at the roofs and walls of your houses. They're so damn full of termites that they'll come down around your ears at the first good blast"—though, at the time, I thought I was lying and using a clever stratagem, for the staff houses were actually constructed of coral concrete blocks and great beams of mahogany. So, with some slyness and very little prescience, I moved all the physicians and their families from their homes (which would all be demolished within a few hours) cramping them, protestingly, into downstairs offices.

Dr. Koloti was at my side, old Dr. Koloti, old-timer on islands, old-timer on many foreign assignments (Borneo, Indonesia, Saudi Arabia); discredited and down on his luck now, a sort of Balkan history in himself of the machinations and intrigues and blood curdling practices of medical care in the far reaches, Guam having been his particular undoing; battle-scarred, darkly despairing, and tired ordinarily, but today excited by the smell of the typhoon and trouble; Dr. Koloti with the elegant, black-bag, bed-side manners: "Oh how joyous it vould be, oh how lak heaven on ze 'eart, if every vun stay sick all ze time so ve vould help zem a little bit mit our luv, mit little pats on ze back, an' mit ze science an' ze art of doktorink"— of course he never actually said this but I always thought that he had that mystical, elaborate sense of possessiveness toward illness that made every infirmity become a thing of glory in his presence, and malformed or idiot children seem sweetly sad, faraway and, somehow, perfumed.

Now he was at my side: "Oh so interesant, oh so ver' interesant! Ve mus' safe da hospital. Ve mus' our oat' remember an' safe da patients. But oh such impossible our doctors who don' give damn an' tink Hippocrates crazy in head. But you an' me safe hospital an' work lak hell. Ha! He! He! Oh, it ver' interesant!" said Dr. Anton Vesalius Koloti as he wiped his sweating forehead with a perfumed silk handkerchief.

He was my durable medical support through the typhoon for he did work like hell that night and in the subsequent reconstruction days until he developed pneumonia and went to the intact Navy hospital for treatment. Yet, on this night of the typhoon, even while working with incredible exuberance and assurance, Dr. Koloti told a confident (who, of course, confided to everyone else) "Ve all die tonight, all die, each doktor, nursey an' patient mus' die . . . an' ve mus' all do it nobly."

Tightly coiled; frowning and severe; pinched; always fatigued and over-worked in a nervous sort of way; unsure of herself now but to gain marvelous confidence in herself before the night was over; classic-featured, though she couldn't have cared less; clear olive skinned, was the chief nurse, Miss Maria Asuncion Cruz. Oh, Miss Cruz, I usually thought you were having menstrual cramps from the way you hated me and my white, father-figure!. A poor kind of introduction for you, Miss Cruz, for overnight and in the subsequent days and nights of reconstruction you grew into a heroine whose statue and stamina, and self-possession frightened and awed me.

Miss Cruz was directing the transfer of the children from the pediatric ward to the physiotherapy quarters when I came to her, scolding too much and looking distraught. "The typhoon had better be a short one," I said to myself, but to her I said, "I'm glad we won't have to use these quarters for more than one night for it is too crowded here and much too hot; and that large fan playing directly on to those children over there would surely get us into trouble." "But it will be safe for the night," she said, having been through the typhoons of 1949 and 1957 and knowing something of the force of winds. "Well, a little pneumonia is probably better than a lot of bashed-in heads," I agreed. And she gave me a smile, a starched, humorless grimace, but the first concession toward friendship that I had been able to wring from her in three years.

There was crying and screaming of infantile protestation about the transfer, the manner of transfer, and, no doubt, the way strange lights and shadows and chaos filled their new quarters.

But suddenly I was no longer attentive to these things or to the sound of gravel hitting the high-placed, secure (I thought then) windows, for the radio was now announcing that "the typhoon will strike at about 6:20 p.m. and the eye will pass over the center of the island at approximately 9:30 p.m." That, we knew, was the precise location of the hospital. That was the last weather announcement for the aerial of the local radio station was soon wrenched from its moorings.

The build-up was slow, and between each development there was an hour or so of waiting. Paul and I, that is Paul St. John, my sanitarian—you remember that ordinarily I am the health officer on Guam and hospital affairs are as foreign to me as a tribal war in Africa—Paul and I, during these lulls, played Telemann duets on two recorders that he had included, like any good recorder player would do, among his emergency supplies. Paul, product of Harvard, dignified but tattooed and lush as a beachcomber, in fact, he is a beachcomber; an encyclopedic perfectionist in all things not conflicting with languor, mathematical abstractions, a brawl, an obscene book, or a rare book. "We had better close the office door as we do this," he said with some self-consciousness, "for it seems a little too British." Each time we played, the tone of the recorders became thinner and we finally gave up in despair and went in search of last minute safety precautions.

"Where is that damn Juan Adams, the hospital administrator, my so-called right arm for the night, my left cerebral hemisphere for the next twelve hours, my left . . . oh well, where the hell is Adams who is supposed to be showing me how to save the hospital?" I asked much more loudly than was necessary.

"Oh, here I am" he said, panting a little from exertion. "I just got through securing things at home" —Juan Adams, the half-cast Guamanian, the slightly dilettantish subordinate who was so wealthy that he would have a $100,000 house blown away that night (a home on a mountain ridge that shared the panorama of the Pacific on one side of Guam and of the Philippine Sea on the other, and, accordingly, the full blast of every typhoon both coming and going; and with picture windows that gathered, not only light rays of fabulous, misty distances and depths, but the full breaking-force of every gale), and the owner of two theaters, a couple of drive-ins, and a number of other businesses—but this is beginning to sound like an appraisal for tax purposes rather than the description of a man! Juan Adams coming to my side—under-developed and limping from varicose veins that were bothering him that night, bifocal, pale from his admixed Boston blood and sedentary life.

"I thought you had decided to chicken-out on us and stay home to watch your property blow away," I said brutally, trying to justify my petulance.

"Oh no," not perturbed by me, "I'm a typhoon boy at heart and I like to be in the center of things." There was a jauntiness about him, and all that night as he hurried about in his limping gallop, giving orders that he usually carried out himself, whistling and wise-cracking, he seemed to be playing with the typhoon. Once he chuckled, "I'll bet that blast got both my picture windows," as if nothing could be more hilarious than seeing his own stateside pretensions shattered in public.

By 5 p. m. the trees were bending almost flat to the ground and shallow-rooted ones, like plumeria, were blowing loose and rolling before the wind like massive tumbleweeds. "This is still not the real thing," said Juan Adams, looking a little disappointed; "this is still nothing but a warming-up exercise. Don't draw any conclusions about our Guam typhoons until the real thing gets here." Winds were not yet up to the necessary 64 knots or 73 miles per hour (a conversion obtained by multiplying knots by 1.14). And I knew that we should expect winds at least double, or possibly triple this base velocity.

It was dark outside by 6:30 p.m. when typhoon winds had presumably arrived. Paul and Juan Adams and I went to the deserted pediatric ward to see how it was faring in its exposed position. The wind was not steady but came at us in great gusts and gasps like a giant undergoing an irregular excess of passion. It obliterated the surf sounds from below and became a surf of its own and we sensed billows of air piling up against us, compressed and full of energy, shaking the ward, and then sucking back almost like an undertow so that our ears crackled. Metal window frames in banks of three were being buffeted loose from their concrete moorings, and some of them bellied like canvas sails in and out of the room with each ebb and flow of the wind. A bank of windows, right in front of us, suddenly sucked out into the night—no sound of crashing from below!—and we were looking into the darkness that hung over the bay, the wind momentarily calm as the pressures reversed themselves. Then the typhoon poured in through the gap. Chairs crashed and beds blew against the opposite wall; and there was a strong taste of salt in the stinging rain that came at us like bullets.

We hurried to the upper floors of the north wing of the hospital where winds seemed less apparent though windows were beginning to bang. Dr. Kolosi was there ahead of us, "Ve move patients to hallways maybe now? Vindows go pouf-bang all over place; eye out here, jugular there, leg off some oder place. Oh mighty messy, huh? An' scientific, like experimental, huh? An' oh so vonderfully for doktorink! Ve move kvick! Here nursey, nice nursey, here vord boy, move patients kvick lak gut ol' Doktor Kolosi say." And he started pushing a bed into the hall while the nurse and orderly stared blankly out of a window.

"That probably will not be enough," I said, "Ve mus' be ready, an' ver', ver' kvick, too, to move the patients to the second floor in the public health offices," I said, damning myself for my red-handed, not-quite intentional mimicry.

"Ve try, ve try ver' hard an' ve safe da patients, you an' me, too, also," and he smiled gaily. His chin and nose seemed to be waving at each other across an edentulous valley like two mountain yodelers.

By eight o'clock the typhoon was on us in full force, roaring like a flight of jet planes, and shaking the hospital so that its thick, over-designed walls trembled. Wild singing of aeolian harps came from the elevator shafts and ventilators. Louvered windows began to break their wire restraints and to bang and chatter; and the wind, having worked its way into the area above the acoustical ceiling, tore loose the fiberglass and asbestos sectors and began to heave them up and down—very gently at first, but finally with violent plopping—so that they showered us with glistening, irritating dust fragments of their material; and finally, later in the evening, with whole sections of their compressed boards. There was a feeling that we were rushing pell-mell into a dark tunnel, a feeling of embrace by something that was wild and sinful, and I kept thinking, "This is something that I shouldn't be doing."

The electric power was still on, and in the parking lot the streaked floodlight beams showed a curious animation among the parked cars which were becoming restless and social, constantly nodding and moving from one group to another; one rolled sedately into a ditch and lay over on its side, lugubriously, exhaling a drunken sigh; another reared its front end in the air, whinnying, I fancied, pivoted about in a determined sort-of-way and crashed on top of another car.

"Looks like it's trying to breed," said Paul with the rapt intensity of one taking a Rorschach test. Workmen were still frantically trying to apply their little restraining wires to the windows, but the crazy, wild louvers snapped like teeth at their fingers. It was beginning to look dangerous and futile.

Lania hao, screamed a workman at a window that had just bloodied his fingers. [The Guamanian obscenity is of such depth and shock that no decent person would translate it, though the meaning is precisely that of the most common GI obscenity.] When he saw that I was watching him he said, "Nothin' 'hol' still. Evert'ing shake an' jump all time. Dis no typhoon lak we supposed t' have, it's a goddamn eart'quake."

"Or like a whore with St. Vitus dance," said Paul whose preoccupation with sex had been increasing lately.

The wind was beginning to roar in the stairwells, and the grandiose, two-story-windows that were coming loose in the concrete, thundered as they bellied and whip-cracked. Every so often there was the crash and curiously musical tinkle of a glass panel being whipped to pieces. The typhoon was getting loose in the hallways and blowing at us, unsteadying us as we walked, flooding some areas. Earlier, when the windows had been securely closed, it had been hot and humid, now it was cold in the damp, salt wind that was whipping through the halls. Our clothes were wet and our shoes half-filled with water.

The upper wards in the south wing were being evacuated and the patients came crowding into the central hallway, most of them standing. They were calm and they smiled in unconcerned mood as I passed. The windows in the physiotherapy section were giving way under the impact of flying gravel, and nurses were pushing the children's cribs into the hall. Juan Adams and Miss Cruz supervised the moves and all was uneventful as a scheduled fire drill.

Up the hall away from this central area, but still within view of it, a bank of six windows began to loosen and slowly bulge inward. Alarmed workmen brought long planks to lean against the top of the frames, hoping somehow to force them back into proper position; but as they struggled against the pressure from without, the wind suddenly slackened and gave a mighty suck and the entire bank of windows, still being pushed by the workmen, huffed outward, crashing in the hospital yard. The typhoon howled into the hall, victorious and proclaiming liberation from whatever tyranny we may have been under, and rain slashed through, forming a little surf that worked its way toward the patients. Slowly, other windows in the long hallway gave way until the entire front lay bare. The louver-fronted offices lining the hallway were ripped open. Patients huddled in the central hall where they were protected by a bank of elevators on one side and a solid wall on the other. Several physicians sat there among them, pale, not working and trying to avoid my attention. I felt better when I didn't see them.

Lights began to flicker and finally blacked out, but only for a few seconds, then the emergency generator, taking over, lighted the central areas and the stairwells.

Power remained for a time for one elevator. Juan Adams came down the stairs with his funny three-cornered limp, panting, "OB. and nursery are cut off. Can't get the patients out."

I went to the fourth floor. Many workmen followed me for they had given up the defense of the windows; and also a missionary physician: thin, intense, just out of his internship, unnaturally pale as if he had been spending too much time in a dark, secret place praying. I had never paid much attention to him and I wondered how he had gotten to the hospital through the typhoon.

We stood in the protection of a wall and looked across a broken space that seemed like a yawning chasm though the floor was really quite intact. Both sides of the building had been blown out, and the full force of the typhoon at this fourth-floor elevation shrieked its 210 mile-an-hour wind through the dark, desolate space, sucking at us so that we held back with effort. Partitions were down, and beds, desks, all kinds of equipment, and fragments of ceiling were junked four feet high in a restless, shifting terrain of ridges and valleys and ziggurats. Metal strips, hanging from the broken ceiling, swept scimitar-like through the air, or, breaking their wire fastenings, shot across the space with the force of spears. Broken glass filled the air with comet tails when caught by the beam of our flashlights. The rain streaked horizontally before us. Far across the space—miles away, it seemed—we could see the emergency lights of the closed obstetrical suits, with dark figures crowding against the glass doors.

And suddenly I was 'swimming' against a strong current, my fins and snorkel gone and my mas' leaking, the incredibly muscular tentacles of the wind jerking me, man-handling me, teasing me toward the brink of the broken wall; black objects in the air struck my head and shoulders. Halfway across the space I lay mashed on a heap of rubbish, resting a moment, trying to get a breath of air that did not contain salt water, trying to get my bearings. The lights of the obstetrical suite seemed very far off, almost as if they were receding, and I knew that the workmen and the missionary were watching my progress from the black hallway behind me. Then I crawled the rest of the way. It was a tremulous crossing, and when I slipped through the door, holding myself back so I wouldn't shoot into the room like a projectile, it was with a feeling of some kind of symbolic achievement, like Grace Attained. But I formulated my impression no further for it was bright in here and calm enough to stand upright, and faces were welcoming me with interest.

There was a momentary illusion of haven and serenity. Pregnant women, and women who had recently delivered, and a sprinkling of husbands stood there, each woman holding a nursery infant, some holding two. The tenderness of a Madonna and child tableaux was repeated twenty times or so. In the front stood Miss Cruz, her olive face classic, maternal and loving. She showed me the infant that she held. "He's beautiful, and he hasn't cried once." she said. Though I was thinking, "This is just an ordinary infant. It is you, Miss Maria Asuncion Cruz, who is beautiful, and it is your radiance that is filling the room."

"We must get them out of here," she continued, "for the roof and the partitions are beginning to collapse and, as you can see, there is water up to our ankles. I can carry this one across and come back after many others."

"How did you get here?" suddenly suspicious that my own heroics had been undermined. "I thought you were downstairs."

"Oh, I crawled on my knees. Look at my uniform" and she laughed scornfully down at her dirty, torn skirt. "It wasn't difficult. Miss Quenga came with me. We were afraid these people wouldn't know what to do."

"Well," I said, "I am sure I couldn't possibly carry a baby across there without getting it injured and I just don't see how anyone else could do it at this time." I looked at my watch. "But in 10 or 15 minutes, according to the predictions, the eye of the typhoon should be here, and at that time it will be easy to come across. I think you will have to wait until then. The ward will hold up till then." But at that moment a section of ceiling fell just behind us and a partition leaned a little more into the hallway. "Yes, it will be safe for the next 15 minutes," I reassured myself for there seemed to be no alternative.

Then I went back through the black current, holding a pillow over my head against the flying debris. I told my decision to the missionary and suggested that he and the workmen wait there for a lull that might permit safe evacuation. And I went to the north wing.

My plan for evacuation, I am sure, was good, and it would have worked except for one thing: the eye never came. It missed the hospital, which remained in the full, crashing force of its central winds and crossed over Merizo. When Miss Cruz saw that the winds were not slackening she crawled to the workmen and she and the missionary organized the men into a bridge, a sort of poorly covered bridge of male bodies, sufficient, though, to break the impact of flying objects, and the women, each clutching an infant to her breast primordially, crawled across the abyss. It must have been a terrifying trip. It was heroic. And I felt cheated that I wasn't involved.

The women came down the stairs and crowded into the hallway at the foot of the elevator, joining shoulder to shoulder with the other patients. One woman promptly went into active labor, and the missionary, laying her on a desk and rolling up his sleeves, delivered her while he elbowed the crowd that pushed against them.

But I was not present, for things had gone wrong in the north wing and were keeping me there.

The psychiatric and tuberculosis patients were lying on mattresses in the Public Health offices and in the hallway. Water stood several inches deep and the mattresses on which they lay were sodden. Little waves rolled the length of the hall, like an experiment in physics to demonstrate the propagation of sound waves, for the door at the end of the hall had broken in. "We'll have to segregate the tuberculosis patients," I mused, for in the rush and darkness, Koch's postulates had been ignored; and I went along the hall flashing my light from face to face, trying to plan some reorganization. "But," suddenly and with a start, "where are the chronic patients from third floor? I don't see any of them." A nurse said, "Maybe they are still on the ward."

Paul and I and a string of Detention Home boys ran up the stairwell bright from the emergency generator's electricity, through little Niagara's that cascaded about our ankles. "Lania, oh lania," I heard Paul say haltingly and unfamiliarly as he lost his footing on the slippery steps.

When we opened the door to the ward, there was the thunder of havoc breaking through it and a feeling of bats for the air was full of flying objects. The windows were all gone; partitions sagged and lurched; the ceiling had disintegrated into a kind of brown mud that splattered the walls; the metal rods that had once supported the ceiling hung from wires and clanged furiously. Furniture flopped about, broken and animated, seeking heaps against the partitions to lie in. I looked back and saw Paul pausing for just a second in the door way. It was just a second, but during that second, he told me later, his legs were carrying him in the wrong direction. "I would start to follow you, but my legs, without any command from me, would be carrying me back to the stairwell. It was a funny sensation for at the moment I seemed to be numb from the hips down. It was like riding a horse that keeps trying to bolt back to its stable, but then I got control of my legs and had no more trouble." There were thirteen bed-patients still on the ward, the beds having been pushed for slight protection to the lee of the nearly-collapsed partitions. Young student nurses were with them, holding on to the beds for support, fighting to keep the patients partially covered by mattresses. I hurried to the first patient, uncovered the face and shone my light on a mongoloid child, slobbering, prematurely aged and nearing its natural time of death. Her face, in the glare of the flashlight, showed as brightly as an illumined shrine, and there was a sort of infantile sweetness in her grimacing that reminded me of the nursery. She reached a hand jerkily toward my face and made a happy gurgling sound. But re-membering my survival priorities, I covered her face and left her, feeling, though, a little guilty as if I had been usurping the rights and privileges and despairs of God. The next patient was a very old, fat, senile woman whose hands were restrained to the bed by ties. An indwelling urinary catheter led to a bottle suspended below the bed. Rapidly I broke the restraints, discon-nected the catheter and carried her dead-weight toward the door, lurch-ing—a student nurse steadying me as best she could. Just before I reached the door, feeling that I might fall, I leaned momentarily against a pillar. The old woman was talking in Chamorro and I put my ear close to her lips to hear her say: *"kao man mato esta y Americano? , , , Dabe de on lortasia yan y magas Japanies, ya yangin heneno hao to diebe de on resiste y hagaho.* ("Have the Americans come yet? . . . Always bow at the waist when you meet a Japanese soldier, and if he pushes you to the ground, do not resist, O my daughter.") Two Detention Home boys took her from my arms and carried her the rest of the way and I hurried back for another. Paul was busy carry-ing out other patients and so were the Detention Home boys. The last one I carried out was the mongoloid child.

One of the student nurses, as lithe and handsome as a South Seas model, but very serious now and as challenging as Florence Nightingale, came to me: "We did right didn't we? We wouldn't move the patients until we got a doctor's order. That was the thing to do, wasn't it? Those wild boys kept coming and saying that they were men and that they wanted to carry out the wounded, but we wouldn't let them. We knew that we must stay. We knew that we were doing our duty."

In the morning the ward looked as if it had been bombed, the walls and ceiling gutted down to basic concrete, the furniture blown away or lying twisted and worthless in heaps. No living thing could have survived the entire night there—not even a Crimean War Nurse, nor a myth.

We added the chronic patients to the crowd in the Public Health corridor and lay them on mattresses in the water. Dr. Koloti moved among them as if he were making his routine ward rounds, possibly a little forgetful of time and place: "Vell, vell, all my liddle patients are here, I see, an' all improving nicely, all MIT roses in cheeks. Oh, so happy. Oh, so contentible. All so vishful to tell happy thoughts to ze director an' ze congressmens."

The Detention Home boys asked me "Which are the crazy ones?" and took their places with them, shepherding them expertly for the next several days, never leaving them except when we needed a special work crew. "They like us," the boys told me, "An' they don' even know we're delinquent an' gotta be locked up jus' like them. . . . Crazy ain't it?"

When Paul and I paused for a moment to catch our breaths, he said, appearing a little startled at his own words when he said, "I know I have been working at top speed for hours, my aching muscles tell me that, but I can't remember much of it, probably no more than five minutes of actual activity. I've sort of blacked-out since about the time we stopped playing the recorders. What we're doing at any one time seems very clear, very, very intense and important—like something that I have been trained for all my life; like something I came to Guam for—but my brain just won't hold on to it once it's past. I think I know what it feels like to be an idiot." Nervously, I tried to reconstruct my own activities but could pull only an isolated face or gesture or an edentulous smile out of an amorphous black jungle of lost sensations. Though over the next few weeks most of the details returned, usually with precision and clarity. I went back to the south wing and pushed my way through the crowd of standing patients. The missionary had just finished delivering another baby. The nurses were counting and recounting babies, for the rapidly increasing numbers had confounded their statistics. "There seems to be one missing," they kept saying as they made frantic rechecks. "There must be one still on the fourth floor."

The missionary and I didn't really believe it—after all, nurses are always miscounting sponges and getting doctors unnecessarily upset, but we took our flashlights and climbed to the fourth floor. In the obstetrical suite and nursery the partitions were all down, and the concrete walls had a sandblasted appearance. We crawled through the rubble, flashing our lights in every crevice, listening as best we could for crying. "They're wrong. There is no baby here," we finally agreed and left. But Miss Cruz was not satisfied with our search, and a little later she commandeered an expectant father and the two of them went back to the ward. She told me how it happened: "I was on my hands and knees crawling under a collapsed partition when the wind slackened just enough so I could hear a squeal that seemed to come from a linen cabinet. When I opened the door and reached into the dark, something grabbed my finger so that I jumped, thinking it might be a rat. But it was the baby, still in its bassinet, dry and happy and just as safe as if it had been downstairs with the others. I don't know how it ever got into the linen closet.?

"Nice going, Maria," I heard Paul say, a familiarity in address that surprised me.

The winds had reversed their direction sometime earlier and were beginning to slacken. A radio call came for me and I went into one of the ambulances to receive it. "This is the Governor's Aid calling from Civil Defense. The Governor wants to know the condition of the hospital. Over."

I fumbled with the microphone and the controls saying 'over' a couple of times by mistake before I finally got the hang of it. "The hospital has been largely destroyed, but no one has been injured; however, all patients will need to be evacuated to the Navy Hospital. Tell the Governor that there has been some real heroism going on up here among his people, that the Detention Home boys," . . . I could feel my exuberance soaring as little fountains of cortisone, somewhere in my adrenals, sprayed my physiology into greater magnitudes.

"Hell," said the governor's aide in his burly state-side voice, "I'm not interested in heroism, "I just want to know about the damage. Over."

I had a flashing image of the aide huddled over a microphone in the heavily-reinforced, battened-down security of Civil Defense Headquarters, looking like a hero. "Do you have your crash helmet on?" I asked.

"Sure, we gotta take all the proper precautions," he said, "but how did you know I had a helmet on? Over."

"Something about the unusual resonance of your voice."

"Very good, very observing," and his voice deepened. "Yes, the Governor will be interested to know that the Detention Home boys caused you no trouble and I will convey your message to him. But we need a doctor down here, can you come? Over."

"Sure, I'll come right now. Over and out," I concluded with a precision that must have surprised both of us.

The ambulance was heavy and powerful as a tank; the wind could sway and shake it, but, compared to the windowless hospital, it seemed like a typhoon-shelter as we drove down Marine Drive. Our busy spotlight picked out the dark shells of houses, roofs off, walls down, sometimes only scattered remnants of lumber and tin roofing remaining. Trees had become branchless stumps. There were no lights and no signs of life. It was spectral and lonely as a graveyard laid open.

"This is just like the war after the bombardment," the ambulance driver said. "No," he added a moment later, "it is worse than that." There was dishonesty in the spotlight's narrow beam: it was too yellow, and it seemed incapable of picking out familiar landmarks. "It will be different in the daylight," I assumed with some conviction. "Surely a truly great catastrophe would have more reality to it than this and I would be overcome with horror. As it is I am merely bewildered."

The business sections of Tamuning and Agana, which lay flat along the lagoon, were filled with coral rubble and good-sized boulders that waves had rolled in at high tide, and we picked our way in low gear, jolting and teetering over the paved, four-lane street that had become a boulder field. Electric poles were nearly all down, and wires festooned the street like

Christmas tree ornaments. Transformers dangled and swung rhythmically in the wind.

Wires made the motions for rope-skipping, and we timed our progress with their swing. But sometimes we became entangled so that we had to back up to make a lunge that would break their hold. Once we became so hopelessly snarled that the ambulance driver stepped out on the running board and with his bare hands lifted the wires from around us, saying, "I'm pretty sure the current's been turned off."

Near the Agana boat basin large ocean-going fishing boats rested on the street and smaller fishing boats were scattered far inland, almost all the way back to the cliff. Madeleine's Dress Shop, across from the boat basin, seemed to be intact—except, of course, for the roof, for missing roofs had begun to look normal—and there was a familiar-looking car propped against its front door as if seeking entrance.

The Civil Defense Headquarters was crowded with many Guamanians, and a few State-Siders, a number of Filipinos and Trust Territory Islanders—polyglot and huddled. I knew many of the Guamanians and we exchanged greetings as we might have done on any casual meeting. There was my little secretary among them, who had been married just recently enough to be seven months pregnant, and bulging now as if she were concealing a watermelon beneath her dress. And there was her husband. "Oh, good evening doctor," she said, smiling amiably as she might before determining if I wanted cream or sugar in my coffee at coffee-break. "Isidro cut his foot. I guess that's the reason they sent for you."

"How did it happen?"

"Oh, he cut it when we were walking past Madeleine's Dress Shop."

"My goodness, what were you kids doing out there," a horrid thought crossing my mind, 'You weren't looting, were you?"

"Oh no." That was all she said then and I didn't get the full story for several weeks. Here is the way Isidro cut his foot:

Isidro and Teresita live in Sinajana in a solid concrete house that sits high on spindly stilts, sensationally high even in a village where stilts are the mode, and it gives the appearance of waiting for a flood. When the typhoon came on, the house began to sway, and Teresita, never quite over her first months of morning sickness, became a little bit seasick. At the height of the typhoon, at about 10 p.m. the door blew off the hinges, tables and chairs sailed across the room, and the house seemed to sway more wildly than ever.

"Oh Isidro, oh Isidro," Teresita cried, repeating his name so as to indicate special alarm and emergency, for Isidro, being a calm individual, was difficult to excite. "Oh Isidro, the house is going to collapse now. We must get in our car and go for shelter in the Navy Hospital, which is a very strong building since it cost thirty million, five hundred and thirty-eight thousand dollars to build, the cost of patient-care each day is . . . but don't mind, Isidro, we will discuss such details after we get there; the important thing is that we leave this house which was most certainly improperly constructed and cost less than six thousand dollars, as rapidly as possible."

The direct road up Nimitz Hill to the hospital was blocked by fallen debris; and electric poles and transformers were crashing wildly on all sides of the car. So they turned back and drove down through Agana toward the alternate back route up the hill, picking their way intuitively, for visibility had become nearly extinct, and the few available landmarks seemed unfamiliar and misleading. They were driving along Marine Drive between Madeleine's Dress Shop and the boat basin when the waves rolled in, lifting the car and 'surfing' it toward the dress shop. Water came up about their necks and, as they rode the crest of the wave, they could see large boats racing past. In alarm Teresita cried, "Isidro, Isidro, we are going in the wrong direction. Somewhere we took the wrong turn for we are now in the middle of the boat basin and heading rapidly out to sea. Turn back before it is too late, Isidro, for there is a severe storm on the ocean tonight."

Then they crashed into the front of Madeleine's Dress Shop. The water chilled them and their teeth chattered. Waves continued to pour over the car. Teresita's first thought, there in the breaking surf, was of her pregnancy. "I have lost the baby for I no longer feel pregnant. Put your hand down through the water on my stomach, Isidro, and find if it is still there."

As the waves began to recede Isidro carried her to a slightly protected window ledge and ran to Civil Defense Headquarters for an ambulance. In the water he lost his zories and that was the way he cut his foot.

The gash was not serious but it would require suturing, and as I studied it and made arrangements for its care, I listened to the conversations of people around me. A peroxide blonde, brassy and hard and whore-like, sat beside a shriveled, dejected man who looked like a pimp. She talked without let-up in a west-side-Chicago accent. "Me an' Toughy—that's this here muscle man I'm shackin' up with—had a close one. When the house started ta go, he says ta me, 'You'se the one with a brain, you'se the one that listens ta them broadcasts—what're we supposed ta do now? Tell me quick, Sweetie, bafore the walls fall down.' I tries hard ta remember, but nothin'' comes straight, an' this guy who thinks I'm a brain, who shacks up with me cause he thinks I'm smart, him a' standin' there stupid an' shakin' in his pants like a kid, an' wantin' ta know somethin. 'Gosh, Toughy,' I says,' I know it but it won't come ta me, it's in my head but it won't come out. We're supposed . . . we're supposed . . . it's beginnin' ta come, Toughy. I know we're supposed ta keep calm an' collected, that much I remember fer shore, but the rest is tougher. . . Oh, yes, we're supposed ta keep sanitary, extra sanitary like brushing our teeth a lot. Yes, that's it, that's what we're supposed ta do. We gotta brush our teeth.' So we went ta the kitchen sink an' brushed our teeth, me sayin' all the time, 'Brush 'em up an' down, not sideways like usual, up an' down, Toughy, up an' down.' An' then a wall fell in an' the roof went off, an, 'You're rememberin' fine,' he said, and I said 'We pack our suitcase nex'.' But the house was comin' down fast an' I didn't have time for any more rememberin' so I just tossed our tooth brushes in an ol' suitcase along with a couple of pillow cases, an' an 'lectric skillet cause the 'lectricity was off an' I was thinking about the stores being closed. So that' all the crap in the world me and this guy Toughy got right there in that goddamn suitcase."

And that is all I will say about the night of the typhoon.

Malawi mother and child. The mother has active tuberculosis and is being treated in the sanatorium that can be seen behind her. In Malawi, it is impossible to separate a child from its mother so the child stayed in the sanatorium with her and was treated prophylactically. As can be seen from the photograph, the child has Down's syndrome.

CHAPTER FIVE

INTERLUDE: MALAWI, AFRICA

After four and one-half years on Guam, my wife and I went to Malawi, Africa (1965) where I spent three years—as Director of a Public Health Project under the auspices of the University of North Carolina. For reasons I still do not understand, I almost ceased to write. Perhaps I was overwhelmed by the wonders and perplexities of this 'unknown' world. Certainly nothing that I had experienced in Rongelap or Guam had prepared me for the savagery of back country Malawi: our cook, when accused of witchcraft, was forced to drink a poison concoction that killed him, thus confirming his guilt; four burglars ransacked our house one night; a witch doctor who was hired to kill a woman near us transformed himself into a crocodile that did the actual killing, though the court ruled that no man should be held guilty of the murderous ways of a crocodile and the case was dismissed; lions patrolled the jungles and sometimes the villages and their houses, searching for prey; entire families of baboons, sometimes several dozens of them, often crossed the road in front of you and if you stopped your car to avoid hitting them, they would jump up onto the hood to peer at you through the windscreen, and try to reach through a window to touch you. I had been warned that if ever I came upon a serious accident in which an African had been injured by a 'European' driven car, I shouldn't stop for the anger of the local people would be directed at me and I would be savagely beaten; instead I was to drive to the nearest police station and report it. . . . I, a physician running away from his Hippocrates' prescribed duty! I'm sure that I couldn't have done it and would have stopped and attempted to give emergency aid.

Now something about the politics of Malawi — its jungle politics, and a word about its president, Dr. Hastings Banda, a physician who had earned his MD. at Maharry, an' all Negro' college in the United States. He directed the revolution that had just ousted the English colonialist government, and had become the first president of this new nation. I learned to know him and regarded him as an honorable man who would save his country in spite of the rough way in which he handled some of its initial problems; for instance, minor rebellions kept arising against him, so he hired Israeli military officers to come to Malawi and organize young men in each village into semi-military clubs, called Young Pioneers, whose duty was to catch anyone who disagreed with Dr. Banda and beat him and burn his house. Often, when I was in a village at night I could hear the Young Pioneers running through the streets screaming their hate, and in a following newspaper I could sometimes see pictures of these same Young Pioneers laughing and joking as they beat one of Dr. Banda's enemies — sometimes to death. My favorite memory of these Young Pioneers came when Dr. Banda called me into his office and said, "Things are quieting down and I no longer need the Young Pioneers to beat up my enemies and burn their houses, but I must find ways to keep them busy and out of mischief. I want you to try to find ways to keep them occupied." I said that I would try and I extended the University's Health Program to include well-baby clinics in several villages in which I used Young Pioneers to weigh and handle the babies and act as nurse assistants. I shall never forget how tenderly these Young Pioneers, who had just been committing atrocities, set about carrying and kissing and weighing the babies. Photo-

Two tuberculosis patients and a Peace Corps volunteer who is trying to save them from starvation in the "sanatorium" partially shown in the background.

graphs showed them smiling just as happily as they had smiled when they were beating Dr. Banda's enemies; and the well baby clinics were a success that I extended to many more villages.

Unfortunately, once Dr. Banda began to feel powerful, he became a selfish, cruel, paranoid tyrant. He made all political parties illegal except his own. He appointed himself president for life, and he began systematically killing off his rivals. All who approached him were required to address him, not as President or Dr. Banda, as I had been doing, but as *His Excellency the Life President, Ngwazi Dr. H. Kamuzu Banda.* Anyone who failed to do this would go to jail. And anyone who disagreed with him on an important issue could expect to be executed. Finally, long after I had left Malawi, he began to demand that his high officials should learn to speak Latin and Greek so that they could discuss ancient philosophies with him.

I am not presenting these examples disparagingly for at one point my wife and I even considered the possibility of retiring in Malawi. I wrote one poem while I was in Africa which I never published until recently. It has to do with our handsome, young African gardener's assessment of my aging process. His name was Francisco. Here is the poem:

A huge Malawi baobob tree that may outdate Jesus Christ. The car was my rental car.

POEM
On Aging

A garden boy I had in Africa
(when I was an ersatz colonialist)

obsidian and handsome (always) and
brave (usually), and a good companion

when I went mountain climbing for orchids
or wanted to make friends in any hut

or village where I stopped, said "You are old . . ."
He didn't say Bwana nor Master as

other servants in those parts would have said for I
had schooled it out of him, just: "You

are old an' ready ta die anyhow
so it's O.K. you take risks an' act fool
But me, ah me, I is yout'ful an desirable ta many womans who I
mus' please an' give babies — enough ta prove
fa sho' I don' sit up in chair all nights;

so many t'ings; one enemy who needs
poisoning, several who need huts burned down,

friends ta be taught my strengt' an' courage, an'
how I can out-drink an' out-smart 'em all."

So he wouldn't go with me up a mountain
on Chirwa Island where I knew I could

find many pythons and black-mounted mambas,
nor into Mpatamanga Gorge at dusk

where lions I wanted to spy on would
be prowling, nor into leopard country

if I took my dog which attracts leopards
nor up a peak on Mlanje Mountain

where misanthropic little men live invisible lives . . . which irritated me

until I got to thinking he had named
the kind of freedom I was looking for.

Our neighbors in Malawi expected my
wife and me to employ three of them
for servants. The one in the center is
Francisco, our gardener. The one on his
left was our cook, and the one behind
Francisco was our night watchman.
Francisco is the one we brought to
Saipan with us hoping he would
become a member of our family. But it
didn't work out.

I had just climbed a tree and carefully removed a beautiful orchid. This woman grabbed it from me, fastened it on her head, and went dancing wildly away. I couldn't catch her, but she finally surrendered it to me, laughing at my poor attempt to catch her.

When Francisco first came to us as gardener, he had only one year of school and could not speak a single word of English, but within several months he could carry on fairly complicated conversations in English with us. Then my wife and I became so entranced by him that we decided to make him a permanent member of the family, and, after three years, when we moved back to the Pacific, we brought him in the plane with us.

This was Francisco's first airplane trip and it was probably the first time he ever gave way to serious philosophical contemplation's. Looking down at the ocean beneath him and at the horizon on all sides of him, he said quietly but with conviction: "*I think the world must be round* " And suddenly I found myself comparing him with classic Greek philosophers who had required centuries of intense thought and discussion and argument to come to the same conclusion.

But another observation that he made was not so profound. In Malawi few Africans risk learning to swim because of the danger of contracting bilharzia from African fresh water snails, and I looked forward to teaching him to swim in Saipan's pure water; and soon after our arrival I took him to the beach and told him to paddle around in the clear water. He did, but came running to me shouting, "I'm getting out of here. Someone put salt in the water."

Saipan islanders accepted him readily—too readily for his comfort—and when a group of them invited him to go on a picnic at which a dog was butchered, cooked, and eaten, he came home crushed, saying: "If they'll eat a dog, they'll eat an African. I want to go back to Malawi." After that there was no consoling him and we had to send him back to Africa.

⊕　⊕　⊕

Here I am on Saipan's coast, relaxing
from the stress of intense office duties.
My companions are my two local dogs
and several Saipan neighbors.

CHAPTER SIX

LONG ROUTE TO THE TRUST TERRITORY

Africa had been a delightful place to spend three years, but finally my wife and I began to long for the Pacific Islands and for the empathy that we had learned to develop with islanders; and when I heard that the Trust Territory was trying to recruit a Commissioner of Health Services, whose office was on Saipan in the Northern Marianas, I applied.

The old Trust Territory was notoriously careless in its recruitment and almost any statesider who applied could get a job, so I was amazed at the meticulous way it looked me over and quizzed me before I was hired. I applied for the position while I was still in Africa. Poor, poverty-stricken Trust Territory paid my way to come to Saipan for interviews, kept me there for a week of inspection by almost everyone on the staff, and then sent me to Washington to be interviewed by many people in the Department of Interior and the USPHS, including Sargent Shriver. Then they sent me back to Africa to get my wife and furniture and, also, our African gardener whom we had become fond of, and our dog. Actually this entire trip circumscribed the earth one and one-half times, crossed the Atlantic Ocean once, the Pacific Ocean twice and the equator three times. The reason for such immaculate and intensive and expensive care in my selection was that a year before, the High Commissioner and the Commissioner of Health Services had gotten into such a disgraceful public quarrel that they had both been fired; and all of the MD's except one, a Belgian pathologist, had quit out of sympathy for the Health Service's Commissioner. This reduced Health services to shambles which would need to be reconstituted from scratch. Recruiting a new High Commissioner was easy since filling this position was a simple political matter and there were many politicians who wanted the job, but recruiting a single MD for a hospital position had been impossible. I knew this but it did not disturb me because I had confidence in my recruiting ability. However, that was not the main problem, and this they concealed from me (fortunately, for I would not have come had I known it) and I learned about it only after I was installed in my new office and was being oriented to my responsibilities. Then a high-ranking official from the High Commissioner's office said:

"Now we will tell you why we took so much care in selecting you. Painfully we have learned that American physicians cannot be recruited for hospital positions in the Trust Territory. For the last year we have worked very hard, both here and in Washington, but have failed to interest a single physician. We are convinced that this cannot be done by any of us who are experienced recruiters; you, who have just arrived, will be unable to do any better; so we have decided to place Health Services under the control of the Indian Health Service. Recruitment will then be easy because young doctors who are refusing to go to Vietnam have been forced to join the Indian Health Service which now has more physicians than it can use, and their excess physicians can be forced to come here. The only problem is that the natives don't like the idea since they think it means that their islands are being turned into Indian Reservations. We feel that you with your overseas experience can convince the natives that this will be good for them."

And I, who had once checked on the Indian Health Services and found how poorly and inhumanely it was being administered, refused. Everyone argued with me and they finally sent for four high-ranking officials to come from Washington to overpower me.

I told the Washington officials that I refused to participate in the plan, but said that I was certain I could recruit and that I could prove it if they would give me ten months trial. At this they withdrew into a whispered, corner confab for about half an hour. When they returned they said, "We know you cannot recruit doctors in 10 months, nor even in a year, but we have decided to give you a trial of two years. But if these positions are not filled by then, you are out and we will engage the Indian Health Service to replace you. This delighted me and I got very busy contacting all of my sources which included the American Medical Association, the World Health Organization, many State Medical Associations and several medical schools, and in ten months all positions were filled and there was a reserve pile of applications two inches thick on my desk.

And then I set about the very serious task of creating a system of modern medical care from the tattered remains of a system that had just been ruined: training and retraining the far-flung Health Services' staff, assuring a constant supply of drugs and equipment over a three million square mile area, building or rebuilding almost all hospitals and many dispensaries in the Northern Marianas, Yap, Palau, Truk, Ponape and the Marshalls; initiating many Federal Health programs. It was like inventing a new world. But political events that had nothing to do with health care began to overwhelm all other considerations: demand for independence and the end of colonialism . . . burning down of the Congress . . . extensive night-time damage to the High Commissioner's home . . . damage to Trust Territory administrators' homes and cars . . . progressive weakening of all Trust Territory authority. . . . Thus my five and one-half years as Commissioner of Health Services: progressive and exciting years so far as improvements in the health and well-being of islanders were concerned and in medical achievements, but dismaying politically—for the Trust Territory was dying.

DECLINE AND THE FALL
(AND THE MIRACLE) OF THE TRUST TERRITORIES

Dr. Dirk Anthony Ballendorf, now a historian at the University of Guam, and I wrote this chapter cooperatively in December, 1987, soon after the demise of the tired, old Trust Territory. Then we said:

It seems safe, now that the Trust Territory of the Pacific Islands has been disbanded, to attack it or praise it however one pleases; and in this postmortem viewing of its corpse, we shall try to place ourselves in the position of a pathologist performing an autopsy on a stranger found dead on the highway, marveling at the life and death factors that his scalpel reveals, and searching for causes. This kind of objectivity will not be easy for either of us for we were both loyally involved in the Trust Territory in its early formative years (W.M.P. as Commissioner of Health Services and D.A.B. as a Peace Corps official who also lived on Saipan and worked closely with the Trust Territory administration) and so we must each bear responsibility for some of its failures as well as for its several successes.

It is a truism that the United States was a fumbling colonial giant, for its misadventures in Micronesia and elsewhere have amply demonstrated its lack of serious talent for developing and administering consistent, overseas policies that deserve intellectual respect; and it would be difficult to find a written statement by a single qualified observer, during Trust Territory days, that did not deplore or ridicule its system of administration and its policies; for instance, the ridiculous, fantastic 'Zoo Theory' (to be discussed later on) that dominated its early policies.

Everyone at that time, sometimes even including us, was so busy criticizing and damning poor old, understaffed, under-trained, under-financed, misdirected Trust Territory that no one had time to see that right there before our skeptical, unseeing eyes, a miracle of wondrous proportions was occurring. Do you believe this, dear reader? Probably not, for you have been too long indoctrinated with TT's dismal aspects; so let us draw back for a moment, and look at the islanders themselves—their psychic-being, their competence, their self-respect, their initiative—and see how these personal qualities changed during TT's administration.

Here is an example from Rotanese oral history that is unrecorded in any textbook, but is clearly recalled by Rota's elder citizens: Shortly after World War II, and before the official creation of the Trust Territory, three Texans said to be millionaires, came to Rota. They inspected its high-rolling Sabana and proclaimed, "This is where we will establish our 'Texas ranch,' here in this tropical paradise. But first we must clear the island of its inhabitants." And they made plans, presumably Washington-approved, to move all Rotanese to neighboring islands.

What happened? Was there a riot? Was there court action? Were the Texans chased off? Were appeals sent to Washington? No, there were only lamentations: "If they tell us to go, then we must go," they told one another. Fortunately for the Rotanese, the Texans decided that Rota's harbor was not adequate for their enterprise and the project was canceled. Compare this submissive, heart-broken attitude, learned from the Japanese, the Germans, and the Spanish, with the reaction those arrogant Texans would get today if they made a similar proposal on Rota or anywhere in the Western Pacific: they would be ridiculed as idiots, laughed at and sent away in disgrace, or, if they persisted, they would be hauled into court and thoroughly trounced. They might even be assassinated.

Such rapid, incisive maturation into democracy of a subjected, beaten people! Has it ever occurred as decisively and in such short time anywhere else in the world? Can any other colonial power claim such a success?—if, indeed, that was ever the purpose of such colonialist efforts.

But it happened here. Neither through design nor astute administration; only minimally, if at all, through compassion. Certainly not through budgetary largess—none of these virtues—but through sheer, marvelous, reckless serendipity, where the most flagrant and outrageous plans that anyone in the Trust Territory or Washington could concoct somehow got fouled up and resulted in its finest achievements. It is almost as if the Trust Territory, like the Big Bang itself, had been created to fulfill a universal destiny. We will give instances to substantiate this unorthodox belief.

Dr. Van Schoote was a young Belgian physician, brother of an important Belgian archbishop. His wanderlust, or perhaps his Albert Schweitzer tendencies, also took him to the Congo for a stint of medical practice. For some strange reason he specialized in pathology at a US medical school, though pathology was foreign to his inclinations (life interested him; death did not) and he never practiced his certified specialty. When he came to Truk (Chuuk) hospital in the mid-1960s, he worked as a general practitioner; even extending his patient-care capabilities by spending several weeks at Guam's Naval Hospital to learn to extract teeth.

Dr. Van Schoote not only looked like Oliver North [this was written during Oliver North's hey day when to be compared to him was a compliment], but matched him in charisma, aggressiveness, ingenuity, sense of dedication and uncontrollable eagerness. Hospital practice could not contain these impulses and very soon he, a landlubber up to then, bought a sailing ketch and without waiting to learn the rudiments of sailing and navigation, was soon taking off, often by himself, to all Trukese outer islands, dispensing medical care and kindness as he went.

But this did not satisfy him. He organized a support club on Guam and also in several countries in Europe so that he could raise essential funds to build a sturdy, attractive dispensary-hospital on Pulap Island where it still stands as a memorial to him.

But for Van Schoote this was only the beginning, for he visualized a whole system of similar island dispensary-hospitals throughout western Truk and eastern Yap, a system that he hoped might eventually obtain political as well as medical autonomy. Read the Guam newspapers of those years and you will see how citizens on Guam rose to support him with praise and dollars. The Trukese themselves idolized him with affection and reverence almost mounting to deification, and some of them still become misty-eyed when they recall how he sailed off toward Japan with a crew of one young Trukese man, to get his ketch dry-docked and repaired. They never returned. At first his Trukese supporters could not accept the reality that he had been destroyed by a typhoon that crossed his path, and they created a myth that somehow he had survived—just as heroes usually do—and had reached China. For a while reports circulated that he had been seen here and there in Asia, always doing good.

Though Dr. Van Schoote was sanctified as a living legend, he never saw himself in this light, thanks to his good sense of humor and his earthiness. Here is an illustration:

Dr. Van Schoote, as far as we can ascertain, obtained his ketch in Saipan, or at least he arrived there shortly after purchasing it. Then, knowing nothing about sailing and less about navigation, and despite Coast Guard admonitions, he took off for Truk. A day or so from Saipan a storm struck, disabling the ketch. His radio reception was destroyed, but he could still transmit messages and this he did, night and day. Everyone with a radio on Saipan listened to the high drama of this intrepid physician lost at sea. And when the Coast Guard found him and hauled him in his ketch (stalwartly he had refused to abandon it) back to Saipan, there was a crowd on the beach to welcome him, including the effusive, attractive wife of the chief of the Trust Territory radio system.

Hero-worship and awe overcame the crowd, and when Dr. Van Schoote leaped from his ketch, threw himself prostrate on the sand and kissed it, the effusive lady could contain herself no longer and rushed to his side. "Dr. Van Schoote, oh Dr. Van Schoote," she cried as she leaned over him, "I've been listening to you night and day, day and night. Oh, Dr. van Schoote, it's almost as if I've been living with you." And Dr. Van Schoote, looking up from the sand, said, "Lady, I hope you are not pregnant!"

When the Interior Department took over administration of Micronesia from the Navy in 1951 it was prepared to administer the area as though these Pacific islands were an integral part of the United States. This was consistent with the utterances of the various American officials who had testified in Congress in hearings pursuant to the passage of the Trusteeship Agreement. This provided that Micronesia, unlike the other ten Trusteeships which had been established following WWII, would be a 'strategic trusteeship.' This meant that the UN Security Council rather than the UN General assembly, would have ultimate jurisdiction. And since the Security Council, at that time was dominated by the US militants, it meant, in effect that the Navy was still actually in charge of Micronesia. Thus, historically, we have the beginning of great ambiguities: Micronesia was a foreign area but administered by the Interior Department; but the Interior Department was not the ultimate authority for it had been officially outranked by the Navy. It was the Micronesians who would come to understand this ambiguity best, and to learn how to manipulate and work it to their advantage.

The 'zoo theory', as described and named by popular journalist E.J. Kahn in 1967, was actually applied to all Trust Territory islands by the newly created Trust Territory administration. Today it chills one's concept of civil rights and human dignity but not at that time for the new Trust Territory administration loaded itself with academic anthropologists and the anthropologists promptly made a major policy decision which was enthusiastically approved by the universities from which they came. This was based on the then highly touted 'zoo theory' which was straightway applied to all Trust Territory administered islands. The technique for doing this was to sequester each island by restricting its contacts with the outside world, thus preserving the citizens in primal purity so that destiny and its slow, evolutionary process would determine, over the course of years or centuries, their islands' eventual social and economic order. This was a harsh method for forestalling acculturation and it pleased the theorists; but it horrified the Micronesians when they learned that their role was to be that of penned-up animals in an experiment. This 'zoo theory' was still in actual application when I lived on Guam and tried repeatedly to visit some of the Trust Territory islands. But I was never allowed, at that time, to visit any of them for fear of my contaminating influence. The Trust Territory's 'zoo theory' was reinforced by Washington which required its own clearance before allowing any person to enter Guam from which one might, if very lucky—I wasn't when I tried—to enter the 'zoo.' Was that the way we were trying to introduce Democracy? Was that an improvement over Japanese times?

This idea had not only ideological appeal, but also intense budgetary interest, for it would cost very little and require minimal initiative and effort. What recently appointed administrator, sitting awkwardly at his new desk, could disagree with that? The theory was implemented by default if not by design almost as soon as Trust Territory Headquarters' office was established, and it continued to function as the administration's highest, though inadvertent emblem of faith and commitment for almost two decades, that is until the Peace Corps came in 1966 and shattered it overnight.

This brings us directly to the matter of serendipity and how serendipity saved the day for the Trust Territory islands.

That Peace Corps was able to function at all in Micronesia is a marvel, for no two authorities in Washington agreed on its purpose or how it should function; but somehow, serendipity-wise, it managed to survive to finally become, at least in retrospect, a catalytic factor in preparing island populations for self-government.

Criticism of lack of economic and social development had become acute, not only from the islanders themselves, but from the United Nations and from our own US Congress. And politicians started searching for ways to redeem their sorry record, preferably for ways that would cost very little, such as the introduction of Peace Corps . . . for the Peace Corps functioned proudly at poverty levels and had become a leading intellectual challenge to the Third World. The first request for Peace Corps Volunteers in Micronesia, however, was made in 1962 by the Micronesians themselves through the office of the High Commissioner. The idea was to help the Micronesians get a few volunteers to assist with various community development projects, and the request was for a total of only twenty volunteers . . . a small, manageable group that would disturb no one. The Peace Corps headquarters in Washington, however, rejected the request because it said Micronesia was a domestic place since it was administered by the Interior Department and was budgeted by the US Congress; however, following the admission of many 'Third World countries' into the United Nations in 1967 and the appearance of the infamous Solomon Report in 1964 and the establishment of the Congress of Micronesia in 1965, a new evaluation was made which daintily skipped over previous pronouncements thus permitting the Peace Corps to come to Micronesia on the basis of en para matoria, which said in effect, that Micronesia, though controlled by the US domestically, was not physically a part of the US and, therefore, 'foreign enough' for the Peace Corps.

President Kennedy appointed a Commission to study the development in Micronesia and make recommendations as to how best to proceed from that point (1963). The Commission was headed by Under Secretary of the Treasury Anthony J. Solomon, and his charge was, implicitly, to suggest programs that would soothe the criticisms that were coming abundantly from the islands themselves and the entire world. The Commission came up with lots of expected answers: provide better infra-structure, establish industries, provide better education and health care, and so on. These routine suggestions were highly publicized and promptly forgotten. . . . However, the Solomon report also came up with secret, under-cover strategies as to how the United States might affectively establish political hegemony over the islands through a series of swift plebiscites. Peace Corps Volunteers, the report enthusiastically (and secretly) suggested, should be a means to this end, and they should be sent in large numbers to the islands as a way for advocating closer ties with America by setting a good example of what Americans are like, thus encouraging Micronesians to vote favorably in a subsequent plebiscite. . . . Thus would Washington bureaucrats craftily control the islands.

Looking back now, it seems incredible, even inconceivable, that accredited individuals could have been so naive as to think that volunteers fresh from the rebellious campuses of the 1960s would submit to such subversion. And, of course, they didn't. The doctrines that they were willing and eager to spread dealt with civil rights, personal freedom, even civil disobedience—issues that they regarded as the very essence of American democracy as they had learned it during their campus demonstrations; and when they arrived in the Trust Territory and went to their assigned villages, they were a group of highly-trained, committed activists who loathed colonialism and autocratic governments, and were determined to circumvent the very principles—'zoo theory' principles—that had brought them to Micronesia.

Was the Peace Corps successful? If, at that time you had asked harassed Trust Territory administrators (including myself), most would have replied angrily that the PCVs were a nuisance that disrupted day-to-day administration—their numbers having reached a whopping total of 800 volunteers and trainees. But if you had asked the islanders themselves, you would have gotten varied judgments. The younger ones would have said that the volunteers were great because "they taught us to think for ourselves and have made us realize that we have the same abilities and rights as all other human beings." But their elders would have lamented, sometimes scathingly, that the volunteers were long-haired hippies, who were teaching island children to be disobedient, to love loud rock music, and to dream of leaving their islands.

One of the most dastardly and unfortunate aspects of the entire American administration in Micronesia was the perpetration of nuclear testing in the 1950s. Bomb testing occurred within the geographic confines of the Trust Territory during its administration, and it must bear some responsibility for the damage that was caused—though it is easy to see how this newly-created, politically weak organization would have been unable to face up to the military and drive it from its test sites in the Marshalls. We do understand, however, that Mr. Delbert Nucker, one of the High Commissioners during those times, may have had some influence in canceling one particularly dangerous and ill-conceived detonation during the 1958 series of tests. This bomb was meant to be spectacular for it was to be detonated from a rocket some fifty miles out in space directly over Rongelap Atoll (and over me, stationed there at the time), and it was actually scheduled and carried to the point of several countdowns before it was canceled. Such a detonation just before dawn, as planned would have permanently blinded any islander who happened to be star-gazing at the moment. If we are interpreting Mr. Nucker's influence correctly, some of the dishonor of bomb-testing in Micronesia is removed from the Trust Territory Administration. This particular test was moved from the Marshalls to unoccupied Johnston Island, and the bomb was detonated from its rocket on August 2, 1958, its glare visible in Hawaii.

Finally, an old Trust Territory friend of ours recalls a remarkable incident that occurred in 1960 when a delegation of senators from the now-defunct Congress of Micronesia came to the Palau high school in Koror to answer some questions of the students regarding the future political status of education programs. Discussion was mostly derogatory, and a defiant student finally stood up and demanded, "What has the Trust Territory ever done for us? Name one thing!" And Senator John Mangefel of Yap—later to become the first Governor of Yap when it became a Freely Associated State, and who was always known for cleverness and keen objectivity, answered, "It has taught us democracy. Now we are simply asking that we be allowed to practice it."

It was a simple statement which struck through the old layers of Trust Territory's disorganized and failed policies to its very heart where its genius and true benevolence were concealed. Could anyone now—some twenty years later—offer a more succinct and gracious summary of its achievements or a more respectful final tribute? Certainly we cannot.

INTRODUCTION TO POEMS

I was shocked when editing the manuscript for this book to find that there were only scanty references that document the five and one-half years that I spent as Commissioner of Health Services in the old Trust Territory, for those years were the culmination and the apogee of my life-long career. How could I have been so negligent with those exciting, creative, adventurous, sometimes depressing, but always very personal years . . . years when I knew that my day-to-day survival depended on the soundness of my plans and how I adapted them to local expectations and culture (new hospitals, copious Federal programs, extensive training programs for physicians, nurses, technicians, and arrangement for frequent medical referrals) and that one wrong decision could destroy the elaborate structure of health care that I was struggling to create. And I had no time for writing prose. But I did have time for writing poetry, plenty of time; all of those sleepless, restless, nervous nights! And writing poetry became the way I strove for absolution and to clear my soul for the next day's encounters with reality. It was like a confessional that healed my wounds.

Prior to becoming Commissioner of Health Services I had written only three poems. But then, suddenly and to my amazement, new poems began to appear every few nights. These I regarded, not as literary art forms, but as effective tonic that sustained me through my bouts of insomnia; though now, as I reread them, I believe that they are best seen as honest revelations of the way I thought and felt and reacted to the trauma and exuberance of those years. I think that these insomnia-induced poems recount those years more honestly and more poignantly than chapters filled with daily events. Here are a few of these poems that I have found in my desk.

'Lesson' in Composition

The throes of a phrase that won't fit
A cadence that won't calm down
Like epileptic convulsions
They keep jerking and
Tearing at the poor muscles of my brain;
Tongue bleeding and in the emergency room;
Still-birthed clauses and pauses
And macerated fetuses
                                        awaiting burial;
Good words wary and running for cover
Till there's nothing left —
Certainly no poem.

EXPLANATION OF 'ALAMAGAN'

Remote islands, at that time, presented special medical care problems and I visited as many as I could depending on freighters' routine schedules and on the availability of seaplanes at time of emergencies. Alamagan is a small, lonely, beautiful, volcanic island in the Northern Marianas with no more than 50 or 60 people on it. I wrote the following poem about it several nights after I had returned from a routine visit by commercial freighter.

Alamagan

This place is nowhere
Except on an ocean's map
And the unnatural imaginings
Of a few insularites ...
                Volcano crater, like a chalice
                Held up to God's smoking fingers
                Clouds walk its rim
                As attentive as temple pigeons
                Employed to watch its mysteries
Then down cliff by cliff
Basalt ridge to basalt fall
Burned, branched
Last lava spills
Forever lost in jungle

Down to the village
That seems suspended over the sea
        (or so I remember it, for a typhoon
        destroyed it soon after I left)
By swarms of flies and angelus dreams.
On down the cliff trail
Where pigs
        Not sacrificial pigs (which would be seemly) but
        Commercial pigs who understand market day principles—
Are pulled by front leg-rope
Bleeding ears and broken tail
Squealing, screaming
Some fighting back magnificently
        ("Pig power shall overcome" and
        "Pigs of Alamagan arise!" I ventured
        with no results)
Some trembling sick and
Beaten from behind by
Beautiful brown children
Down to the little boat which
Like a wild thing
Driven crazy by the surf
Bangs its head on the rocks and tries to run.
Wait here. Now there's no hurry. Wait patiently for
A time will come when the waves turning on themselves
Will hold the boat immobile for one split- second.
Push then, everyone push!
And the pig will drop the last four feet
On to the slippery deck
Docile and too stunned to fight
        (though two jumped into the surf)
Then I
Nearly as frightened as the pigs
Jump
        (my fault: one-half second too late)
Slip, sprawl, fall belly-flat in manure
And we
The pigs and I
Smelling alike
Reverence alike
Leave for the big ship

That is waiting for us
Out in the safe
Deep water.

INTRODUCTION TO 'ON RECEIVING DIAGNOSIS'

As Commissioner of Health Services for the Trust Territory I was given frequent reports by groups of US physicians and statisticians who were studying the after-effects of radiation on the Rongelap citizens. These reports were alarming and showed that many Rongelap citizens were developing cancers of the thyroid, some of whom I had once known and shared radiation hazards with during the 1958 bomb tests. Once, while I was reading a report, my hand rose nervously to my thyroid—and there it was: a mass the size of a small walnut. I hurried to specialists in Honolulu who emphasized the probability that this was cancer and, because of my age, probably the more malignant of the two common types. I returned to Guam and entered the Navy Hospital (which, at that time would accept Trust Territory patients) and was scheduled for surgery the next day. And that night, sleepless and bereft, I wrote the following poem. I showed it to the pleasant, young surgeon as I entered the operating room; I thought he was not disturbed by it, but the anesthesiologist was alarmed and spent considerable time trying to comfort me before putting me to sleep. Here is the poem.

On Receiving Diagnosis

Lord
        You have kissed my neck
Where it is bound
        To cause death.
The trouble with this courtesy

        Lord
(Being hale and hearty and virile
        Everywhere else)
Is that I'm really not ready
        For it

Nor deserving either
        When I contemplate the problems
        It will solve.

Though, nostalgically,
Those long, sweet years
Of gentle decay
Leave a debt unpaid by
One of us,

Though I'm not sure
By which.

INTRODUCTION TO 'MANIFESTO'

Immediate microscopic analysis of the tumor (described in the preceding poem) failed to confirm my tragic plight for the tumor was nothing more than a cyst, and when the young surgeon came to the recovery room to tell me, I was still so sleepy that I have no memory of seeing him. But I do remember the heavenly vision that descended on me, brilliant, flashing unearthly lights, with a chorus that was singing Handel's Hallelujah Chorus—the best rendition I had ever heard, except that the words had been changed to: Benign, Benign, Benign.

Then I woke up, walked to my room, visited fellow patients, carried water to them, and went to a party that evening with the surgeon. This occurred on my 60th birthday and, to bury my recent past and to announce my new beginning, I wrote a poem to commemorate my birthday which I labeled Manifesto. Here it is:

Manifesto

Glorious   Glorious
Glorious is the knowledge
That sometime during the night
            (perhaps as I turned restlessly)
I became sixty
            years
                        old. . . .
I didn't know that responsibility
Weighed so much

For now I feel
        as light
            as a
                feather
Adolescent, or probably less
(Let's say well under thirty),
I can now protest
Get up late
Cultivate eccentricities
'Till they become 'centricities'
        of harpsichord
        of orchids
        dubious conceits–
        allowable distortions,
Blame a poor memory on age
        without any excuse at all.
Become
        a dirty
            old
                man
Or a bigot
If such things should please me.
The world, to hell with it now,
should know that I'm
        sixty years old—
and take
        all due
            precau-
                tions.

INTRODUCTION TO 'REVOLUTION IN THE MARIANAS'

As the prematurely aged Trust Territory weakened, it's islanders' op-position strengthened, and as a loyal Trust Territory employee, I tried to support it, even on its death bed. Here are several poems that I wrote (at night, of course) as I tried to organize arguments to justify its poor performance which might prolong and soften its death struggles.

Revolution in the Marianas

O they burned Congress down
To black crow char
                        last night
Tried to legalize pot
                        and got
                        almost, a lot
Of free abortions
In this Catholic community.
Wrote a Proclamation of Secession
That would have paled Jefferson
And pained Paine
Arranged confrontations
                        marches, rhetoric
                        dreams of military muster
                        dreams: gory . . . glory . . . Custer
And backed down
When politicians
Looked around
And found
It wouldn't pay
And that's the way
They and I with them
(Forgetting our ancestors—
                        mine ghosting '49er plains and lost causes
                        theirs in each others' cooking pots)
Have changed
O

Song From the Pacific

Unhappy   Unhappy   Unhappy
            is paradise these days
            T 'would be better
if there were more money
            and no one ever had to work again;
if all who wanted to be philosophers
            were
                        and without effort
or doctors or political scientists
or were elected to Congress

(Well, not quite: the present membership would object
    on jurisdictional grounds);
if emergency rice and spam rations
    once started
        could be continued forever
    and no one ever had to
        fish
            grow taro
                pick bananas, breadfruit,
                or mangoes
    except on ceremonial occasions
    when sad remembrances
    of ancient hardships
    would be in order;
if tourists, Buddhists, the Japanese and Javanese
    the Russians, the Slovaks, and Egyptians
(anyone with a dollar or yen or kopek in his pants)
    could be here . . . and not here;
if Peace corps could be phased-out
    and AID, OEO, Welfare phased-in
        (or is it the other way around?)
And O that confrontations
    and mimeographed editorials
        and resolutions
            and petitions
                and speeches
    that mortify all administrative flesh
    could increase in violence and power and shock
(O beyond even Bikini's wildest, proudest apocalypses)
    earth jarred slightly out of orbit and atremble
    in the glorious, greenish glare of God's glaucous love
and everyone's stunned approval.

Thus saith the Congress in Paradise
Which is unhappy this season.

INTRODUCTION TO 'TERMS OF AGREEMENT'

Africa was a paradise of tropical plants and trees, many of which I
had never heard of before, and straight way I had become an amateur bota-

nist. And when my wife and I moved from Malawi, Africa to Saipan I brought my most loved plants and seeds with us, this being possible at that time when there were few restrictions on such plant transfer. The fact that none of them survived has nothing to do with the following poem where I am referring to them nostalgically and using them only as metaphors

Termσ of Agreement

First, though,
      The orange seedlings must bear
        However briefly.

Breadfruit season
      Must come and go enough times to give
        An illusion of
Eternal superfluity.
      Those baobob seeds from a tree antedating Christ
        Must spring into
New life expectancy
(2,000-4,000 years?)
      That only a line of Pharaohs could predict.
        And orchids!
Oh those orchids
      For which I risked my foolish life from
        African mambas and leopards
And from coronaries
      (for I was too old to be climbing mountains)
        And argued past
Quarantine inspectors
      At every port across Asia. Orchids must drip
        From every tree
Overfilling
      With useless magnificence and rapture any void
        That is left
And the tuna!
      Of these no end shall be tolerated, unless
        Our ends coincide—
My boat
      Opening its seams as they depart distractedly
      (tropic's white sea birds still believing in them)
        For arctic seas.

But then, O God
> Let it come, not in the kind of cataclysm I seem
>> To provoke, but
Quietly, inconspicuously
> As is right when everything is
>> Completed.

But as an impertinent request
Let me ask
> For a rising mist with many islands coming out
>> To greet me

And the odor—
> Of an orchid that grows rank on Sochi Mountain that I
>> Couldn't transplant—
And the momentary recapitulation
> As indifferent and tranquil as a memorized prayer
>> Of maybe six shining events.

INTRODUCTION TO 'INSOMNIA'

Insomnia was my retaliation to an ocean that had just knocked me down, torn strips of skin off my back, and nearly drowned two landlubber friends whom I had undertaken to introduce to an ocean that I thought I could control. I fancy that I had approached this Saipan ocean, and its particularly hazardous segment of reef, like a lion tamer, whip in hand, enters a cage of performing beasts. . . . I wrote *Insomnia* that night while I was hurting, immensely ashamed of my performance, unable to sleep, and thoroughly hating the ocean. I wrote *I Lay My Dreams in Your Lap* later, after several days of reflection.

Insomnia
Wind
Great sea wind
Wind that watches at the louvers
Speak of sleep
More effectively &
Let your busy salt Trades
Carry me off

Sheep
Sheep keep leaping   lambing   gamboling
Being counted   all things
Sheep are monotonously good at

Surf
Bang   dance   thunder   shake
Me to sleep
Lift up your hoary head
That weighs many tons
And let it drop on rocks
Clutch the sky
With cyanotic fingers
And demand forgiveness
For the mayhem you have just committed
Become festive and deck
Yourself in garlands
Spray perfume   stretch and sigh
Graze in spacious coral meadows
Munch boulders   belch salt strew shells
Wail

Wail
Wail at your stone wall
Recite your thousand sorrows
And commit suicide
In your deepest cathedral voice
Command the land to disappear
Into primordial void
Writhe and whine   convulse
Copulate beneath your blanket of foam
Vomit on the beach
And slumber me
Into unconsciousness

I Lay My Dreams in Your Lap

Great sea
Mother tortoise ocean
I lay my dreams in your lap
With devotion and tears
But you, great sea
  your stomach empty and rattling conches
  retching bones
  roaring typhoons, and ravenous
Swallow them whole.
I shout my hates at your wind
  foul-mouthed, searing, sweating, savage, evil
and you muffle choice obscenity
To mucoid sighs.
I extrude my soul
On your broad abdomen
Like a starfish extrudes its stomach
  to devour coral
  (though my intent is quite different)
And you pay it no mind.
When I cast my bread on Thy Waters
  (skeptically, I must admit)
The fish eat it, leaving no trace.
O placid, atheist sea
O bellowing slaughtered sea!

When I try to interest you in a game
You take off my hide
With one swat
Wham me across your knees
Process me in your surf-factory.
Great sea
Beggar at my gate
Why do I keep giving you alms?
Why do I keep ascribing you virtues
You don't possess
Nor want?
Why do I glorify disdain
From the likes of you?
Why did I write this?

Folk Song; Murky Waters of Micronesia
(Written to introduce a program in Environmental Protection)
> Pollute
> Pollute
> Lagoons
> Like wounds
> Dilute
> With a lute
>> If required.
> Neglect
> Or infect
>> If desired.
> Censors are out
> And all about
> Changing words
> Like 'turds'
> To: "A sewer
> 's more pure
>> Than moonlight"

> Rout
> The lout
> Whose millipore
> Shows all
> Is sore
> In out-fall
> 's gore

> Adore
> Much more
>> All landscape.

INTRODUCTION TO 'REPORT FROM THE ISLANDS'

Most Trust Territory Administrators and their staffs—just like me—had been recruited from the States while they were searching for paradise, and we found each other difficult to work with. Without them, however, I would have had no insomnia and no urge to write poetry . . . perhaps I should feel grateful to them. Here is an ode I wrote late one night to commemorate my fellow coworkers.

Report From the Islands

O, the old ones are going off to Honolulu
To get their cirrhosis taken care of,
Or simply disappearing with no trace left
(though I suppose there are forwarding addresses
   In Personnel) to nurse and to die of
Expatriate wounds (mostly coronaries and hypertension
And harmless, cackling senility—or is this a kind of
   Enlightenment and Grace?)
And the new ones are making unreasonable demands—
Peace Corpsish, missionarish, hippish, or new college-
   protester type (all much the same once you
   boil them down under a tropical sun)—
And threatening to quit or write their senators
Unless they
   Get the house
      Or the jeep
         Or the new laboratory technician
            Or a new bridge and a new school
            and fifty water-seal toilets
              on Yap
They want
   or by the mystique of press releases or edicts
   become instant civil-servant heroes
And enjoying their culture shock
Like one sometimes enjoys seasickness
Or the knowledge of distant disasters
And I, O, I!
Who don't see myself in either category
   (no beard, don't cackle, only want forty
   water-seal toilets on Yap, rarely preach)
Still clear-eyed (I think), and
Capable of righteous indignations

And the tempests that go with them.
I, O, I!
When I read what I've just written
   must have gone cynical
   which is worse than either.

FINAL STATEMENT

Quest

Perigrine, perigrine falcon, I
Into the badlands
Into the wastes
To love it
To find it
Flesh feel it
Lost
Hurt
O

To understand it
No

O
Ere you molt
Go

I don't recall where this photo was made—but it could have been on any of the small, southern Pacific islands for they all share such comfortable ways of life and artistry.

CHAPTER SEVEN

TRUK (CHUUK)

In 1972 I stepped-down from my position with the Trust Territory and was sent by the University of Hawaii's School of Medicine to organize and direct a Physician's Assistant course (MEDEX) in Truk (now renamed Chuuk). My wife and I had one reservation about going there and living on it's capitol island of Moen in one of the elegant houses reserved for colonialists, and we insisted that, though my office and classroom would be on Moen, living conditions for us must be on nearby Dublon Island where we would be the only state-siders among 2400 Chuukese. This demand was met and the next three years on Dublon now rank retrospectively among our most exotic and happy years.

The following outburst of prejudice demands a word of apology to my Chamorro friends on Saipan. No, it was not you, dear Saipan friends, who brought on this tirade, it was the Capitol Hill of the late sixties and early seventies, the grand, old, prematurely old, overwrought Headquarters for the entire Trust Territory that I objected to. A road sign at the foot of the mountain on Saipan pointed the way upward (heavenward?) and mischievously, perhaps, misspelled it as *Capital Hill* sometimes it was called the *Golden Ghetto* and, sometimes, *Mt. Olympus—Home of the Gods*. Those who didn't live there felt excluded from its colonialist prerequisites and lusted for them; and those of us who did live there felt like colonialists under perpetual siege by barbarians. To many people Capitol Hill was Saipan; to some it was more than that: It was the total Trust Territory of the Pacific Islands (all three million square miles of it) . . . it was power . . . it was vision . . . it was the 20th Century brought to the Stone Age. . . . Its lights shown far out to sea and were like a beacon.

And when we went to Chuuk we were sort of fleeing Capitol Hill, nee Capital Hill, nee Golden Ghetto, nee Mt. Olympus, and the image of it that I had constructed and fixed in my mind; so I insisted that my wife and I must live six miles of rough water away from the expatriate community in Moen…hence Dublon, an island without water supply, sewerage, or electricity, and that was inhabited only by Chuukese, most of whom spoke no English…and Dublon Island became for us a 'blessed hermitage.'

When we came to Chuuk from Saipan, my wife and I felt that we had become surfeited with too many state-side neighbors in Saipan, and we insisted that we live on a lagoon island where they didn't exist. To our delight, Dublon island fulfilled this dream for it was five miles away from Moen, the capitol of Chuuk, and had a population of about 3,000 Chuukese and no others. There was a house there that had been built to entice stateside teachers to come and live in it, but no one ever came—possibly because there was no public water supply on Dublon (you can see the large tank that we used to collect rainwater) and no electricity or sewage disposal. We loved it.

LETTERS TO DOROTHY

Here are a series of letters I wrote in 1973, 1974 and 1975 to my sister Dorothy in Detroit, that define the lives my wife and I lived on Dublon Island in the Chuuk Lagoon. Having tired of colonialist-style living in Saipan and Guam, we insisted on living as far from the ex-patriate community on Moen (the capital of the Chuuk district) as we could get. Hence Dublon. Hence our lives on that island where we were the only state-siders and were protected from familiar American influences by six miles of rough lagoon water. Hence these letters to Dorothy written at times of rapture and of occasional despair or horror, but always at times of profound amazement in finding that we were there and that those things I was putting into letters were actually happening to us.

Some things are very easily and properly forgotten; for instance Comet Kohoutec (a fizzled-out, scarcely visible, no-account comet) which I mention at the beginning of my first letter. Why did I do this and in such an unseemly fit of mystery and reverence? Because it set the mood: Comet Kohoutec, touted as the greatest celestial phenomenon of the century, even by respectable astronomers, was predicted to burst over us with a radiance never seen before by man. Radio and newspaper commentators were making free use of such terms as 'spiritual–cleansing' and 'rebirth of human values'. Comet Kohoutec was a deceptive oracle, and I became its easy convert. . . . Now let's get on with the letters.

December 25, 1973
Dear Dorothy,
The occasion, I agree, is Christmas. . . . Solemnly Barbara and I are waiting for Comet Kohoutek to appear from behind Mt. Tonomuan which screens the southeastern horizon from us; and, for those first subtle, comet-induced transformations that should automatically, with absolutely no effort on our part, change our lives radiantly and spiritually now that we are living on Dublon Island. That much for Comet Kohoutek, which never arrived, and which I never mention again. The subject is easily dropped.

Every morning we get up early to test the primordial silence that exists here except at high tide when lagoon wavelets, speaking softly and apologetically about their great cousins that are pounding the outer reef, lap into our backyard to surround the bases of palm trees and fill a little salt water pond that has mudhoppers in it for Chida, our dog, to chase; and to get ready for my five-mile trip to Moen. The boat trip doesn't take much physical preparation, for we have a young Chuukese man living with us who gets the boat ready, the motors running and then snakes it and the two of us out through the tortuous channel and on to Moen. It's more a matter of working myself into a proper emotional fettle for the big waves that we must meet broadside all the way to Moen, there and back. But this commuting is the invigorating part of the day, and it has me working harder, feeling more fit, and playing the harpsichord and clavichord more than ever before. Also it is the happiest fellowship part of the day for there is usually a flotilla of twenty or more boats making the trip at any one time, and we are all waving to each other, sometimes racing, and watching each other for catastrophe. It occurs to me for the first time, as I write this, that I am always the only American in the group.

Such problems as we have fall mostly on Barbara. A plumber from Moen spent much of the last week trying to stem the thousand leaks in our water system, and to unplug those lines that had become choked with algae …with perhaps 25 percent success. We have a 2,500 gallon catchment tank which should be adequate if most of our fine rain water weren't being lost through leaks. Twice we have had to get 1,000 gallons of water shipped to us from Moen. Cooking is done on table-top kerosene burners (no oven). Barbara is trying to bake something for Christmas dinner on top of one of them; and our refrigerator, a cantankerous, xenophobic creature, uses kerosene.

If there is propane on the tanker that just entered the lagoon, we will try to change over to propane as our chief fuel. Kerosene mantle lamps work well and are almost as bright as 100 watt electric bulbs. Barbara is trying to learn to use a kerosene pressing iron but so far it has succeeded in outwitting her at every ironing crises. The amount of kerosene we need to keep us in these amenities is astounding, and with a fuel shortage coming on, we may soon find ourselves burning coconut husks. Space is not the problem we had expected for Public Works has built on to our partially decayed, two-bedroom (concrete block) house, a lanai that is 48 by 12 feet, screened in and with a good overhang that cuts out most of the rain. This is where we do most of our living. It is where I am writing this letter. Usually there are people outside looking in, but we are getting used to that. So far, though, we are living mostly on the floor since we have no beds nor couches nor proper chairs. Curiously, we get a sense of graciousness by sitting and sleeping on the floor—maybe the ghosts of Japanese, if there are any left about the village, think we are propitiating them.

Women and children, Barbara's almost constant companions, do not speak English, so Barbara spends most of her day in solemn coffee convocation with several young village women, learning each other's language. For her it is almost like the Peace Corps' effective but traumatic total immersion in language. Everyone is very friendly and we are being absorbed into village life and responsibilities a little faster than we find comfortable; in fact, this instant acceptance is probably our chief problem. There are usually one or two village people in our house at any one time, and last evening we suddenly realized that we haven't eaten a meal by ourselves since we arrived. Barbara—imagine Barbara!—has suggested that maybe we should start going to church, not as Trukese do twice a day, but once in a while.

Children are everywhere, but they are the best behaved children we have ever encountered. Ordinarily our tolerance for children is low, but here we enjoy them, especially hearing them sing their improvised songs, or beat out rhythms on a series of tin cans and coconut shells. They get along well with both our dogs, and not one of them has tried to ride big Chida.

We hired two young Trukese men; our boatman, Shoap Orininko, and Benessed, our handyman (actually spelled Blessed and intended to mean blessed, but Benessed is the way the lagoon Chuukese pronounce it as they struggle with the unnatural 'L', and his last name is either Neekaifes, from his grandfather, or Iriasari

Shoap (our boatman), our boat and our dog. Our house can be faintly seen among the palm trees on the right.

from his father, a matter about which he vacillates each time he signs his name. He is lithe and muscular and nearly always shirtless as all young Chuukese males should be with their sculptured torsos. They seem to be constantly dramatizing something about the South Seas, about centuries of whalers and sailing ships, and of a millennium of perfect bliss before that, but, of course, they don't know they are doing it.

Shoap finished high school in Moen and had one year of training in subsistence agriculture in Papua New Guinea, but like so many other recent graduates, has remained unemployed. "We pay him fifteen dollars a week, a rather elegant salary. He understands English very well (he read our *Two Years Before the Mast* and spoke of it with suitable excitement), but he speaks English with heavy accent, and with amusement. We think he is one of the most engaging Micronesians we have known. Benessed, who lives next door with his wife and young child, speaks and understands English poorly, but has an ingratiating smile (we pay him $2.50 a day—some days he prefers to take off for fishing or gathering breadfruit, or just to play pool—poon, though is the way he must pronounce it. We thought he was becoming a little too insistent on appearing at mealtime, but yesterday at noon (the meal he is entitled to when he works) he said to Barbara, "Me eat home this day. Got food in house this day." Then he returned after the meal with a present of several fish. I guess hunger is the reason he stays so lithe and spare and well coordinated.

Few of the men in this village are employed, and the amount they can make from copra can hardly keep them in kerosene and beer. Yet, Terageyo, an old cripple and a favorite of ours—a sort of landlord for the community since he was the one who planted coconut trees through this area twenty some years ago—keeps a stalk of bananas hanging in our lanai and brings us choice breadfruit. But hunger, like a pall, hangs over the village and we have not learned to live comfortably with it. (To comfort us a cynic told us that once one member of a clan gets a salary job all others stop working and the beautiful, millennia-old rhythm of subsistence living disappears overnight. Then the rhythm becomes: for one week after payday everyone lives high, and the second week all go hungry…fish jumping in the lagoon, breadfruit rotting as it falls. Everyone seems to be honest, though I suppose some light-fingered person will eventually surface. At the moment, though, I feel that locking up the house at night is one of the unnecessary things we do.

We brought our jeep to Dublon quite unnecessarily and undesirably as I am now discovering. When I get to Moen I wish I had it for getting from the dock to the hospital. Instead I take a taxi. A Chuukese taxi requires a word of explanation. No other American, so far as I know has ever ridden in one. They are all Datsun pickups, and you ride in the back end—rain or shine or coral dust—for 15 cents. It's an humbling, purifying, exalting experience like participating in a righteous civil disobedience demonstration or visiting the Vatican.

There are no stores on Dublon with one important exception. This is the bakery. At the bakery bread is baked in a backyard, old mud kiln—delicious bread that costs 35 cents a loaf. While you are waiting for it to come out of the oven you are served slices of bread, and coffee—free. Once the bread was wrapped in a Barran's newspaper—where the newspaper came from I could never find out. The bakery was open and selling bread at 6 o'clock this Christmas morning. Benessed and I went there on our bicycles and bought several loaves.

Years ago, Dorothy, you visited us on Capitol Hill in Saipan in our typhoon-Micronesian-proof house, and then you toured Truk as a fee-paying tourist. But now is the time for you to come. Now you would be able to savor the entire Micronesian universe. This time you wouldn't have to rely on travel agents, as you did then, for the essence of this whole, vast area is immediately apparent when you walk through little Dublon villages and smell their salty, sometimes fetid air, feel the earth turn beneath your feet, feel the cool trade winds blow the sweat from your brow, and smile admiringly at the slow-moving, friendly people. . . . And then the unexpurgated truth of all small Pacific islands and their islanders will be revealed to you as in a dream.

P.S. I haven't mailed the Christmas letter yet so I will add an important postscript. Last night a tropical storm walled us in with sheets of water that sounded like a thousand water taps turned on and a hundred toilets flushing. Water filled our lanai as if it were a ship sinking. So today Shoap, Benessed, and I have been building dikes and drainage ditches around our house, and Barbara has been drying things out. Tomorrow, house guests are coming (recorder and harpsichord playing, mostly). I think we will be ready for them, and prepared to convince them that this is the good life.

Yesterday we distributed a few gifts of rice to our neighbors, somewhat to their bafflement, I think. And today here came a gift of shells from one neighbor and another neighbor whom we scarcely know sent us a large supply of pounded taro wrapped in giant taro leaves. . . Eden . . . Eden.

December 28, 1973

Dear Dorothy,

This morning Benessed said to Barbara: "If anyone in village bother you or Dr. Peck, I kill heem."

"Won't that be going a little bit too far?"

"No, not too far. I kill heem."

August 17, 1974

Dear Dorothy,

I am sitting in the lobby of the Eastern Gateway Hotel in Majuro, Marshall Islands, right where the trade winds are converging on me and keeping me cool and pleasantly salty. Yesterday I was in Ponape, tomorrow I will be in Kwajelein. If it weren't so hot outside I might look up your old friend, Amata Kabua, to ask him to deliver your island immediately. [Note: Dorothy took a guided tour through Micronesia in 1970. Amata Kabua, president of the Senate of Micronesia at that time and 'crown prince' of the Marshall Islands, took her for a boat ride through the Majuro Lagoon. When she excessively admired a tiny island, he gallantly offered to give it to her.] As you can see this is a rapid, island-hopping, junket-sort of trip that is for the purpose of orienting a new physician to Micronesia, and not at all for my own improvement or gain though, actually, I'm having fun doing it. I am anxious to get home, however, for just before leaving Dublon I had to discharge Benessed, who had moved from handyman to boatman (previously I had to discharge our 'trusty' Shoap for he had become too drunken to trust with the boat). And now I had to discharge Benessed for the same reason, a painful thing to do for his tears and 'when I love you so much,' and then more tears, made me feel like a heartless tyrant. But to partly compensate for my heartlessness I have hired his younger brother,

Andon. I will send you Andon's picture since I suspect that your chief orientation to our Dublon lives is by way of the boatmen we hire and fire.

Andon is a handsome boy (he looks like a boy and is a 19-year old one, though he has a wife and three children—the secret, perhaps, being that his pretty wife is said to practice love magic on him constantly. I can imagine that even though children continue to accumulate like clockwork, clock hands will stand still and he will continue to be 19 years old and passionately in love as long as Dublon remains above water.

It is pleasant to watch him work. He is so strong and agile that he can swing my 40 horsepower outboard onto his shoulder and stride through the surf with it, laughing. I would simply collapse a couple of vertebrae if I were successful (very improbable) in hoisting the motor to my shoulder. Even thinking about it makes my vertebrae feel like jelly. Andon speaks no

This is our neighbor, Andon, nineteen years old and married with three children, two of whom are in the picture. Andon was the last of my several boatmen.

English which, in a way, after the deviousness that Benessed developed as his English improved, is a relief. . . . I think that deviousness is impractical, and certainly no fun, unless one has sufficient fluency in language to realize all of its nuances and variations that can make an art of it.

Barbara is now taking Chuukese lessons with a group of Peace Corps trainees, and has just one more week to go. She actually is beginning to speak Chuukese, though so haltingly that I think she must be several months from being able to dream in it, at least without using a dictionary, but even so she tells me that our neighbors, when they don't want her to understand their Chuukese conversation, resort to whispering and watching her stealthily for signs of comprehension; and some of them, even those who speak tolerable English, are beginning to ask her to translate for them.

You were justified in your recent letter, though not correctly, in remembering Dublon as being very close to Moen. When one stands beside the Continental Hotel on Moen where you stayed, and looks south, Dublon seems to be almost within spitting distance, so deceptive are distances over water. Actually it is three miles away. It is about three more miles in the other direction to the dock on Moen so actually I must drive about six miles to get to work, as opposed to the five miles I estimated in my Christmas letter when the trip, being novel, seemed shorter. Your memory of Chuuk seems to be pretty good, though I think it is obvious that you must return if you are to enlarge your Chuukese universe by these essential parameters: a never-never land where a boatman is nourished on love potions, and seasonless island days run on and on with the rhythm of overripe breadfruit falling; a strange back country where tide tables and the sounds of tides entering our yard, and the way the sun sets and rises behind massed clouds or passes clear and naked into and out of the ocean are the clocks and the weather forecasts that order our lives; where a house with a dog population of four (two of ours and two of the neighbors) is even at this moment increasing as one of the bitches is delivering a new, as-yet-uncounted litter of pups in Barbara's room, squealing as they come; where a garden in the backyard is now producing hikamus, winged-beans, wild yams, tomatoes, eggplants, and that has trees started in it that should one day bear Polynesian chestnuts, star apples, mangosteens, papayas, avocadoes. But there are also grim aspects to it—lost counterbalancing fragments of paradise: Boatmen who get drunk, wreak some kind of dreadful damage and must be fired (one became drunk one night, stole our jeep and drove it to the bottom of the lagoon where it has remained, a relic for divers to admire). And Andon, our most recently appointed boatman, has succumbed and joined the long succession of his discharged predecessors—just retribution, no doubt, for my sin of having tried to mix my weak capitalism with their fragile subsistence lives. And an ambiance of ghosts that hover over us, especially of the recently departed which are always the most troublesome.

Especially Kifiku's ghost. Kifiku died in childbirth with massive pulmonary infarction just a month ago. Before death she was by all odds the kindest, hardest-working woman in the village, but her ghost is a brat that is knocking on houses at night, chasing people out of the mountains, threatening her brothers and sisters who ever had an unkind thought about her. To placate her vindictive spirit a taboo has been placed on all of the clan's coconut trees for three months, which means that everyone will have three months of hunger; and her husband, Tosiwo, will be forced to leave the village if he fails to marry one of her close relatives within this span of time, a very real catastrophe in itself since he is the only reliable food-provider in this clan of poor food providers. His six children, favorites of ours, must stay behind since they are the property of the clan. Wailing and keening, the special province of women, were absolutely monumental in volume, in tuning and invention. They started the moment her death was announced, and kept us awake for many nights. At times I thought that the keening was becoming competitive and I tried to sabotage the front-runners by giving them tranquilizers. The province of the men manifested itself a couple of weeks later in the form of a massive village drunk: Tosiwo, from the time he staggered off his boat at twilight until two a.m., came running through the village screaming 'Kifiku! Kifiku!' and pounding his fists to a pulp on the sides of

A Chuukese physician, born and raised there, looked at this photo and with a faltering voice, said, "Chuuk must be beautiful." This was the first time he had given critical thought to his everyday surroundings. This was how he discovered the amazing beauty of his home islands.

houses, while others ran behind him encouraging him with shouts and drunken bravado to seek out and confront a ghost.

Here in Dublon we must divide our attention between two worlds of almost equal importance: (1) the marvelous Pacific idyll which is the Chuuk Lagoon with its occasional rampages of actual terror; and (2) the subtle treachery and clamor of an unseen world that is crowded with ghosts and their ghostly ectoplasm. As you looked out of your window in the Continental Hotel, Dorothy, I'm afraid that you were aware of only the paradisiacal, post-card half of Dublon. You must return for enlightenment. We have an extra sleeping mat and a choice place on the floor for you any time.

December 20, 1974

Dear Dorothy,

I've started this letter several times without finishing it. Each time a crisis diverted me. Here are scraps from those unfinished letters. A week ago I asked Andon (whom I have rehired and whose name, incidentally, turns out to have been derived from a Navy officer, Commander—or perhaps Admiral—Landon, minus the impossible 'L') to show me where the weather-warning flags are flown. This is on a pole at the head of the boat pool in Moen, where, indeed, there was a square red flag with a square black center waving in the strong wind. Andon was unperturbed by it and merely said, "No typhoon!" Each day, for the next week, I checked and found the same flag, sometimes so flattened by the wind that it appeared to have been made of sheet metal. It wasn't until early this morning that I got around to referring to an atlas on navigation and found that there are four weather flag signals:

1. One triangular red flag means small craft warning.
2. Two of the same means gale.
3. Square red flag with square black center means full gale with winds from 55 to 73 miles per hour.
4. Two of the same means typhoon.

That, I suppose, substantiates my impression that it's been a little rougher than usual this last week since our winds have been just short of typhoon velocity.

Actually I have been feeling quite secure in the way our narrow, deep—prowed Chuukese boat (which Drs. Kumangai and Ngas, two Micronesian physicians who are knowledgeable in the ways of small craft, refuse to ride in) feels its way through all the cross-currents with their pattern of crazy waves slamming into each other, and I have never thought it was in danger of capsizing or of being swamped. But one statistical probability does seem to be moving in the wrong direction: Dr. Jones' boat (built by Chuukese boat builder, Niro) broke a hole in its bottom and sank when it hit a large wave. Two hospital boats (each built by Niro) collapsed in heavy waves recently, one with our good MEDEX, Herman, in it, Herman somehow holding his walkie talkie above water long enough to send a message for help, and finally being picked up by a rescue boat, sometime, though, after the hospital boat had sunk). And my boat (alas and alack, and a double alack for good measure) also built by Niro! When and how far from shore, and will someone in a good strong boat come along at the right time.

These are not the reasons, though, for our preparing to move back to Moen; neither is the bit of nastiness between Barbara and Benessed which developed when he butchered and cooked, in our backyard, one of the dogs Barbara had been feeding and nursing into good (succulent?) health. Barbara who still has agonizing dreams of the way the dog implored her to save him, shook her finger angrily at Benessed, which to him was the equivalent of putting a hex on him to blind him, whereupon he tried to knock her down, but she got a gun, a ferocious- looking revolver that shoots BBs, and chased him out of the yard. Exit Benessed, the same Benessed who once said, "If anyone bother you or Dr. Peck, I kill heem." We haven't heard from him since, even though he presumably still lives next door. No, these things are simply part and parcel of the kind of aggressive lives we have elected to live. I think that the real reason is that we feel that our 'Dublon period' is coming to a normal and fairly triumphant end and we should leave while we are still flush with the excitement of having 'discovered' a stark island way of life, and of having proven to ourselves that we possess some of the sense of adventure, the hardiness, and faith that pioneering has always required. After all, that is the kind of stock we think we came from.

Nor is it due to Barbara's Achilles tendon. But this is another story that I have neglected to tell you. Several months ago Barbara went into the back yard to empty the garbage. In her usual flamboyant way she hurled it at the 55-gallon garbage drum, but the container and all that was in it sailed high over the drum and into the swamp, Barbara in hot pursuit. Somehow, as only Barbara can do, she lost her zories, got mired up to her knees in swamp muck and, incredibly, completely severed an Achilles tendon on a piece of broken glass. She was hamstrung and bleeding profusely. I was able to track her route when I came home that evening: from the swamp, into the house, into the various rooms she entered and to the window from which she was able to call for help. As you know, Barbara doesn't panic, and she was able to send for the local Health Assistant who applied a pressure bandage, loaded her into his little motor boat, and brought her to the hospital on Moen, all within two hours of the accident. That's when I learned about it—Barbara on the operating table in the emergency room, and Dr. Jones, the surgeon, reaching far up into the calf of her leg to retrieve the retracted tendon. The tendon has healed very well, but she broke the wound open one night when she fell off her crutches in the bathroom—Barbara just wasn't built, either physically or emotionally, for intricate maneuvers; and the wound is now slowly healing by secondary intention. The incident with Benessed occurred while she was still tottering about on crutches, gun somehow held menacingly in hand while she chased him out of the yard, and into oblivion so far as this letter is concerned.

January 15, 1975

Dear Dorothy,

During the holidays I spent my time accumulating data that might support a grant proposal for a nutrition program in Truk. But now I'm having second thoughts on the matter. Maybe we really don't need a nutrition program in Chuuk. Maybe we don't even want one; for a thorough survey, if done objectively and scientifically as I had planned, would most certainly incriminate my friend Kan (Carl, actually—note the troublesome 'L' again), an honorable man by his standards and one of many fledgling fish dynamiters who are demonstrating to the satisfaction of almost all lagoon Chuukese that they can have rich, high-protein, low-cholesterol diets without trying. I had been aware of a band of dynamiters on Tol island who came to Dublon occasionally to dispose of fish with broken backs and smashed entrails, but I had regarded this operation as small and without much ecological impact. But I was wrong. On Christmas Eve the dynamiters' workshop on Tol, where old Japanese bombs and torpedoes were being dismantled for explosives, blew up killing four dynamiters and sending four more (including their Mafia-like leader, Kandido, who is also a Chuukese legislator and the brother of a Congressman of the Congress of Micronesia) into the hospital with serious wounds: "Legs and arms all over the place, just like an amphibious landing in Italy" said Dr. Jones, a World War II veteran. And it turned out that there were actually 32 full-time employees, mostly clan members of Kandido, in the gang, who had been diving for explosives, and blowing up schools of fish and peddling them so efficiently that they had probably been netting one to two thousand dollars a week—a vast sum in Chuuk. Most of us assumed that all dynamiters would be so demoralized by the accident that all dynamiting would cease. Quite the reverse! It simply decentralized operations and challenged the manhood of every red-blooded Chuukese male. A government bunker was promptly robbed of 24 cases of dynamite, and now nearly every village has its own crew of dynamiters (our village has two, Kan being the leader of one of them); and the accident made a hero of anyone who is willing to take the risk of being blown apart. I look out of my Dublon window, see a couple of spouts of water, hear applause from the shore, and see fresh fish being sold a few minutes later—though I have been told that the more common procedure is to dynamite, wait an hour for the sharks to come and eat their fill and leave, and then send scuba divers down to pick up what the sharks didn't want. So far as I know legal fishing has been abandoned, the explanation being that there aren't enough fish anymore.

We expect to make our reentry into the 20th Century on Friday by moving back to Moen. The first shock we will encounter will be that this 'cosmopolitan center'—at least that is the way we regard Moen when we look at it across the channel—has just run out of water: no toilet, in or out of the hospital, has been flushed in the last 24 hours.

January 30, 1975

Dear Dorothy,

Moving back was not without incident. The big LCU landing craft, vintage World War II, that came to fetch our furniture, got hung up on the barrier reef as it tried to depart Dublon. We had gone on to Moen in our motor boat and knew nothing about the accident until the next morning when everyone was getting frantic over the missing LCU (an M-boat, a smaller type of landing craft, had sunk a short time earlier), and we were preparing to lament the loss of the harpsichord and clavichord, all of my credentials, books, etc., when we saw the LCU puffing out great billows of diesel smoke on its way to Moen, having just been floated free by a high tide.

We are now living in a rather grand Samoan-type house (high roofed with cedar-shake shingles and louvered sides) high in the

This is Kan, our island neighbor who was chief of a local group of fish dynamiters. He was a dependable friend.

mountain. It's very quiet and cool up here. And since we are beside the District Administrator's house and on his private water main, we share his special prerogative for having unlimited access to water. We are the envy of our friends, a reality that frightens us into pretending that we are also suffering acutely from water shortage; in fact, we turn off our water main in semblance of the water hours below, and self-righteously suffer a little bit.

Oh, yes, the dogs! I seem to have left the puppies in Barbara's room 'whimpering their new life.' Now they are five months old and still with us, all four of them. They are a savage pack, and they nearly tore each other apart during our boat trip to Moen. The lagoon was rough and I think they were all ashamed of being seasick and vomiting all over Barbara; so they took it out on each other, and on Barbara, too, for she, sitting on the floor of our boat, was their battlefield. We hope to give two of the little brutes away this weekend, though Barbara has gotten to feeling protective of them. I think that her being disabled as they were growing up has given a rather special tenderness to their relationship. Kanga, the father wastes no sentiment on them and tries to drive them away. Perhaps he remembers how, as a puppy, he once endangered old Chida's standing in the household. But Chida, our spayed female, is fascinated by them. She roars at them and complains about them constantly, but then accepts their adulation as something that she's been waiting for all her life.

And that's about where we stand now—Barbara, Chida, Kanga, Lug, Bambo, Brown, M'bear and I.

As ever,
Your brother

⊕ ⊕ ⊕

Father Juan Pons, Capuchin priest who
died on Rota during the war, and is
remembered as a saint to whom
countless miracles were, and still are,
attributed.

CHAPTER EIGHT

FEATURE STORIES FROM THE NORTHERN MARIANAS
(WWII Memorials; Historical Recollections and Legacies)

ROTA (LUTA)

Rota! Rota! It has taken me a long time to get here, but now it seems that this was where I have been heading all these years, especially while I was dashing about and sampling one island after another. But now, here on Rota just forty miles north of Guam, I have been able for the first time to completely discard all of my responsibilities as a physician and devote my time wholly to whatever appeals to me at the moment: hiking mountain trails, spelunking, gardening, playing or listening to music, enjoying my island friends, listening to the roar of the surf, and writing. I have kept no diary, and what remains of the excitement and fervor of those activities exists only in the articles that I wrote as they were occurring, and published in local periodicals. Let me see if I can convey a bit of the wonder and excitement of these years by quoting several articles that seem to preserve them. My wife and I came to Rota in 1982 and the following articles were all written since then. But first let me define the term, Blessed Island, which is the designation that is cherished by local islanders:

> But islands of the Blessed, bless you son,
> I never came upon a blessed one. *Robert Frost*

For the short-term need to designate its position within the Commonwealth of the Northern Marianas and to assign it a post office address, the name Rota serves best. But for long-term considerations only the name Luta fully places this little island within its historic-cultural context and involves those deep feelings of identity that each citizen on this island carries in his heart. Many a citizen would consider it an ethnic and ethical error if, when speaking Chamorro, he were to use the name Rota to designate the island of his nativity—this island that he regards as blessed and that Robert Frost, had he lived on it, might have proclaimed as blessed, even to the extent or rewriting his famous couplet as:

> But islands of the Blessed, bless you son,
> Fair Luta, I have found, is the blessed one.

Postulate an experienced and sensitive traveler who comes here and spends a month hiking over Rota's (Luta's) trails and learning to know its people. I think that he might then say: "Yes, this island—this slightly-known island—with its faint jungle trails and its hidden waterfalls cascading one on to another through a mile of steep mountain gorge with the havoc of an earthquake; this island with its jagged, sheer, and dangerous cliffs ('fall/frightful . . . no-man-fathomed' cliffs), and its great basaltic rocks that stand up like totems to warn all to flee who would disobey ancestral injunctions; with its dark, primeval jungles and their massive trees and their shy deer; with its high, cool, orchid-covered Savannah (Sabana); with its stalactite-studded caves that were once sanctuary to rebels (patriots?) fleeing Spanish oppressors! . . . Yes, this harsh island is spectacular in many ways: it is historic and beautiful; perhaps it is the most starkly beautiful island in the Western Pacific though Kosrae, Anatahan, and Alamagan are close runner-ups for this honor."

And if this sensitive traveler is in a philosophic mood he might add: "And the people who live here resemble their island, for they, and a millennium of ancestors who preceded them, have been forced to adapt their needs and pleasures to the harsh realities that exist on such an isolated, sometimes neglected island. Little wonder that they have become a determined, strong-willed, shrewd, basalt-hard, feisty people, and that it takes little oppression, especially out-side official oppression, to bring out the rebel in them that has existed since Spanish times. Many high government officials have learned that to cross them is like falling off one of their cliffs ...and that on this island vengeance is an acknowledged, respected commodity that is measured out with precision and administered with elan."

Such is Rota (Luta) in very brief summary! The point I would make is that to understand it, it must be seen in one piece for its startling landscape, its capable, sometimes contentious, sometimes gentle people, its isolation, its comforts and discomforts, its language and its poetry and song, its history and myths, its huge annual fiesta, its loneliness. This tiny, tidy universe which the post office knows (incorrectly and ingloriously) as Rota!

ROTA TODAY AND TOMORROW

It is impossible to think of Rota today and to judge it without seeing it in its geographic and historic and cultural context, for these things determine the character and attitudes of the people who were born and reared on this small, sequestered island of formidable, dangerous cliffs, of towering trees and dark jungles, of terrifying typhoons, and gentle Chamorrita love songs; factors responsible for their hospitable and gracious traits at fiesta time when they invite the world; for their obdurate and dour traits when their rights are threatened; for their cynical and belligerent traits when they remember their dominated past; for their nostalgia and pride when they recall their heritage, fondling the word *Luta* (traditional name for Rota) as they speak to one another. So let us begin with its geography.

Rota, just forty miles north of Guam is a strange island geographically. There is scarcely any lagoon and not much reef, and the island begins where people live—close to the water's edge, and the most constant sound one hears in them is that of waves crashing on the shore (or was before recent dredging and dynamiting of the harbor and the current hubbub of road repair and construction dominated all lesser sounds). And not far back of the villages are the coral cliffs that rise abruptly to more than 1600 feet to form a cool, lush plateau or Savannah (Sabana, we call it) that is unique unto this island, for it, mostly unused, extends flat and fertile for miles up among the clouds. No one lives there, no citizens own these miles of rich soil, and anyone who wishes may claim a garden plot on it for the season…a beguiling thing to do for many temperate zone crops (strawberries, blackberries, raspberries, asparagus, for instance, will grow there, and cabbages grow to twice the size of those on lower ground.

Here on this high plateau is where great bonfires were once kept burning at night by Spanish conquistadors as signal to their galleons passing through Rota Channel (the 40 mile stretch of water between Guam and Rota.) Here on a central area, called As Manila, from which on exceptionally clear days one can see Guam, Tinian, and Saipan, the Japanese High Command maintained its headquarters and had a Shinto shrine that has since been converted into Rota's Peace Memorial . . . a memorial as spare and understated and as beautiful as the new Vietnam Memorial in Washington, DC. Peaceful and solemn and forgiving are words that describe its mood until one discovers the tunnels that run beneath it, into which frightened Japanese military officers, abandoning their Shinto prayers, once dove to save themselves from Guam-based America planes that would strafe or bomb anything that moved. Then one must add the word terror to describe its mood.

Sabana drips with moisture, and Rota's abundant [abundant in the late 90s], famous water supply is dependent on it, for its strange funnel configuration collects rain and accumulates it at a point called Apuya (umbilicus). Stand there in the clouds on Rota's high, depressed 'umbilicus' and you can hear the collected water gurgling beneath your feet as it gathers itself to seep, rush and fall through underground channels to the Water Cave where it is collected for village use and for irrigating farm crops; or to descend unused in a series of spectacular jungle waterfalls to the ocean.

To most visitors Rota is a slow-moving, languorous, unspoiled island and, for them, that is its charm. And in truth Rota's friendly inhabitants are not in a hurry. At least they are no longer in a hurry, for what is there to hurry for on this neglected, mostly forgotten, pleasant island? Once they hurried and look what happened! They hurried (or were hurried) during Japanese occupation and achieved what must be regarded as a true industrial revolution. Look at old prewar photographs and you will see what I mean: Songsong village with a long, extended passenger bus running up its busy main street, which, at first glance, reminds one of 19th century Boston. Or look at photographs of the potash and manganese mining operations with their great towering (probably clanging) airlifts carrying ore down the cliffs of Sabana to ships anchored off East Harbor, while another, smaller airlift on the other side of the island (not shown in the photographs) carried supplies up to the miners. Look at the record (mostly in the memories of older citizens) and you will find that in addition to being self-sufficient in its daily needs, Rota was manufacturing or processing, and exporting crude and refined sugar; also a kind of potent rum (goseshi) made from whatever was on hand: sweet potatoes, corn, sugar cane; and also charcoal, sea salt, castor oil made from castor beans, papaya siru (dried papaya sap); some rice, beef, starch from German tapioca, a dark purple dye derived from ifil wood, dried tuna (kachubushi), lumber for making furniture in Japan, and a nylon-like fiber obtained from asa plants to be processed into ropes and high-quality dress material. There were major Japanese companies supervising these industries: Nanyo Kohatsu Kaisha, Nanyo Boiki Kabushikigaigha, Tabi Yoka Kaisha, and individual entrepreneurs such as 'Jose' Hattori. At least 5,000 Japanese citizens lived there, mostly in Songsong village, profiting from and exploiting these enterprises and enjoying the social amenities and comforts of their profits.

But what about the Rotanese people, the 873 Rotanese who lived here at that time? How did they profit from this industrial revolution that had descended on them unbidden? For the most part, actually, they were content, even happy with it, for they had been hastily trained to see themselves as an inferior race whose destiny as happy peasants could be secured only by subservience. Indoctrination started in the schools where, on Rota, only three years of education were provided, though a few superior students (once they adopted Japanese names) were sent to Saipan or Palau for two more years of education, and, for a lucky few, on to Japan where they could receive the equivalent of high-school training. In general it can be said that the quality of Rotanese lives, during Japanese occupation, was comparable to that of blacks who lived in the US Southern States at that same time, or of blacks now living in South Africa under apartheid rules: segregated housing (they were evicted from comfortable Songsong village and moved to the hastily-constructed, ramshackle village of Tatachog whose flimsy houses blew apart with each typhoon); segregated education (Chamorro children could attend only the school set apart for them); discrimination in employment (jobs were plentiful but were limited to unskilled and semiskilled work in which the pay was vastly lower than for Japanese performing the same task—a Rota policeman started at 21 yen a month, a postal messenger got 17 1\2 yen a month. There were no radios in Chamorro homes and only one Chamorro (Juan B Barcinas) had an automobile, a Chevrolet (first purchased second hand from Tokyo by Joaquin S. Pangelinan on Saipan, sold to Antonio Rios on Saipan, and finally shipped to Rota for its fourth resale), though a bicycle or a bull cart was owned by most families. When the sea was calm sea food was plentiful, but beef was a luxury that was reserved for fandangoes and novenas and, of course, for the Japanese families in Songsong village.

Leon Taisacan, now [1985] a well-fed, prominent citizen on Rota, construction-contractor, owner of many hectares of good land, began life, however, in a low-income family that was often hungry. Leon reflects on those stringent, though happy times of his childhood and says, "Sometimes when we didn't have food on the table we took pork lard, mixed it with sea salt, dipped a piece of breadfruit in it and ate it, for this was the quickest way we knew to overcome our hunger. And we weren't the only ones who did this, for quite a few others also relied on salted-down breadfruit to keep them going." "How about medical care for you and your family?" I asked him. "For us it didn't exist," he said. "We knew that a few high-ranking Chamorro families could go to the excellent Japanese hospital for treatment, but we couldn't and we relied, just as we always had, on suruhanas [traditional medical experts] and our own knowledge of local medicines, which, incidentally, I still respect highly." "And how about miscegenation?" "That, said Leon, "was a one-way street. Japanese men could marry Chamorro girls, but Japanese girls were beyond our Chamorro reach."

Interesting prewar history, I think you will agree, but what does it have to do with Rota today? What does it have to do with the fact that Rota people are not in a hurry? Almost everything! Those who recall those exploited times know that 'development' is often no more than disguised exploitation and that profits of the exploiters rarely trickle down to those who do the work and are the rightful owners of the island they live on. As you can see there is sound historic basis for Rotanese cynicism, and it is little wonder that Rota citizens, though all of them want true progress, regard each new proposal from abroad with diffidence, and promptly ask, "How are they trying to fool us this time?" Not only do elders react in this way, but also the younger people who have graduated from high school or college (Young Turks, they might be called elsewhere). It was they who took to the street one night, in the early 1980s to subdue aggressive Zee Company fishermen who, with their bomb-like, detonating devices were attempting to convert Rota into their home port. It was these 'Young Turks' who impelled the Commonwealth Government to abandon its attempt to bottle and export Rota's precious water at a time when El Nino was threatening the water supply. Citizens of all ages usually react like seasoned environmentalists whenever any proposal is made to 'develop' Sabana. Then, in alarm, they question the damage deforestation might do to the water reserve, and what havoc extensive cultivation would do to the fragile ecology that now supports a wonderland of ifil trees and other rare trees that are a marvel to visiting botanists: fire trees (serianthus nelsonii), for instance, of which only four or five specimen are known to exist elsewhere in the world; of giant ferns, rare orchids and mosses; of shy fruit doves whose three-part song proclaims this place as primeval and sacred (at least to fruit doves and environmentalists); of deer, fruit bats, and coconut crabs.

These are the things that have determined the character of Rota people, they are the roots that are now controlling and steadying the rate of growth. Though a lot of change has occurred since the Commonwealth Government took over from the malnourished, terminally-ill Trust Territory administration, these changes have been largely limited to infrastructure. The airport has been entirely rebuilt with a runway that, for a time, would accommodate 707 and 728 planes, and with an attractive terminal building that can withstand typhoons and earthquakes.

And the nine miles of once-tortuous dirt road to Songsong village has been transformed into an elegant, scenic, paved highway. The West Harbor which previously could accommodate only small craft, has been blasted and repeatedly dredged so that moderate-sized ocean freighters from

Guam and Saipan can enter and safely store their merchandise in the new warehouse. New high school and grade school buildings and a new gymnasium, have been built, as well as other government buildings and new condominiums. Rota's round house in which its famous fiestas are held, was destroyed in a typhoon, but has been rebuilt in dimensions and quality that match other developments. A new modern hospital was completed in 1986 [Completed in 1986 but in 1991 found to be inadequate so that extensive additions will now be made to enlarge and refine it.] "Several recent typhoons demolished most unsubstantial homes and these have been rebuilt in solid, secure, attractive reinforced concrete.

Nicholas Songsong, businessman and former resident director of Rota's Department of Commerce and Labor, expresses the conviction that most Rotanese citizens held in the early 80s: "Our aim is to create jobs for our young people and I am inalterably opposed to developments that build structures (new hotels, for instance) but do not provide local employment. As a group, our young people love this island of their nativity and want to remain if they can find jobs. Brain-drain needs not occur if only we can create jobs. Neither do I want to see developments that bring in excessive numbers of foreign employees and their families. Right now [1986] there are 130 foreign employees which are about the maximum our culture can accommodate." [By 1993 this number had risen to 1505—this at a time when local citizens were estimated to number 1,455.]

Leon Taisacan, who was station manager for Continental Airlines office on Rota in the 1970s, and who has previously commented on social conditions as they existed in Rota during Japanese occupation, now comments on the emerging plight of Rota farmers. "Rota farmers," he says, "are the victims of material progress. In the early 1970s they were exporting as much as 100,000 lbs. of produce a month to Guam and Saipan, and had won for Rota a reputation as an important farming area. But this came to a crashing end during construction (and all the disorder that went with it) of our splendid, new airport, which has been followed by one disaster after another in air freight services. Delivery of produce has become so fractious and on such unpredictable schedules that outside markets have become wary of Rota produce. Obviously the marketing mess must be straightened out before our farmers can be expected to return to their 1970s' level of production. Melon fly infestation must also be eliminated."

Former mayor, Prudencio Manglona explores modern attitudes that demean honest labor, and says: "Hands soiled by hard labor were once a mark of honor, but now our system is educating people into believing they can accept only white collar work with dignity. This attitude is just becoming manifest on Rota and is one reason that I want to emphasize the importance and dignity of farm work. I believe that everything on Rota (its abundant good soil, its traditional respect for rural life, its former habits of hard work learned from the Japanese, its energetic young people) favors Rota's development as a high grade agricultural center. But success is not assured. Urgently, we need to sit down with US agriculture authorities to develop long-term policies and to plan programs suited to our resources and available markets. I am looking forward to US Government cooperation that we must have if we are to succeed, but I am also looking back across 30-odd years of Trust Territory maladministration. I look beyond those frustrating years and into Japanese times with gratitude and admiration for the initiative and the guidance the Japanese Government once gave us in farming and marketing methods. For this I am truly grateful. I am now pleading for the US Government to show equal initiative and interest in our development."

"But how about living expenses?" someone may ask. They are contingent on the way you want to live. If you are a traditionally-minded Chamorro who believes there is honor in living by the sweat of one's brow by cultivating a few hectares of family ranch on weekends; and if you are surrounded by thrifty clan members who delight in sharing their abundance with one another; and, most certainly, if you are eligible for food stamps, living expenses are minimal and discountable. But if you are a statesider who clings to stateside eating habits and amenities (and I'm afraid that I am one of these unfortunates), then expenses are sometimes daunting. I know that people in Hawaii are indignant that expenses on those islands are higher than state-side, and I know that prices rise almost exponentially as one goes from Hawaii to Guam to Rota (or from Saipan to Rota). Here on Rota, we who have refused to forsake our stateside habits are at the apogee of this cost-of-living orbit. And not only for foods and supplies, but for air transportation; for instance, Rota's airport is only 90 miles round-trip from Guam's airport, but to make that trip costs $ 110.00—well over a dollar a mile…a fact that is worthy of inclusion in the Guinness Book of World Records. But now back to food and supply costs! When you consider Rota's geographic situation, which, of course, is the reason for the expense, perhaps the cost should be discounted for the sheer joy of being a part of this unique, nostalgia-producing, hitherto unspoiled part of the world.

Rota's small population (about 2960) prohibits large, economical size importations of food and supplies, and most orders are too small to interest large suppliers. Moreover, large ocean freighters cannot enter Rota's small (though improved) harbor, and all sea freight must be transshipped by smaller craft from Guam or Saipan, and this spirals freight-costs upward. Air freight, of course, is available for perishable commodities, but this boosts freight charges up to 30 cents a pound. Most of the stores on Rota are small mom and pop family stores which, though adding intimacy and charm to the job of shopping, further escalates the problem of cost-efficient management. And so do the excise tax charges on imports by the Commonwealth Government.

Politics, just as in Guam, Saipan, and Tinian, is the chief recreation, and is a 'sport' in which personalities are pitted against one another in long, pre-election nights of fiery, exceedingly eloquent and scathing oratory, that to a non-Chamorro ear has the impact of machine gun fire (No wonder that cockfighting is the favorite sport on Rota!), I suspect that politics is an essential cleansing process which ends up, once diatribes are exchanged, by uniting its citizens in a common cause to assert Rota's entitlement to a fair share of Commonwealth resources. The powerful common cause is that Rota is the nearly forgotten member of the Commonwealth, and that its rights can be assured only by powerful, aggressive representation in the Legislature. As a consequence, Rota has developed a strong voice and posture, as Saipan officials and bureaucrats have discovered to their sorrow . . . for to cross Rotanese, once they have united in common cause, is a fearsome thing to do, almost like falling off one of their cliffs.

In the early sixties when I lived on Guam, I could—and did—write about it in the same glowing terms that I am now using about Rota, for the same stern, transcendental Chamorro heritage ruled the way its citizens exercised their loyalties and faith; and they lived their daily lives much as their ancestors had done. It was a world that I loved and still do. Most of us felt that it was unnecessary to lock our doors at night, and we all waved at each other on the highways. But now, just 30-some years later, Guam has become a murder capital of the Pacific—rich but sick. How could this have happened to a society that had been stable through centuries of disasters and abuse? Most certainly Guam's acculturation coincided with the appearance of eager, greedy, off-island developers who cared not one whit for ancient values but who loved the dollar; and with the developers came their greed which entered the villages ('dollars have no brothers' is the way Chamorro's explain it) and did its dirty work: a divorce rate that enriches lawyers, corruption of officials, rapes, child abuse, school dropouts, robberies, all manner of juvenile delinquencies and suicides, and, of course, as documented by the daily newspaper, a dismaying sum of brutal and sometimes grotesque murders.

My evaluation of Saipan, when I first moved there in the 70s was about the same as it had been for Guam in the 60s, but now its murder rate is soaring toward that of Guam's for Guam has become the prototype for 'development' in the Marianas. . . . And Rota, where many of us still do not lock our doors, where we all wave affectionately at each other, and fear nothing when we stroll its dark streets at night or wander into its jungles—how long can it remain pristine? . . . We are forced to acknowledge that cultural heritage, no matter how ancient and honorable, is a fragile thing; and that once the greed of 'developers' takes over, it can be shattered—for greed is the gospel of 'developers'.

But moral and social deterioration is not an inescapable fate of development, for development can be controlled and directed by traditional values so as to enrich an island's way of life. But this requires intense, dedicated and sophisticated efforts by local leaders—leaders who, from the time of their mothers' milk, have learned to depend on their ancient heritage to guide them to successful adulthood, and are now in position to use those sound Chamorro principles to shape the route that Rota should take as it enters the Twenty first Century.

Is it too late for this to happen? Fortunately, Rota has always been a neglected island and now, just 30 years behind Guam and 20 years behind Saipan in 'development', it is, by comparison, still pristine, and its destiny has not yet been shattered. But 'developers' are even now drawing up plans to transform simple, neglected, law-abiding, family-loving Rota, almost overnight into a world class resort: All the hotels and golf courses the island will hold, five thousand or more imported executives and caretakers, hang gliding facilities, and condominiums galore. . . . And entrepreneurs are even now begging for the opportunity to make Rota into a gambling casino resort (though currently Rota voters oppose the idea.). Will Rota's ancient principles assert themselves in time to control these changes with honor and with enduring profit to all citizens? . . . It's incredible and nerve wracking. . . . Rota's future hangs in the balance.

THE SEA AROUND US

Rota has a barrier reef to protect itself along only a fraction of its western coast. Elsewhere, the ocean and Rota's rocky shore meet on nearly equal terms, crashing and roaring and threatening each other with destruction; at other times merely lamenting each other's existence. . . . Always the most constant sound in villages along the coast is the voice of the surf. When the ocean is in a destructive mood, its roar rises up beyond the villages to the cliffs where it is magnified and echoed back so realistically that one doesn't know which way to look to locate the source of the sound.

On all sides of us the sea extends without interruption to the horizon—almost to infinity so it seems to us who live here . . . and by measuring that distance (one step closer to infinity) we could calculate the dimensions of this entire planet, at least that was one way ancient mathematicians did it. The ocean is a temperamental being and one learns to watch it carefully for its change of mood may change one's schedule for the next hour, the next week or the remainder of one's life. Once, if old tales are to be trusted, the ocean raged out of control and plunged over the low neck of land where Songsong village stands, destroying houses and landmarks and people. And once, during an earthquake (1767), the ocean dropped several feet below its usual level and remained there (sullenly, I have been told) in semi-darkness for two years.

And there are those wrecked fishing and freight vessels that we see every day, still clinging to the rocky shore and warning us to take care.

But usually the ocean is placid with color changes that are a joy to behold. Its most constant color is a deep, lived blue. . . "a startling blue, a cyanotic blue, blue that is bluer than any blue in the entire Pacific," so says Dr. John Steele, a much traveled physician who comes frequently to Rota for the purpose of medical research. So passionately does he proclaim this observation that my wife and I learned to call this intense coloration 'steele' blue in his honor.

But there are other colors that the ocean assumes as its moods change. Sometimes, though rarely, it is a disappointing 'North Atlantic' gray; but I have seen it turn green, black, copper, and amber. And once, to my amazement, it became luminous pink. This had nothing to do with sunset or sunrise glow. It was pink because it was in a pink mood. And that amazing color extended all the way to the horizon where a thin scrawl of blue, 'steele' blue, separated it from the sky.

ROTA'S FORTIFICATIONS UNCHALLENGED

The history of war years on Rota, as on any other uninvaded island, is easily written off as inconsequential, and there is no textbook to turn to for information. When one considers the excellent documentation of the war elsewhere in the Pacific, these years on Rota are like a cosmic black hole, even though they were of intense importance to those who participated in them. Indeed, the defense of Rota by the Japanese military might have been spectacular had it been tested by American invasion, for the strategy for defense was carefully developed and rehearsed to avoid the mistakes of earlier Pacific battles. Had invasion occurred, American troops would have encountered a Maginot-line type of fixed defense not often seen elsewhere in the Pacific, and would have found it necessary to flush its 4,000 to 5,000 defenders out of an extensive system of tunnels and caves. And they would have encountered an amazing innovation at the moment of landing: Chamorro workmen rushing at them through the surf to impale them on bamboo spears, and some of the workmen would have had dynamite strapped to their chests in such a way that they would have become explod- ing bombs as, kamikaze-like, they threw themselves beneath landing crafts and tanks—though this might have been only a planned diversion that would never have been implemented, for reliance was to be placed on the big guns and fixed fortifications and tunnels back in the hills as shown by an excerpt recently translated from Japanese military records by Dr. Mark R. Peattie, of Harvard's Japan Institute, and sent to the author:

Initially the garrison [Japanese garrison] had attempted to strengthen the island's beach defense in order to meet the en- emy at the water's edge. With the fall of Guam in August, 1944, however, it was obvious that such measures were futile. The main line of resistance was, therefore, pulled back 60 to 300 yards from the beaches and construction was begun that month on a series of tunnels which were to connect its various segments. Because of the hardness of the rocky soil, the work was very slow at first, averaging not much more than three meters a day. Work was speeded up with the use of dynamite obtained from the South Seas Development Company and from explosives extracted from unexploded enemy bombs. At As Manila [Prob- ably an error. Should have been Ginalagan] the garrison was able to take advantage of a natural cave to build a recessed forti- fication. By war's end over 3,300 meters [about two miles that probably included all tunnels on Rota and the labyrinth of tun- nels that once lay beneath Songsong village, now partially con- verted into septic tanks] of tunnels had been excavated, most of which could withstand the force of up to 250 kiloton bombs.

Thus, between June 11, 1944 (when the Japanese military took over full control of every facet of life on Rota) and September, 1945 (when it surrendered), a defense system was created that could protect and give in- stant invisibility to four thousand troops and to four thousand Japanese civilians who lived on Rota through the war. But where are the remains of that system? How could a system carved from solid rock—and durable as the pyramids and as hidden as the catacombs—disappear in forty years? Ask a young Rota citizen you meet on the street about it, ask him to show you surviving war ruins and relics, and he will direct you, or, perhaps, take you, to the two large, well-preserved high angle cannons (and the former site of another) that are touted tourist attractions; but he will appear perplexed when you press him for more information—when, for instance, you ask to see the recessed fortifications built into the cliff at Ginalagan, or the two miles of communication-bomb shelter tunnels, or the three other high angle cannons and other ordinance that are recorded in the Japanese military inventory. Of course he hasn't seen them and has heard of them, if at all, only as myths...so little relevance do these things have with current life problems on Rota (building a new house in Sinapalo, the soaring costs of food, equipment, travel and transportation, and the complexities of food stamps and politics) that he never bothered to ask his grandfather.

I had lived on Rota for two years and knew nothing about the actual extent of fortifications before making the trip that I am about to describe, even though I had become an inveterate hiker through the jungle; and I was prepared then to say, "Rota is the least interesting of the Mariana Islands so far as war artifacts and war memories are concerned." But then, one day I went for a hike with Abraham Charfauros and Gerald Calvo and several other young Rota men to Alaguan Bay. On the way back it occurred to them (Abraham who knew the area intimately from years of intrepid and compulsive deer hunting activities and the field work he does as part of his job with the Department of Culture and Community Affairs, and Gerald who was as unfamiliar with the area as I, but just as eager to learn) that we should drive ('force' is the better word, for one of us had to stand high in the back of the pickup truck to identify the merest trace of an ancient bull-cart trail, shouting "One foot to the right, now turn sharp to the left but watch out for those stumps') and force a four-wheel drive pickup over rocks and ruts and fallen trees through the nearly impenetrable thickets on Jack Atalig's property to the base of Ginalagan Cliff where Abraham had seen evidence of old fortifications. . . .Fred Hocog, the driver and owner of the pick up, lamenting as he drove, "My car, my poor, new car, getting scratched and jarred to hell! Why did I come? Why did I come?"

After such an approach you might expect to find the kind of fortification that such torture should warrant. But at first you see nothing more than a few coral rocks stacked on top of one another, for rank jungle trees and vines and lianas and thick moss blanket the base of the cliff and have returned the area to primeval jungle. It is only after you leave the pickup and climb to the base of the cliff that you suddenly realize that you are at the site of elaborate, man-made fortifications... that from a 1983 Toyota you have stepped into a chapter of forgotten history, that suddenly you are the possessor of facts possessed by no historian. There, just in front of you, is a concrete parapet a yard thick and sometimes higher than your head (though containing gaps for machine guns through which you can peer and see Rota's airfield two miles away, lying vulnerable and naked in the bright sun); and behind the parapet are caves in which you could set up comfortable living quarters (there is part of a sewing machine in one— imagine sewing up a tear in your uniform during an attack!); and caves in which solid rock bases had been constructed for supporting cannons; and live cannon shells and hand-grenades with firing pins still intact, lying on the floor . . . all this extending as far as you can see through the jungle's rank growth. But I am getting beyond my non-military competence and need professional consultation for establishing trustworthy parameters, so let me try another approach. . . . When we returned to Songsong village, Gerald Calvo searched his office files and found a memorandum prepared by the Division of Historic Preservation in August, 1983—an excellent catalogue of the fortification we had just seen, and written by a consultant versed in military ordinance:

The Ginalagan site is an extensive World War II Japanese defense complex built along the base of a sheer cliff approximately 200 meters above sea level. The site was constructed to blend into the natural terrain of the area as evidenced by the use of coral limestone rocks and cleverly placed fortifications. The site consists of gun emplacements, troop facilities, communication areas, man-made tunnels, a generator, housing units, command/observations posts, water collection areas and a parapet wall built along the base of the Ginalagan cliff, providing protection to the positions behind it. The parapet wall which is one meter thick and varies in height from one to three meters, is protected by three concrete pill boxes, periodic firing slits and numerous gun caves which housed 37 mm antitank guns, 75 mm artillery pieces, mortars and possibly a 120 mm gun. Blast walls, constructed of poured concrete, protect the entrances to several shelter and ammunition caves. These caves conform to official Japanese Naval tunnel standards (of the Suidatai Unit) with 'U' shaped tunnels functioning as combat and shelter areas and 'L'-shaped tunnels for housing generators, mortars and 75 mm guns. The caves are littered with personal equipment of the troops, bottles, ordinance and the remains of the wooden flooring. . . . The Ginalagan defensive complex survived the war essentially intact. Today, it is possibly the best preserved example of a fortification resulting from Japan's in-depth defensive strategy during the final days of the Second World War.

Since my first visit to Ginalagan I have prowled the area repeatedly, sometimes alone, sometimes with Gerald Calvo or Lewis Manglona. And each time the area has seemed to expand in magnitude and complexity. So let us get at its dimensions, first its length:

The fortification as described in the memorandum just quoted, and as measured by length of the concrete parapet, is 500 yards long. But actually this is just the beginning of a system that becomes more lethal as it passes into less visible components that continue along the base of the cliff. Perhaps a quarter of a mile west of the parapet these fortifications multiply into a complex that might have been the central 'camp' of the defense system.

Dormitory-like spaces have been cleared under the massive rocks that litter the base of the cliff, and these are often protected by large retaining stone walls and rock walk-ways—some as elaborate as in a Japanese sunken garden—connecting them. There are the remains of a large electric generator. And behind the camp, recessed into the cliff are unusually well designed and constructed redoubts for four 75 mm cannons, the cannons still intact and in their original positions. One demolished cannon, its bore indeterminate, lies on the ground.

Recessed fortifications then continue at intervals all the way to the large 120 mm high angle cannon beside the road to the Sabana, previously described as a tourist attraction. This cannon marks the western end of the Ginalagan fortification whose length can now be measured: a total of one and a half miles.

But here, without interruption, though it must leave the Ginalagan area and pass into the Finafen area, the line of fortifications angles steeply up the cliff along a trail that is marked by half-finished stone parapets, poorly dug caves that may never have been occupied, and tunnels that were begun and aborted after several feet of digging. For half a mile it continues until suddenly it comes onto three large cannons, well protected in large, excellently constructed redoubts, intact and 'full of fight'; one, a 120 mm high angle cannon, twin to the one we saw below but so high on the cliff that it commands a vast segment of ocean, and the other two are large anti-aircraft cannons, one with two barrels, aimed at the sky just as they were the last time they were fired. I am panting from the stiff climb up the awkward trail of rocks and I ponder the question; how could three heavy cannons have been transported here—surely not over this terrible trail—so I ask Lewis Manglona who had guided me to this spot—Lewis Manglona, tough, one-armed 78 year old Rota patriarch, skilled Rota mountain climber; raconteur; farmer; demon to deer hunters and poachers on his property;

once a young rebel but now a treasury and lover of island lore. Lewis Manglona knows the answer for he was here at the time and saw the three cannons lowered by cables and winches from the upper plateau to these carved niches half-way down the cliff. Lewis ponders these recollections for a few moments, smiles at them, and for the next half hour I am inundated by a flood of reminiscences concerning this location and those times. The tale I remember best was:

"Yes, it was fun to watch airplane fights in those days. Once when my friend and I were standing a little way below this spot, an American fighter came over. Several antiaircraft cannons blazed away at it but did no damage, and a Japanese plane flew up from the airfield to challenge it. They were like two fighting cocks dodging and leaping and striking at each other. Now I'm not sure why my friend and I were for the American plane for we had been told that the Americans' sole purpose in coming to Rota was to cut off our ears and tongues, but it was the American plane we were cheering for. Suddenly, it seemed to have been hit for it rolled over in the air and started to fall. But it was only a stunt, for as soon as the Japanese plane turned its tail it recovered, came at the Japanese plane and shot it down. We almost went crazy laughing and slapping and shouting until a Japanese soldier heard us and came running at us with his sword raised. That settled us and we bowed to him and tried to look as if we had been crying."

I asked Lewis why the fortifications in the Finafen area, save for these two gun emplacements, were so much more carelessly constructed than in Ginalagan, and he said it was because they were added late in the war when panic and exhaustion ruled the way things were constructed.

We have, so far as this article is concerned, now tramped the length of these fortifications and know that their total length, their horizontal dimensions, is at least two miles. How about Ginalagan's vertical dimension? I asked Lewis Manglona about it and he took me to his farm which occupies a plateau plot 300 feet above Ginalagan's recessed fortifications to show me its upper extent. Here is an old campfire site to which soldiers once climbed up a nearly perpendicular trail that would have taxed mountaineers, to cook the sweet potatoes that grew on a nearby patch, and to make a kind of tea from tangantangan seeds. Here, also, is an observation cave carved into the cliff's rim from which an observer could clearly see the airfield, Alaguan Bay, and far out to sea (sometimes as far as Saipan), and could report his findings directly by telephone to the gunners down below, to the High Command on Sabana, and even to the emergency hospital in Tonga Cave near Songsong village, for copper telephone lines crisscrossed the island, festooned jungle trees, and brought eventual joy to Lewis who supported himself after the war by reclaiming the wire and selling it. "I know about the communication with the hospital," he said, "for I was there as a patient, having just had my right arm blown off while learning from the Japanese how to dynamite fish to give them, and a night call came from this look-out saying that someone down on Alaguan Bay, probably the spy who had been chased about the island that afternoon, was signaling out to sea with a flashlight. And so it turned out, for 27 Japanese soldiers who went next morning to search for him, found the flashlight (US Army issue) and a pack of US cigarettes neatly placed together on a rock at the point where the spy had apparently been picked up by a boat or a submarine—it was sort of a farewell sneer at them, the soldiers thought, and they were angry about it."

The trip to the top of the cliff with Lewis completes this Ginalagan odyssey and I have nothing more to report. I write it down, mull over it, and worry that, though I may have described caves and ordinance and cliffs adequately, there is nothing that hints at what it must have been like to be a Japanese soldier manning one of those guns. I do not want to leave the impression that they were abstractions and less human than pieces of their ordinance; so I retrace (figuratively, of course) my trail through the fortifications until I remember something I had seen in a cave lying beside a live artillery shell: a fine 'bouquet' of black, branching coral—just like the sea shells and artifacts I collect and horde—that seemed to proclaim the wonders and exoticism of a tropical world, that would document for him the mystic truth and beauty of Rota, and that would forever explain to those back home that this was where he had known courage and fearlessness. I wanted to believe that he had been guarding this black coral as if it were his life, right up to the moment of his capture or his death.

A ROTA SAINT

Corbiniano Ayuyu (pronounced Ajuju) and his wife Francesca: I am in their home this evening, Corbiniano and I sit facing one another and Francesca sits on a chair at the other side of the room, but as the conversation becomes animated, she draws closer and finally sits on the floor beside us so she, as a good Chamorro wife should, can correct her husband when his facts falter. At my side is Chris Ayuyu, their off-island-educated son. I have known Chris for many years: when he lived in Guam and in Honolulu, also when he became the notoriously handsome young desk-clerk at the Royal Taga Hotel in Saipan, and now (1987) when he is the Administrator for the Rota Hospital.

It is Chris who arranged this meeting and who will interpret for us as we take a long journey together of 40 years and more back to the time of the war, a time of mass starvation, a time when mothers' milk dried up and to be born was to die within days or weeks (though I shall note one exception), a time when extermination and even genocide seemed to threaten and were narrowly averted... but also, so the Ayuyus are convinced, it was a time of miracles, for there, back to back with the crimes of war and its war criminals, was an array of heavenly forces dispensing simple physical-act by simple physical-act (miracles?) that saved the island; and where one person, worthy above all others in Rota's long history, was given the semblance of holy sainthood even while he lived and suffered piteously and died horribly (no, gloriously and exultantly!). Thus do I introduce the Spanish Jesuit priest, Father Juan Pons, whose name evokes a look of reverence in the eyes of Rotanese. For them to recount the physical facts of his life and death and ministry is like visiting a holy shrine. To the Ayuyus the war was a device for showing that supreme faith, when severely and ultimately tested, is a glory that survives.

Corbiniano Ayuyu is eager to speak: "I was born in 1917 here in Rota," he begins, "and as far back as I can remember I was an altar boy. Because I respected the church and sometimes thought of holy orders as a possible career, I volunteered my services to do whatever I was able to do: sweep the church, cut the grass, take up the collection. There was a series of priests on Rota during those years. One of my favorites was Father Jose Gumsio, who once, while sharing his lunch with me, said, 'Because you ask for nothing for your services, you will always be provided for. Heaven will see to that.' That was when I was about twelve years old. I believed him, and it has been true ever since, even through the war.

"Now," Corbiniano continues, "let me speak of Father Juan Pons. Father Juan Pons was a Jesuit priest in the Carolina Islands for many years (1921-1935) until he came to Saipan (1935). Once he came to Rota to 'fill in' for several months, a healthy eager priest, white-haired and bearded, who was struggling to learn Chamorro. We liked him, and in 1937 he was permanently assigned to Rota. His ministry was successful and pleasing to him at first for a new, large convent and chapel were just being completed in Tatacho village and he was the first and, for that matter, the only priest ever to occupy and use them.

"I was in my 20s then and married to Francesca Mendiola Masga who sits beside us now, and we lived next door to the convent, and so did my wife's father, Joaquin Masga and his family, and so did Juan Santos and his family, Together we did everything we could to support the new priest. Joaquin Masga's sister, Maria Masga Santos, for instance, sewed the priest's robes and laundered and pressed them and kept them in order. So our three families were in daily contact with Father Juan Pons. One day not long after he arrived, he came to Joaquin Masga to show him a painful, discolored spot that had developed on his ankle while he was returning from saying Mass for a homebound invalid. Joaquin Masga looked at it and told him that it had come from his sandal rubbing his ankle while he hiked home on the narrow-gauge railroad track; but two days later he showed Joaquin Masga a similar area on the other ankle. And from that time on ugly, discolored, painful spots appeared almost every day, and both legs swelled up all the way to the knees, knobby and weeping a mixture of clear fluid and pus; and sometimes maggots would crawl out of the ulcers and fall on the ground.

"'We've got to get you to a doctor,' Joaquin Masga kept saying to him, but it wasn't until Father Juan Pons could hardly walk that he consented to being partially carried by Joaquin Masga and the Spanish Jesuit brother, Miguel Timoner, to the bus, loaded onto it, and taken to the Japanese hospital in Songsong village. But the salve that was smeared over both legs and the bandages that went from ankles to thighs helped not at all, and Father Juan Pons soon gave up all attempts at treatment and waddled about as best he could with his legs bare and swollen to the size of small tree trunks, blotched and purple, dripping (sometimes pouring) pus and corruption and clear fluid, and exuding maggots. This much was bad, but the worst of it was the awful smell that filled the chapel during Mass so that we could barely stay there, and that filled the convent at all times." [Some Rotanese believe that Father Juan Pons' wounds were a result of penance. Corbiniano cannot confirm this though many times he saw him strike at his legs in disgust with a towel. Others, less close to Father Juan Pons, believed that actual self-flagellation may have occurred and could have been the genesis of his condition. All believed that Father Juan Pons' suffering contributed to his holy and exemplary life.]

To illustrate his exemplary life, several Rotanese told me that when he saw a woman wearing a short skirt, he would turn his head and look the other direction even while he was admonishing her. Several informants have insisted that the wounds on his legs first occurred in Truk (Chuuk) and were present, though not so severe, when he lived on Saipan.

"It was about this time," Corbinano Ayuyu continues, "that we began to notice a change in Father Juan Pons: a kind of holiness in the way he accepted this calamity, and he never missed a single Mass up to just three days before he died. We realized that this was no ordinary priest and we began, cautiously at first and then as a daily routine, to ask him to petition for miracles. 'Father,' we would say just after Mass, 'our crops are dying and must have rain.' He would nod calmly, raise both hands to Heaven and invoke rain which came within hours, or, at most within a few days. And it came in an unusual way with lightning streaking the entire sky and great claps of thunder that shook the air and the walls of our houses, which, as you know, is unusual here on Rota. It was like God looking down at us and speaking in a holy, approving voice. And then, when it had rained just enough it would stop, and we would go about our farm work until the soil dried out. Then, just after Mass, we would say, 'Father, our crops are dying and must have rain,' and again he would invoke rain. Or sometimes a fisherman would say, 'The sea is too rough for fishing and my children are hungry,' and the good Father would raise his hands and pray, first in Latin and then in Chamorro, and within hours the waves would become calm and those of us with boats would go out and catch all the fish we needed.

"It was like that day after day. We learned to depend on his intervention in divine affairs, and it made us forgive him for the awful stink, particularly when we took communion and accepted holy wafers from his hand. But by this time he was no longer able to walk at all, even to take a single step without falling. Each day Joaquin Masga, who had become the sacristan, carried Father Juan Pons back and forth from the convent to the chapel, and with Brother Timoner or me, would help him to the altar, one of us on either side, nudging his legs into proper position and positioning him as securely as we could before the altar, and we would carry rugs and towels to place under him to soak up the fluid that seeped from his legs. He could stand there without help as long as he held on to the altar, but sometimes he would forget and let go and almost fall, but we were always able to catch him.

"Well, that's the way things stood right up to the time that we learned that war was approaching and even surrounding us, and we began to feel the panic and hostility and suspicion of our Japanese friends. Up to then the Japanese civilians had been respectful of us and our religion. They had even made it possible for us to build the fine convent and chapel that still stand as war ruins in the Tatachog area. But sometime in the spring of 1944 (probably March 17 or 18, 1944) a Japanese officer, accompanied by a Rotanese policeman who acted as interpreter, entered the convent unannounced and confronted poor Father Juan Pons lying on a couch in his living room. We know what happened then for a dozen or so of us had gathered at the back door of the convent to listen, and every so often Brother Timoner would slip out to give us the details. He told us that the officer looked kind of sick when he first came into the living room and smelled the bad odor, but then, drawing himself up, he became very stern and ordered Father Juan Pons to leave at once so that soldiers could clean up the convent and holy chapel and make them into barracks for the troops. Father Juan Pons lowered his head humbly as if he had been beaten and did not reply immediately, and the officer very angrily repeated his order several times, each time louder than before. It was an insult to the Father and to everything we believed in, and I, had I dared, would have rushed in and hit the officer (though for that I would have been beheaded then and there and without ceremony).

"Father Juan Pons, Brother Timoner helping him, raised himself to a sitting position, lifted his hands and prayed just as he had done so many times when we petitioned a miracle. But nothing happened, and Father Juan Pons, more depressed and ill than we had ever known him to be, said in a strange, weak voice, 'I can do nothing for you, my friend, for I am commanded by Heaven to remain here until I die.' And the officer, too indignant to reply, simply cursed him out, squared his shoulders as if on a parade ground and left.

"Several days later (actually on March 20, 1944) the officer returned prepared to evict our kind, sick priest into the jungle, but by this time Father Juan Pons had regained his composure and from his couch welcomed the angry officer as if he were a compassionate friend who had come to inquire about his health. Smiling gently he tried to reassure him and said, 'My friend, you must not worry, for in three days and with Heaven's consent you shall have this place and the holy chapel, for in three days I shall die. May the Heavenly Father bless you.' For Father Juan Pons it was a supreme moment of revelation and proof of faith, and Brother Timoner fancied that a spirit of glory filled the room. But the officer, only half-understanding him, said, 'Very well, I will allow you exactly three days to leave, but if you are not out of here by then, my soldiers will carry you out.' And shaking his head as if he suspected that he had been tricked into three more days of delay by a clever priest, he left.

"Three more days! Each day I went to the convent and found Father Juan Pons a little weaker than on the day before. At eight p.m. on the third day (March 23, 1944), Brother Miguel Timoner came to me, his eyes wet and red from crying, his voice breaking, and said, 'Come at once, the good Father is dying just as he said he would, and he asks for you,' and I went to his room in the convent.

"The smell was so overpowering that I caught my breath when I entered and could hardly speak. But Father Juan Pons recognized me and when I bent over him I heard him ask for water. I brought him a glassful and helped him drink it. And that was all until 9 p.m. when, once again, he whispered for water, and again at 10 and 11, but at 12 o'clock—at that very moment, just as he had promised the military officer—he died.

"Then I said, 'Miguel Timoner, my good friend, we have a very sad and painful duty before us, for we must prepare Father Juan Pons' poor, punished body for burial.' 'Yes,' I said, 'even his terrible legs which have killed him and are now stinking, yes, we must properly wash and clean them.' And Miguel Timoner, rousing himself to the task, said in sudden bewilderment, 'But I smell nothing, the horrible smell has gone away! The air is clean!' And so it was, for suddenly there was no smell in the room whatsoever. I could not believe it so I pulled the bedclothes back from Father Juan Pons' legs and they were normal and whole, sturdy and intact except for some slight scarring. We looked at each other and fell on our knees for we knew we were witness to a very great miracle. But nothing else happened. There was no sudden wafting of marvelous, sweet and holy perfume through the room as some people maintain who were not there, nor was there a breaking of celestial light about us. There were just the two of us bending and praying over Father Juan Pons' marvelous, intact and sturdy legs. And when we got up from our prayers we were no longer sad as people are supposed to be when a loved one dies, but jubilant and happy and filled with the bliss that had radiated from Father Juan Pons when he had said to the military officer just three days before, "My friend, you must not worry, for in three days and with Heaven's consent, you shall have this place and the holy chapel, for in three days I shall die. May the Heavenly Father bless you."

"Brother Timoner asked me to fetch Benafacio Estebus to help in preparing Father Juan's body, and I did. Then the three of us prepared his body for burial and dressed it in the finest priest's robe we could find, for to us this had become an occasion, not for mourning, but for celebration. And in the morning many Chamorros came to pray at the side of his casket that we had made for him, and to marvel that all foul odors had disappeared. And that afternoon Brother Miguel Timoner said a proper prayer for him and we buried him in the new Tatachog cemetery."

Corbiniano Ayuyu, coached now and then by his wife, continues for he has more to say of subsequent, related events.

"Yes," he says, "the Japanese were prompt and were in the convent the very next day, and in the chapel wrecking the statue of the Holy Mother Nuestra Senora de Consalacion, throwing the statue of San Francisco de Borja to the floor and stealing the priest's vestments that Maria Masga Santos had been so carefully pressing and keeping in order. I slipped into the chapel as soon as they left and rescued the fallen, undamaged statue of San Francisco de Borja which I hid in the jungle. But the statue of the Holy Mother was ruined: there was her head broken from her body with the hair torn off, and one hand (the left hand) which had been broken off at the wrist, but the legs, the arms, and the right hand were missing. So I took the head and the left hand and hid them in the jungle.

"From then on I could hardly bear to look at the ruined chapel and rarely went back to it, but my wife did. Now let her tell her part of this story."

"I came to the chapel many months later," Francesca Ayuyu began, "long after Tatachog village had been bombed by the Americans (June 11, 1944) and the roofs of the chapel and convent smashed, and we had been forced to flee to the mountain to find caves to live in. It was probably in January, 1945 that I came down one morning to get water out of the cistern that you can still see by the ruined convent. My baby Guadalupe, just eleven months old was tied to my back. [Guadalupe Ayuyu, now a school teacher, was one of the few infants to survive this period]. There we were, just the two of us with no cover over our heads, when an American plane came over at treetop level shooting at anything that moved. I was terrorized and ran to the chapel, not that it could give us protection for the roof had been bombed off long before, but because I remembered it as a holy place. So there in the roofless chapel I bowed to the floor and prayed. By that time jungle weeds had grown up through the broken floor, thick and tangled, and as I bent my head through them almost to the floor I saw, just a few inches from my face, the other hand of the Holy Mother. I kissed it and prayed some more and suddenly I was no longer afraid for me or for my baby. So I went back to the cistern, got a bucket of water, and climbed back up the mountain carrying with me my most precious possession of all time: the right hand of the blessed Holy Mother. I gave it to my husband who hid it with the other holy fragments until finally we found time to construct a crude wooden structure for a body onto which we attached the precious head and hands, and dressed it as best we could. And that is the statue of the Holy Mother that stands so proudly and serenely in our large church in Songsong village . . . except that the crude body we had made of boards has been replaced by a proper one carved in the Philippines."

"Were there other wondrous events?" I asked the Ayuyus, "Yes, many," said Corbiniano Ayuyu. "Take this one, for example. It was a true miracle, we believed, and we gave credit to the dead Father Juan Pons.

"For us on Rota the war began June 11, 1944 when American planes first bombed Rota and neighboring islands preparatory to the invasion of Saipan four days later. Then the military officers ordered us to leave our damaged, now-dangerous Tatachog village and find whatever shelter we might in caves or under overhanging rocks up in the mountain. This we did promptly but with loathing because we knew that mosquitoes up there would make our lives unbearable. We prayed to our dead priest to protect us just as he had once protected us against droughts and rough seas; and he did, for we cannot remember seeing a single mosquito up there until after the war when they returned in full force.

"And there was another thing," said Francesca Ayuyu, "that had to do with the priest's elegant robes that my aunt, Maria Masga Santos, had sewed for him and kept in a closet in the chapel. The soldiers took all of them and tore them up to wrap around their hips as lava lavas. And it was a fact that everyone knew: these sacred materials gave all who wore them a severe, persistent itch as punishment for their disgraceful behavior, and whenever we saw a soldier scratching his hips or his crotch, we knew that he had been desecrating one of Father Juan Pons robes."

Corbiniano Ayuyu was eager to speak again: "Shortly after the Americans came I was working on Francisco de Borja's statue, cleaning it up, when two American soldiers came upon me. Apparently they were looking for Japanese stragglers for they pointed their guns at me and yelled, 'Are you a Japanese or a Chamorro or an American?' 'Cha-Cha-Chamorro,' I managed to stutter. Then they looked at the statue, acted ashamed of themselves as if they had been caught yelling in church, crossed themselves several times and left.

"And one final event that I can think of this evening," he continued. "It goes like this: After the war I worked as cook for the US military, and I and my family had a house not far from the big Tonga Cave. It was ramshackle just like most other houses on Rota at that time, except that in the center of the living room the statue of the Holy Mother, that we had saved, stood on the table, now dressed in the finest yard goods we could find. She stood there surrounded by candles that we kept burning day and night just as is the custom in our religion. At that time a very bad typhoon swept over Rota destroying almost every local-made house except ours and doing it no damage except (while we were in the Tonga Cave seeking shelter) upsetting the candles which set fire to the table cloth under the Holy Mother, but the fire touched her not at all, not even scorching her fine robe. And we have been asking ourselves ever since: why did this happen, why was our ramshackle house spared, why did the fire do no damage? Was this another miracle?

"Now the Holy Mother stands in our church in Songsong village, but most people have forgotten the proud story that goes with it, and do not ask themselves such difficult questions.... But it's getting late," Corbiniano Ayuyu said, yawning, "so let us finish this discussion some other evening."

That concludes the conversation with the Ayuyus. I then wrote to a friend and well-known historian in Truk (Chuuk), Francis S. Hezel, S.J. of the Micronesian Seminar. Father Hezel sent me documentary material from church records from which I have inserted data into the story by the Ayuyus. In addition he furnished the following pertinent facts of Father Juan Pons' life prior to coming to Rota: Father Juan Pons was born March 26, 1867 in the town of Manresa, Spain, near Barcelona. He entered the Society of Jesus on June 22, 1892 and was ordained as a Jesuit on February 2, 1911. For almost ten years he was rector (superior) of a college run by Jesuits in Zaragoza, Spain, and then volunteered for the new Spanish mission in the Carolines, coming to Truk in 1921 where he became superior of the Mission, traveling extensively through the Carolines, Marshalls and the Marianas. He spent a couple of years in Saipan (1935-37) and then went to Rota (1937) where he remained until his death on March 23, 1944. Father Hezel states that at one time plans were made for sending him to Japan as a medical referral but the war prevented this and the Japanese refused to let him go.

EXECUTION OF BROTHER
MIGUEL TIMONER (SEQUEL TO A ROTA SAINT)

An account of Father Juan Pons' ministry and death should not close without mentioning the fate of faithful Jesuit Brother Miguel Timoner for he was executed several months after Father Juan Pons died. Prudencio Hocog tells me that Brother Timoner (Frater Michael Timoner as he signed his name in church records) moved out of the convent following the priest's death, into Francesco Songao's house in Tatacho village and was there on June 11, 1944 when American bombs first fell on Rota. At that point all Tatacho village residents were ordered to leave the village and seek refuge in mountain caves. Two refused: Brother Timoner and Ignacio Dela Cruz (Chala). Both stayed on in the vacated village, which, of course, raised Japanese suspicions of them and they were watched. Brother Timoner was seen waving a white towel at an American plane which was enough to incriminate both of them as spies and they were both executed. Here are some of the details of Brother Timoner's execution: Corbiniano Ayuyu says: "There I was on the way to Tatgua where the executions were to take place. My hands and arms were full of oranges that I had just picked while I was waiting for the execution group. When it arrived, all of them, a Chamorro policeman (whom I won't name), Brother Timoner, Ignacio Dela Cruz (Chala) and four or five Japanese hechos'. Brother Timoner tried to stop to speak to me but the policeman kept pushing him along. Even so he managed to stop long enough so that I could see he was crying, and for him to say, 'My good friend, my best friend, give me two of your oranges to take with me to my death to comfort me and to remember you.' I managed to pass a couple to him, and on he went."

And this story from Carlos Calvo who spoke to an Okinawan who had met the hechos' coming from the execution, heard their excited account of the event, and then followed them up to Japanese Headquarters where he saw the hecho' who had executed the two 'spies' undergo a ritual purification ceremony in which salt was rubbed over his shoulders.

Details of the execution itself come from Emilio Inos, Rotanese patriarch. Now I am interviewing him in his home. He has no additional information on the sequence of events that led up to the executions; but the details of that tragedy are as crystal clear to him as if they had occurred yesterday, for he heard the story first hand from the man who had executed him. On that day Emilio Inos was working as usual digging a tunnel in the Tatacho area when his bossman, Hecho' Koyama, returned from the execution he had just performed and the ritual of purification that cleansed his soul. Koyama was excited and pleased with his performance and proudly drew himself up as if he were going to address an audience. "A number of us hechos' were there and we all volunteered to kill him for we all hate spies. But I was the one who was chosen and honored to do it. So we stood the first spy, who was some kind of priest, up in front of the grave we had dug for him, and I aimed my gun at his heart and pulled the trigger but nothing happened. The damned gun wouldn't shoot. So I aimed it at the sky and pulled the trigger and it shot like it was supposed to. So I aimed it again at the spy, pulled the trigger and once again nothing happened. By this time everyone was laughing at me and I got mad and threw the gun on the ground, grabbed my sword and ran with it and jabbed it into his chest. But that didn't kill him either. He just sank down on his knees and looked up at me and said in the funny way he tried to talk Japanese, 'My friend, it hurts.' By that time everyone was laughing and making me feel ashamed, so I grabbed his face, threw him to the ground, put my foot on his head and chopped it off with one, clean blow. Then everyone clapped and shouted respect for the way I had done it."

Emilio Inos speaks little English and Richard Manglona, recent high school graduate, was my interpreter. He was as eager as I at uncovering this testimony, and sometimes would leap ahead of me in his eagerness to reconstruct the details of those nearly forgotten, often proscribed years. Once he asked Emilio Inos, "Were you alone when Hecho' Koyama told you this?" "Oh no", Emilio Inos replied, "there were the two of us who were working in the tunnel at that time. The other man's name was Renaldo Manglona." . . . "My God," gasped Richard Manglona, "he is my father and he never told me this. I didn't even know that he worked in a tunnel or had anything to do with the war."

OFFENDED ANCESTORS

Is there anything truer than truth? Yes, legend.
This gives eternal meaning to ephemeral truth.
—*Nikos Kazantzakis*

What a way it must have been to live on this island at a time when phantoms outnumbered human beings: phantoms that took on human (or any other) form whenever it pleased them; phantoms that could be heard rustling in the dark corners of your house while they watched your every move; phantoms that moaned and wailed like forsaken souls in banyan and nunu trees; mischievous phantoms; phantoms who could pinch and torment and even create sheer catastrophe for those who trespassed into their special jungle living quarters.

Inconsolable and bitter were those phantoms, and, from their point of view, for good reason, for their once-loved-and-trusted children had betrayed them by adopting foreign Spanish beliefs. History was unfair to those ancestors and there developed a true 'generation gap' that has persisted ever since the first Jesuit Father set foot on this island. On one side of the gap are stern, offended, demanding, unforgiving 'first ancestors', the *taotao monas*, thousands of them in phantom form dating back to the first Chamorro; and on the other side of the gap are their few two thousand, living, unrepentant island descendants.

This is the way life went on for most of the last three hundred years. Unfair to the outnumbered survivors? Yes, but even so, a clever Rotanese who learned the ways and weaknesses and conceits and favorite haunts of the *taotao monas* could outwit them and even profit from the encounter. A few fortunate Chamorros developed enduring friendships with some of them, thereby becoming *gai taotao* (possessed ones)—actually the village representatives of friendly *taotao monas* who had forgiven the ancient betrayal and were seeking reconciliation. There are no *gai taotao* on Rota today but Ursula Atalig's mother, whose name was Rosa Maratita Hocog, was a respected one with unusual mystic powers for she could command the services of four (three males and one eunuch) friendly *taotao mona gachongs*. [*Gachong*: intimate Chamorro friend.] She could lean back leisurely in her chair, call for a banana, confidently reach out her hand and grasp a special ripe one from an unseen *taotao mona gachong* attendant; or she could command all four of them to help build a house next door—at night, of course, so they would not be seen. Once she commanded them to appear in human form before her four daughters. Ursula was too frightened to look at them, but her three sisters watched their apparitions closely and reported them as being human-like, of average height and color, and fully clothed so that they were unable to determine which one was a eunuch. Curiously, her mother spoke to them in Spanish rather than in Chamorro.

These were some of the advantages of being a *gai taotao*. But there were disadvantages that her mother had to endure; for instance, whenever she tried to enter the church, phantom hands reached out and pulled her away from the door; and she, by her *taotao mona gachongs'* injunctions was never able to charge money for the time she spent organizing and supervising the work they performed for her neighbors.

All *taotao monas* were easily offended and woe betide a careless person who offended one, for there was no forgiveness, and from there on that *taotao mona* became obsessed with evil (*taotao tiamulek*) and constantly plotted the careless person's destruction.

But those days when phantoms dominated life on Rota are gone. *Taotoa mona* are diminished and have become an endangered species. Now they are seldom encountered by anyone but hunters who trespass their few remaining jungle sanctuaries (reservations?). Acculturation is hard on phantoms, especially on ones that will not change their ways. This is sad for it is now only through nostalgia that one can reclaim the reality of those times when destiny could be comprehended and sometimes controlled through the grace or malevolence of one's ancestors. Those were perilous times, mystic times, almost sacred times, and they have become a heritage that gives strength and identity to those who are born and reared on this island.

But historians have shied away from those chaotic, formative years and have never documented them. You ask, "Is it too late to do so now?" and I answer, "Almost, but not quite, for there are still a few elders on Rota who are eager and competent to recreate those times, as they knew them, so they may be recorded; so let us waste no time and start our first interview at once.

Ursula Atalig, Gerald Calvo, and I are sitting in the Office of Aging: Ursula, a strong, determined woman, spokeswoman for the elderly on Rota, and passionate in her convictions—she could have been an actress, a poet, or an artist had she been born where such arts flourish. Gerald is the young administrator of the Aging Program, articulate and meticulous about facts, and he is a sensitive translator. I need his skills today for I speak no Chamorro and Ursula is uncomfortable with English.

Ursula speaks: "I was born Ursula Hocog in 1909 right here in Songsong village. This was during the weak German administration five years before the Japanese took over. My father died when I was one year old and I was reared by my godparents, Badomero and Maria Mendiola. Gerald

Calvo, here, knew them because they were his grandparents. The first event that I will relate occurred in 1917 when I was in the first grade. Songsong village was then almost like an ancient Chamorro village for only a few Japanese had arrived by then. I can remember that the Japanese *honcho* (governor) had a substantial concrete office about where the mayor's office stands today (1985), and that there were a few concrete Japanese homes scattered through the village, but the rest of us lived in simple frame structures with thatched roofs. My godparents' house was in the Sasanhaya section of Songsong village at the foot of the hill below the Japanese *honcho's* office and across the road from where the Rota Dive shop now stands, and behind the Rota Dive shop location was a grand old kamachili tree, a tree that may have outdated Songsong village by many years. That Kamachili tree, the road down from the *honcho's* office, and my godparents' house are the landmarks I want you to keep in your mind's eye for this is the area that became enchanted one night and for part of the next day.

"One evening about seven or eight o'clock my godmother handed me a water jug and told me to take it to our neighbor, Juan Mendiola, and fill it from his water tank. The moon was full and shining and I wasn't afraid as I would have been had it been dark. At the corner of the yard I met my 25 year old sister, Maria Hocog, who welcomed me kindly as she always did, and told me to leave the water jug in the yard and go with her. Since she was older than I, I knew I should obey her and together we walked up the road to the *honcho's* office, sometimes holding hands and speaking to one another as we were accustomed to doing. I don't know why we went up to the *honcho's* office for we did nothing there but open the door to a tool shed, look at its contents, and then turn back down the hill, though maybe I was experiencing my first wave of enchantment for I questioned nothing. We didn't return to my godparents' house but turned to our left at the bottom of the hill and went under the spreading branches of the kamachili tree. 'We will spend the night here,' my sister said, and suddenly she had in her hand a beautiful, intricately made sleeping mat that I had never seen until that moment. She unrolled it on the ground and we lay down together and went to sleep, certainly she did, but I was awakened every so often by my godmother's voice from across the street begging me to come home, but I paid her no mind and never answered. That seems strange to me today for I was an obedient child and never before had disobeyed her. It was as if I had been struck on the head and was only partially conscious, or like a person who has been stunned by a vision.

"At daybreak when I woke up, my sister was gone and so was the beautiful sleeping mat, and I found myself sitting on the ground in the same area; but now six strange plants were arranged so as to form a perfect circle around me, each one rising from a carefully tended mound of sea-shells, and each supporting a large red blossom that seemed to be bowing to me. I couldn't keep my eyes off of them because I had never seen any-thing so beautiful in my entire life. But then, even as I was admiring them, I heard men shouting up on the hill by the *honcho's* office, sometimes call-ing my name, and soon I could see them marching down the hill. Vicente Masga was leading the way and he held a crucifix high in the air as if he were leading a Christian army against infidels. When the men saw me they yelled, 'She is here, we have found her' and came running toward the kamachili tree. And at that very moment I could feel lively motions all around me: the plants with their red blossoms and mounds of seashells were whisked away, and a hand that I couldn't see but could feel grasped me and carried me to the trunk of the kamachili tree and stuck me to it so firmly that I couldn't have moved even if I had tried, but I didn't try for nothing worried me and I simply sat there as if this was what I was sup-posed to be doing. The first men who reached the tree's trunk tried to pry me loose and pick me up, but they couldn't for I had become part of the tree trunk, and they hastily stepped back in alarm, realizing that they had en-tered an area of magic—that is all but Vincente Masga and Justa Hocog. Vicente Masga placed the crucifix that he had been carrying against my chest, murmured an incantation, and I was released and able to stand up. Justa Hocog embraced me and picked me up in his arms. All the men shouted with amazement and marched triumphantly with me across the road to my godparents' house. But the spell still dominated me. I could walk and keep up with them, but I couldn't speak, and I simply didn't care what was happening.

"Almost everyone in the village had assembled in the front yard where they were preparing to start an island-wide search for me. When my god-mother saw me she rushed to me, picked me up in her arms and carried me to the center of the crowd, all the time crying out, 'What happened to you, where have you been?' But I couldn't answer and became sullen because I didn't want to answer. Some of the neighbors became so upset by my be-havior that they became hysterical, and one of them, Maria Goigue Songsong, screamed to my godmother, 'Beat her, take off your holy belt and beat her hard because she is possessed and has evil spirits in her. O beat her until she screams and the evil spirits fly away.' And my godmother did just that. She unbuckled her holy belt from around her waist and struck me several times as hard as she could. It hurt worse than any pain I ever had but I didn't cry. Instead I threw my arms about her and kissed her, for the numbness in my head had disappeared and suddenly I felt like a normal little girl. It was a wonderful feeling that I shall never forget and it made me feel grateful for what my godmother had done... and I began to talk. 'I went for a walk with my sister, Maria, last night,' I said, 'and we slept under the kamachili tree'...but I got no further for there was my sister, Maria, standing in the crowd and screaming, 'No, no! I didn't do it! I wouldn't do a thing like that. No, not to my little sister whom I love. O Ursula, speak the truth. I was just as worried as everyone else and that's the reason I came to search for you.' And then my real mother joined us. She hadn't been worried and she came now just to see what was going on. She kissed me and calmly told my godmother, 'You must not beat her again with your holy belt because she has been in no danger and there have been no evil spirits in her. My *taotao mona gachongs* love her and have been with her all through the night. Even if she had been absent for a month you shouldn't have worried for they would have been walking with her, talking with her and caring for her every need. And you must understand that my daughter, Maria, had nothing to do with it for she was with me all night and knew nothing about it even though one of my *taotao mona gachongs* took on her shape and one of her dresses.' That relieved the tension and all went back to their daily chores just as if nothing had happened.

"Then my godmother (not my real mother since she was a *gai taotao* and couldn't enter the church) took me to Father Rodez who blessed me with a rosary to cleanse my soul of demons that might still be hiding there. He said to me 'Hereafter you must wear a rosary at all times, for demons that have once found your soul will return to it again and again.'

"And I have followed his instructions and have worn a rosary ever since; see, I am wearing one today even as I speak to you." Ursula hesitated a moment and then continued, "No, that is not quite right, for once I failed to wear it and suffered pain for my failure. This was when I was a young woman and had gone to Tatagua beach to hunt sea crabs. I wasn't wearing my rosary that day and when I saw a large sea crab scuttling along the beach I chased it to a rock which stood protectively over a small freshwater spring. The sea crab dove under the rock into the spring. Hastily I pushed the rock aside intending to grab the sea crab and put it in my sack. But I didn't, for there beside it was a large black, slimy creature that I had never seen before and that seemed to be protecting the sea crab. This frightened me so that I replaced the rock and went home, but even as I was replacing the rock I felt a tingling run up my left arm and change into a pain that stayed there. When I got home I applied local medicines to my arm but they did no good, neither did the medicines and massage that the *surihano* [medicine man] gave me. This went on for three months when suddenly, without much thinking about it, I knew that I should pray to St. Anthony for his divine help. I went directly to church, lighted candles in his honor and knelt in silent, intense prayer, and there, even as I prayed, I felt the mystery of St. Anthony's presence and knew that I should return to Tatgua beach and seek out the sea crab and the *taotao mona* that been protecting it and apologize for my rude behavior. So I went directly from the church to Tatgua beach and to the rock that sheltered the sea crab and its protector. This time I moved the rock courteously and as gently as I could, and there were those two same creatures, the sea crab and its *taotao mona* friend, just as I had seen them three months before. I apologized to them and felt so ashamed of my behavior that my voice quavered. Over and over again I promised that never again would I trespass into their area. And even as I spoke to them my pain subsided and then disappeared entirely. That was a lesson I've never forgotten, and I've worn my rosary ever since."

Ursula has finished with her stories and I, having just lived with her through the anguish of those times (or so I thought) lean forward and with quavering voice say, "Ursula, those were terrible times to have been born and raised. You were brave and strong to have lived through them and to be with us today." But Ursula, touching my shoulder to calm me, said, "No, no, that is not what I've been telling you. Those were wonderful times. We were content and happy in those days because we knew just what to do and how to keep out of trouble. Father Rodez told us, our Japanese bosses told us, and, of course, our *taotao monas* kept us up to date on their rules. And when we did get into trouble we knew what we had done wrong and never did it again. We had solid, dependable rules to go by, and it wasn't at all like today when everything keeps changing without reason. Yes, if I could have my way we would still be living just about as we did when I was young."

TALE OF TWO TAILS
First Tale

Prudencio M. Manglona, the oldest man on Rota, was born in 1903 during German occupation, missing Spanish times by only five years. He lived through Japanese colonial rule and the war, and on through Trust Territory preceptorship and into Commonwealth times to become a true Rota patriarch. One son is now (1990) the Mayor of Rota, one son is the Lieutenant Governor of the Commonwealth, and a grandson is a Senator of the Commonwealth. All told, there are now 42 of his descendants living on or near Rota. How better, then, can one learn the personal details of those nearly-unrecorded, important times than by speaking to him?

He is still an active person—tall, spare, erect and handsome…and if subsistence living were still an issue as it was most of his life, he would now be spending most of his days and many of his nights hunting or fishing, or tending his cattle and hogs and crops on his ranch.

But times have changed, and so has he. I see him walking about the streets of Songsong village silent and distant, solemn and contemplative. And that was the way I learned to regard him—that is, until I asked him about *taotaomonas*. Then everything changed. Suddenly he became a happy, exuberant adolescent, maybe 18-years old, who was inviting me to come join him in the orderly world of his youth where there were no distractions from living the life one had been trained to live—nothing, that is, except when a vindictive taotaomona sought to ruin one's day. . . . Here is how Prudencio M. Manglona learned about taotaomonas in his first amazing encounter with one that disliked a cow.

Now we are sitting in the living room of Prudencio M. Manglona's house in Songsong village—Prudencio M. Manglona, Gerald Calvo, and I. Gerald had arranged the interview and would act as translator. Mr. Manglona speaks: "As best I can remember, I must have been about eighteen years old when this incident with the cow and the *taotaomona* occurred. I was living with my parents in Songsong village. I was just a kid, of course, but I had finished three years in the Japanese school for Chamorros, and after that I had been working as a man on our farm, and hunting and fishing. But I didn't resent being put to work so early —especially when the work involved hunting as it does in this story that I am preparing to tell you.

"One day our neighbor, Jose Camacho Atalig, whom I respected and often worked with, came to me and said, 'My mother is having a novena this week-end and I must go into the jungle up by Dugi to hunt wild pigs and maybe, if I'm lucky, to kill a wild bull. Will you go with me?' 'Of course,' I said, and rushed home to get an old cow to ride on, and a machete and several hunting dogs; and the two of us set out, both riding our female cows, Jose Atalig leading the way. The trail from Songsong village to the Machong area was well-marked and our cows followed it naturally, but the trail from Machong on to Dugi was seldom used and our cows had difficulty following it. Much of the time it was so overgrown by jungle that it could scarcely be seen and heavy branches spread across it so that we could not sit upright on our cows.

"'We must get off and lead the cows,' Jose Atalig finally said. 'We can't see the trail and the cows can't see it, but the ancient landmarks are still visible to me and they will lead us to Dugi just as they led our ancestors.' But just before we got to Dugi we came to the area called As Nieves where hundreds of small papaya trees grew and covered the ground with a thick carpet of their leaves, so thick that we couldn't have seen a trail even if there had been one. I remember the area well for I still lie awake many nights trying to recreate that scene and the event—perhaps the most important single event of my entire youth—that occurred there and that I will now tell you about.

"So there I was leading my cow and following Jose Atalig's cow through this open space carpeted with papaya leaves. And it was there, right there on almost level ground that Jose Atalig's cow stopped and refused to move forward. I heard Jose speak softly and encouragingly to the cow, but nothing happened and then he started shouting at it and jerking at its rope and kicking at its front legs. 'My son,' he finally shouted at me, 'nothing will make this cow move. Take your rope, double it up and whip her sides.' And that is exactly what I did. I doubled my rope and whipped her as hard as I could on both sides. Here, watch me and I'll show you how it went." Prudencio M. Manglona, right there in his living room, acted out an event that had occurred 60 years ago about 10 miles from there. "Now I'm the old cow. See how I've got myself all hunched-up and grunting and trying to go forward but getting no where but acting like I'm really trying to pull something. Then see me, an 18 year old boy, standing up behind the cow and whipping her on both sides with my doubled-up rope, really laying it on and yelling at her each time I whacked her.

"Then see what happened! Suddenly there's nothing holding her back and she lurches forward and almost knocks Jose Atalig to the ground. Then look at me. Now I'm standing there back of the cow with my mouth open, all confused until I look at the ground behind the cow and see her tail lying there, pulled loose and smeared with blood. I look at the cow's rear end and see the rest of her torn tail still hanging there and bleeding.

"'Something's pulled your cow's tail off, right here in front of me,' I yell at Jose Atalig. 'Something I can't see, something that doesn't make sense. And I didn't do it,' I cry at him, 'I couldn't even if I was that kind of a guy for I've let many cows pull me up a hill with their tails and nothing ever comes off.'

"And he, crossing himself, said, 'Jesus, Mary and Joseph, something awful is happening here.' And becoming very solemn he drew himself up as if he were a priest and said, 'Lords of the Woods! O Lords of the Woods! What have we done to offend you? Don't be angry with us for coming here for we are not going to play tricks on you. We came here searching for food just as you, our ancient ancestors, once did and in this very spot. O forgive us.'

"He stood there for a moment, listening intently. I heard nothing but he suddenly appeared reassured and said to me, 'We can go now. Our *taotaomona* ancestors are angry but not at us. We are safe. They are angry with the cow and have punished her by pulling off her tail, and it will be safe for us to go on; in fact, they may even be willing to help us find a hog.'

"And they did. That's exactly what they did, for it was only about 75 feet further on that the dogs found a hog, ran it down and held it while we killed it and tied it onto the back of my cow—not on the back of Jose Atalig's cow because that one was acting as if it had become sick, and it kept on acting sick for the next week."

Second Tale

I am Leon Inos Taisacan. I have spent my entire life on Rota and I am now 50 years old, but when these events occurred that I am about to tell you, I was 25 years old. Emillio Atalig Inos, my uncle, now dead, who is the leading character in this story, would have been about 52 at that time.

These were Trust Territory days, happy days of subsistence farming, though my uncle supplemented his farming activities by working in the Department of Agriculture and I supplemented mine by teaching fifth grade classes in the school. These were times when to be Rotanese meant that you were part of the very island itself and not just a person who happened to live on it. Then each one of us represented Rota, it's history and its hopes, and felt responsible for its successes and failures.

We led sturdy lives and respected one another and our traditions. I had my own farm which I worked on regularly, but I enjoyed going with my uncle to his farm to marvel at the way he could foretell how crops would mature, or when cows would give birth and he would make these forecasts by noting the phase of the moon. "This cow," he would say, "will have a calf two days after the full moon." And at least 90 percent of time he would be right. I could never understand how he did it, but I thought that if I watched him closely enough I'd be able to do it too. So often times I was at his side when he was at his farm at the border of As Nieves and Gampapa areas.

One Saturday morning my uncle and I stood at his pasture fence while he called his cattle. All five cows came promptly, including a bull and a pregnant, black Angus cow. My uncle looked her over carefully, checking her udder and her sides and said, "She will deliver on full moon which is tomorrow. We must return and check the calf right after Mass tomorrow morning."

So right after Mass we drove to Machong and then on to his pasture. My uncle called the cows just as he had done the day before, but only four came, the pregnant cow being absent.

"See," he said triumphantly, "the cow has delivered just as I predicted and is staying with the calf."

So we climbed the fence and started searching the pasture and found nothing until we came onto an ancient latte stone that was hidden among a group of trees. The latte stone column was intact and stood about five feet high, but the cap had long since been displaced and lay on the ground. It was an unnerving site for us to come onto for the black angus stood despondently beside the holy latte stone cap as if mourning the dead calf which lay on it covered with blood and torn placenta.

We approached the calf cautiously for the cow had been dangerously protective of her three previous calves, but this time she did nothing. So we checked the calf and found it was cold and stiff as if it had been dead for some time. Then we examined the cow and found nothing until we came to her rear end and found that there was no tail, that is, nothing but several inches of dried-up stub-end tail that was smeared with dried, clotted blood.

"Some neighbor must have done it with a machete," I ventured.

My uncle thought for a moment and said, "But he couldn't have done it by just standing out there and whacking at it in mid-air; he'd have had to hold it against a rock when he did it." So we searched the latte stone, both the pillar and cap, to find where they might have been chipped by a machete but we could find nothing. Then we started searching for the tail. We spent hours searching over every square meter of pasture, but we couldn't find it, nor any trace of blood that might have been splattered on the grass. We kept on looking, hour after hour, until late in the afternoon, for, if we couldn't find the tail and evidence that it had been chopped off with a machete, we knew we were in trouble.

"If some human being didn't do this then a *taotaomona* did it," my uncle said, lowering his voice to a whisper for the area had suddenly become very quiet and alarming. "This is *taotaomona* country and right over there about a mile from here is where a *taotaomona* pulled the tail off of Jose Atalig's cow—right there while Prudencio M. Manglona was watching. And, of course, we all know that latte stones are sacred to *taotaomona*."

My uncle began to shake and I whispered, "Maybe we'd better get out of here," but my uncle said, still whispering, "Yes, but not until we've made peace with the *taotaomonas*, for they're watching us and listening to everything we say. I can feel them slipping around us."

And he drew himself up like a Holy Father might do, faced the latte stone pillar and said in a loud voice: "O Great First Ancestors who guide our lives and tell us what we should do and not do, we respect you and your wishes. This ancient latte stone, we know, is sacred to you and must never be disturbed by either man or cow. This cow should have known that and deserved having her tail pulled off and her calf killed. We beg your pardon, Great Ancestors, and we will now bury this calf and clean up the latte stone and leave this sacred area in peace and in your care."

And that is the end of the story about the calf, but not about the cow which we moved to another pasture so she couldn't possibly have another calf on the latte stone cap; and then we gradually began to forget the *taotaomona* incident, save when preparing for a fiesta or novena, when someone would suggest that it was about time to butcher the black cow, but then some of us 'old-timers' would remember the tail problem and say, "No, we had better wait another year."

This went on until after my uncle had died and my uncle's grandchildren, who may never have heard the tail story, went to the farm, slaughtered the old cow and brought her carcass back to the village, cooked it and served it at a fandango.

My wife and I were suspicious of the meat, thinking that it might contain the spirit of a *taotaomona* and we watched people carefully as they ate the tough meat from the poor old cow to see if any one choked to death, but none of them did, so I made several attempts to help myself to the meat, but each time I tried I became nauseated and felt the same terror I felt up there on my uncle's farm when I knew that taotaomonas were watching me and probably blaming me for something I hadn't done.

And that is the way I learned about taotaomonas and how we, if we are to live contentedly on Rota, must respect their jealous and contentious ways."

INTRODUCTION TO WAR YEARS ON ROTA
(Pacific Islanders Recollections of WWII)

Introduction (Mortality-Rota; Effects of War)
Rota, many people will tell you, was a safe place to be during the war. Historic battles, almost too dreadful to be remembered, were fought on all sides of it, but it somehow remained an island of serenity, a sort of privileged sanctuary, even though it was at the epicenter of a great war's holocaust . Or, so they say, citing the fact that there was no invasion of Rota and that no World War II battles were fought on it, as they were on nearby Guam and Saipan. "Oh, a few bombs were dropped here," an informant may tell you, "but only in target practice (not anger) as planes were being lightened of their bomb load prior to landing on Guam; and, of course, gunners sometimes practiced their strafing skills on Rota citizens and their buildings." But if your informant is a young Rotanese, he may add at this point but without a trace of bitterness and as a sort of footnote that you are not expected to remember, "Though my parents did tell me that my brother, an infant, starved to death."

It is footnotes such as this one—not the apologies—that tell the true and awful story of those years. But such isolated, unsettling footnotes must be confirmed, so look further. Look for data that is objective and that can be measured; for instance, go to Rota. San Francisco de Borja Church records of deaths during those years that were recorded, not at the time for there was no priest on the island during most of the war, but later when bodies were exhumed from wherever they had been left in the jungle and reburied in sanctified ground in 1946 or 1947. Look at those immaculately maintained church records, compile the names into lists, count them, and, if you are at all scientifically committed, record your results on graph paper, though I warn you, you will be frustrated on your first try, for the 1944 and 1945 deaths peak to such heights that they will go quite off the graph paper you had intended to use. And you will be shaken by a new concept about war and the way it destroys, for here is powerful, objective evidence that deaths *per capita* on *uninvaded* Rota surpassed those of its *invaded* neighbor islands. And in irony you will be forced, just as I have been, to understand that invasion, though terrible during the days or weeks or months it may last, nevertheless brings resolution and surcease to the agony of such a cataclysm. Had it occurred on Rota it would have brought an end to enemy military occupancy that had panicked into near insanity and sought refuge in barbarity and savagery as if these were safe 'caves' to hide in. But during the prolonged siege that was Rota's World War II fate, there was no escape, not even into sudden death provided by enemy gunfire…and its population sickened, and died slowly by starvation, never for a moment sustained, as in an invasion, by visions of heroism.

THE PIT: ACCEPTED CHAMORRO VERSION

Most Rota citizens who lived through the war have put those tragic years aside as if, by a simple act of forgetting, they would be purged from their lives. Mention the Pit and you will see the same recurring look of disgust—disgust with you for having forced them to recall it. But not when you mention it to Manuel Ogo who was personally involved in the drama of the Pit. An act of friendship—an almost heroic act of friendship meant to save him from death in the Pit—now transcends all else and is the memory he most cherishes. He sits in the office of Rota's Program for the Aged, alert, lithe, smiling, and eager to take me back 40 years to that time of exhaustion and despair, of chaos and panic—there to meet Katashi, now long dead. Katashi had been a young Japanese soldier-cook, stern and militant, rule-book enforcer and rule-book breaker, and cruel at times, but who became his trusted friend and confidant and gave him information that would have saved his life had the disaster of the Pit materialized.

For Manuel Ogo the war started not on December 8, 1941, with Pearl Harbor and the fall of Guam, but sometime during the first half of 1944. In January, 1944 there were only six Japanese soldiers on the island, and, except for some disruption of its shipping lanes, Rota continued to function as it had become accustomed under a beneficent Japanese occupation—that is as a miracle of industrial achievement.

Citizens took for granted the five-story sugar refinery (turned liquor distillery); the extensive mining operation with its huge aerial transport across Rota's vast mountain top (its Sabana) and down its 1600 foot cliff to an elaborate storage and ship-loading facility; its well-organized, self-sufficient agricultural fields tucked into every arable space; its thriving salt and charcoal manufacture and export; its efficient narrow-gauge railroad which hauled sugar cane and other freight as well as passengers all the way around the island. An old photograph shows a passenger bus as large as a freight car passing along a busy street in Songsong village, that makes one think of Boston in the nineteenth century. But perhaps one should choose some pleasant, quaint Japanese city with which to compare it, for Chamorros, early in Japanese occupation, had all been moved to Tatachog, a strictly 'native', ghetto-type village created for that purpose three miles north in the jungle. Only Japanese were allowed to live in Songsong village and enjoy its amenities. This was before the term 'Apartheid' had been invented and no one seems to have regarded the move as inappropriate, or as any more racist than required by the immutable verities of those happy, prosperous years.

Manuel Ogo, with his family and neighbors, had been moved to Tatachog and there he was hired by a private employer to boil down sea salt for export. He was content with this arrangement and he did not know that a war was going on elsewhere in the Pacific until early 1944 when these things occurred: The Japanese military presence increased from just six soldiers in January, 1944 to 4,000 by late spring; a military airfield was started at the site of the present airfield and completed and in full operation by April; six large cannons were placed in several positions judged to be of tactical importance, along with a number of small artillery pieces, their barrels aimed toward the sea; machine guns appeared in profusion, and poked their muzzles from the mouths of caves; naval, shore and air units appeared and took up their battle positions; armored ships and armored planes came and went.

There were already four thousand Japanese civilians on the island. Add them to the military and you get eight ,thousand individuals who expected to be sustained by the bounty of Rota's subsistence economy. What were the logistics for fulfilling this responsibility? Theoretically, as viewed by Tokyo's supreme command, they were not too bad, for, by military count there were 186 able-bodied Chamorro men of proper age to undertake this task. But actually there were only 26, also by military count, for 160 of them had been sent to Saipan, Tinian and Guam on various work details. And of these 26 men only a handful were actually assigned to food production, the others being ordered (for military necessity and panic soon ruled all decisions) to help prepare the extensive fortifications that were never to be used. And for the first time in Rota's long history food became scarce.

"We all lost weight," Manuel Ogo recalls, "even the Japanese who, of course, had first claim to the food that was produced." Thus, the war was first perceived by Manuel Ogo and all Chamorros as a long, inescapable hunger pang.

But late in the afternoon of June 11, 1944 another kind of war came to Rota. This was the afternoon when American planes bombed Guam, Rota, Tinian, Saipan, Pagan and Iwo Jima preparatory to the invasion of Saipan. It came with a roar of exploding bombs that destroyed Rota's airfield installations and parked planes, and the roar of bombs being dropped indiscriminately over the entire populated island, including Tatachog village. Tatachog residence fled into the jungle, for, to them, this was the true beginning of the War in the Pacific. At this moment their lives were forever changed.

Now, for the first time Japanese military personnel (who seemed to have become almost as anti-Chamorro as they were anti-American) took full charge. They rounded up the Chamorro men who were regarded as deserters for having fled into the jungle, disarmed them of their machetes and knives, and put them in jail at Songsong village—that is all who could be crowded into its limited space. The others, including Manuel Ogo were forced to lie on the ground nearby while armed guards threatened them with drawn swords. Others, still hiding in the jungle, were summarily scheduled for beheading—a schedule that, when announced, caused them to surrender at once.

The next day all Chamorro men were presented with an option: stay in prison forever or go to work under military discipline, full-time, no pay. All accepted. First, though, they were given one day to find their families and move them about five miles up the mountain to the Akodot area (now the site of the Atalig betelnut plantation) into caves they might find or under the shelter of overhanging rocks. Then the men were brought back to the military camp at Tatachog and divided into work crews, each under an armed Japanese supervisor or honcho. None were permitted to visit their families and they worked seven days a week from sunrise to dark.

Once each week, representatives of their families were called down so that food, when available, could be distributed to them. Otherwise the families lived on the wild yams and roots and berries they could find, and on African snails (though several persons died before it was discovered that snails should be starved for a week to render them safely edible), and jungle breadfruit when it was in season.

For them to return to their ranches and butcher a cow or hog or chicken was illegal, for such resources were reserved for the military and the hungry, Japanese inhabitants of Songsong village. Chamorro workmen grew so gaunt and weak that sometimes they could scarcely recognize one another. "It was kind of scary," Manuel Ogo told me, "for sometimes meeting our friends seemed like meeting ghosts." The milk of nursing mothers dried up so soon after birth that nearly all nursing infants starved to death, there being no milk from other sources. Every child, beyond infancy, became malnourished and sickened and many died. Manuel Ogo had three children: a daughter, Solidad, born July 24 during the height of military panic. She survived for several months (longer than most infants) and died of starvation on Nov. 20, 1944; one son, Ricardo, aged 2 years, died Nov. 1, 1944; and another son, Salvador, aged 5 years, died August 8, 1945, just one month before peace was declared. They were all buried hastily, without benefit of religious ceremony, in shallow jungle graves.

Though the Chamorro men were demeaned as traitors for having fled to the jungle with their families, they were not to be deprived of the glory of defending their island, and each one was ordered to equip himself with a sharp bamboo spear which he was to keep constantly at his side so that when invasion occurred he could join in a banzai charge that would repel the American invaders. "And we believed that we could do it," Manuel Ogo said, "and sometimes under direction of our *honcho* , we practiced our attack on imaginary hordes of American barbarians coming through the surf, who, if we failed, would surely cut off our ears and our tongues and who knows what else—for that was their purpose in coming to Rota, so we were told and so we believed."

At this point we must interrupt events as they were revealing themselves on June, 1944 and insert information on the Pit, for that is the subject of this chapter. You can see it today just as it looked 40 years ago at war's end: an inconspicuous hole in the ground near a great bamboo thicket in an area called Sakaya which is about one-and-a-half miles from the former Tatachog camp site. It is seven feet in diameter and carved with remarkable precision to about the depth of a tall telephone pole. Inconsequential in appearance and undocumented by official records (not in Japanese or US military records, nor in Trust Territory or local government accounts), it is now a threat only to deer, stray cattle, and clumsy hunters; and it takes a determined intellectual effort for a visitor to look at it and see in it the horror of genocide and of extinction. But those who survived the war remember it clearly and with loathing and are haunted by it just as Guam citizens are haunted by memory of the infamous Merizo Massacre and its cave.

Now Manuel Ogo picks up the story of the Pit, carries us back with him 40 years once again and continues:

"Juan Manalo and Francisco Quichocho were ordered to dig the Pit. They started in June, 1944 and continued without letup through bomb and strafing attacks (for they could dodge and hide in the bamboo thicket) right through the periods of greatest famine, right up to the very day of surrender while American planes were dropping leaflets all over Rota to explain that honorable peace had come. They worked on it almost as if they were crazy or were being driven by someone who was crazy."

"Sometimes we would sneak over there and watch them work—one of them at the bottom of the Pit hacking away with his hammer and chisel as if his life depended on it, and usually coughing, and the other hoisting rocks, bucketful by bucketful, to the surface. 'What you digging this crazy hole for?' we would ask them, and they would stop working just long enough to say, 'The soldiers tell us it's for water but we know there's no water in these dry rocks. They tell us not to talk about it and to keep to ourselves. And also, they tell us we're behind schedule and must work faster if we don't want a beating'—and at that they would start working again, faster than ever for they were scared for having stopped to talk."

"We knew that a similar pit was being dug in the Uyulan-Hyulo area where many Chamorro and Okinawan work crews lived, and that maybe another was being dug somewhere up on the Sabana, though we never knew much about that one. Sometimes we gossiped with each other about these pits, but not too much, for many things, even stranger, were going on. For instance, the tunnel we were digging under Tatachog village and the ones that were being dug under Songsong village and in Ginalangan and Tatgue and Agusan and Machong etc., and we just had to accept the fact that the Japanese officers knew what they were doing, and that they were meant to save us from having our ears and tongues cut out by the Americans—and it wasn't until some time in August, 1944 that I learned the real purpose."

Manuel Ogo was first assigned to a work crew that spent its 12 hour work days and its 7 day work weeks, stringing telephone lines from one military post to another, all the way to the airport. They assisted Japanese soldiers who were uprooting pengua trees by the hundreds, roots intact, and dragging them to the beaches where they were placed so that they could be mistaken for anti-aircraft guns. These were his jobs until December, 1944.

But Manuel Ogo's mind, much of the time was on his family, for his wife was eight months pregnant when the family moved up to the Akodot cave, and his two sons were ailing. Once he saw his wife standing in line waiting for several handfuls of food she was to get, obviously near term but so shadow thin! "How can she nurse the baby when it comes?" he asked himself? That night he and three companions slipped away from the camp and stole breadfruit from a tree hidden in the jungle, and tramped with it up the mountain. But they were caught by a Chamorro neighbor who had been elevated to supervisor. "He didn't beat us as a Japanese supervisor would have done," Manuel Ogo recalls, "but he took the breadfruit from us, saying that it must be distributed equally to all, though we knew he was lying and that this was his way of keeping himself fat."

Solidad Lizama Ogo, a mere shadow of an infant, was born July 24, 1944 and, to everyone's surprise, managed to survive until November 20, 1944, a very long time, for death had become the fate of nearly all infants born during the war and usually occurred within days or weeks.

Soon after the baby died the Chamorros were once again relocated. This time it was to an area of similar caves and overhanging rocks near Sokayo. Why Sokayo? Well, for one reason it was closer to Tatachog, just one mile up the mountain side from it, and well hidden in the jungle, and for another reason: it was near the Pit!

Coincident with this move, Manuel Ogo was assigned to a work crew that had responsibility for digging a tunnel under the Tatachog military camp in which all soldiers in the area could hide, and from which they could defend themselves. The work was brutal and painful, for the tunnel was being hand-chiseled inch by inch through solid rock; and it demolished its workers in short order, for the coral dust suffocated them and brought on uncontrollable attacks of coughing and wheezing and breathlessness. The heat in the tunnel was intolerable and the pressure for haste unrelenting.

But this is where Manuel Ogo met Katashi. This is where the story of this improbable friendship begins, continues, and ends. He waits impatiently to tell his story and now, given the opportunity, tells it (in Chamorro, interpreted by Gerald Calvo) with gusto and high spirits, acting out many incidents, and laughing at his own performance. Here are his approximate words, though often the sequence has been rearranged and phrases restructured for the sake of clarity, and phrases inserted that are meant to express the emotions of situations that he created so vividly in pantomime.

"Yes, as I was saying, on Rota during the war the most useful and sometimes the best friend one could have was a Japanese cook. Katashi was cook for the Tatachog Military Camp and he was my friend; in fact, I considered him to be my 'gachong' [most intimate Chamorro friend] even though he knew no more than ten Chamorro words and we always spoke in Japanese. Since there wasn't much food to cook in those days, Katashi had additional duties: he was bossman (honcho) over us who worked in the tunnel, and, because he was a good climber and the officers trusted him, he had responsibility for climbing the largest banyan tree in the area to spot American planes that might be heading our way to unload unused bombs on us prior to landing on Guam. Also, since talk among the Japanese officers was all about the expected invasion, his job was to spot and evaluate the intention of American ships that were beginning to come into our area. So he was often with his officers and heard them discuss their worries and plans, and sometimes, after we became friends, he would tell me what he had heard.

"At that time friendships between Japanese soldiers and Chamorros were illegal and severely punished, even by beheading as another soldier/cook by name of Noman almost discovered, and would have if he hadn't stolen a canoe and escaped to Guam. So how could one become a friend of a Japanese bossman who knows he's tough and wants to show that he can get more work out of his crew than anyone else?

"Well, here is how it happened to me. 'Workman Manuel,' Katashi ordered me one afternoon, 'Go down tunnel and find how many buckets of rock need be carried out.' I did what he told me and reported back as, 'Soldier, there are only two full buckets of rock.' That was all I said, but he jerked me forward with one hand and with the other started slapping my face, first on one side and then on the other, 'Don't call me Soldier, stupid Chamorro dog. I'm not Soldier to you! I'm Honcho! Hear that! Honcho! And he kept on slapping me until somehow I got knocked to my knees so I must have looked like I was begging for mercy. Then he stopped, whirled around, squared his shoulders, and marched to his kitchen as if he had the build and power and persuasion of a sumo wrestler (which he didn't, for he was a skinny kid like me, and about my age which was twenty three). I might have kicked him had I dared try, but for that I would have been beheaded, there, then, legally, and without anyone paying much mind.

"I hurt all over, my face swelled up and turned black and blue, and I was trembling so I could hardly stand, but I got up and brought the two buckets of rock out of the tunnel. I can't remember now if it was that evening or the next that Katashi walked up behind me and slipped some food into my hand. He did that for several evenings in a row, then one evening he slipped me twice as much as usual and said, 'That's for your wife. Take it to her.' 'Not me,' I replied terrified at the idea, 'I'll get caught and whipped.' 'No danger,' he said, 'I'll see to that.' So I asked him to come with me and he did, and together that night we climbed up the mountain to a space that was sheltered by an overhanging rock and not large enough to be called a cave, but which began, from that night on, to seem like heaven. For there was my wife beside me, and here was Katashi, all smiling and feeling good, and with more food than we were used to and the girl from the next cave got to coming over and became Katashi's sweetheart . . . though that meant, as time went on, that Katashi had to steal more food and that we had to carry more food up the mountain, for now there were four of us to feed.

"Sometimes Katashi stole a bottle of Rota-manufactured liquor from the soldier's mess (actually distilled in Rota's sugar mill that had been converted into a distillery) and the two of us would get drunk together just like friends are supposed to do. Sometimes we carried up the mountain fish that Katashi had dynamited on the reef. And that was the way this gachong business got started and the way it continued right up to the very moment Katashi was killed . . . his head blasted off by an American bomb after he had unloaded sweet potatoes from a truck and was preparing to take his turn up the banyan tree to watch for bombers.

"Actually it was not long before his death that Katashi risked his life for me. It was then, late one afternoon when I was alone in the tunnel carrying out the last bucketful of rock, and coughing while I was doing it, that Katashi came into the main tunnel, hesitated a few moments, cleared his throat nervously, and began, 'Manuel, my friend'—which seemed strange for usually he didn't speak that way until we had started up the mountain—'I want to talk to you. You are coughing too much on this dusty job and I'm going to change you to making salt down on the beach. I'm doing this for the sake of your health.' He cleared his throat several more times, looked over his shoulder, listened carefully for sounds of anyone who might be listening, and continued, 'I will do something else for your health, something, in fact that will save not only your health but your life. But first, as my most trusted friend, you must promise to keep it secret between us, for I would be killed for telling you, and you would be killed for knowing about it.'

"I promised that I would tell no one, thinking that it had something to do with dynamiting fish and carrying them up the mountain. 'This is it,' he said, whispering so faintly in my ear that I could barely hear him, and standing so close I could hear his hard breathing and could feel his heart beat against my arm, 'When the Americans attack us, this is what will happen: all Tatachog work crews and all their families from up the mountain will be called together to meet at the Pit. That is when you will all be shot and thrown into the Pit. Maybe I'll be one of them who has to do the shooting. That's what the Pit is for. That's the craziness that our officers have, and what they talk about when they are alone and scared. They want you out of the way when the fighting starts, and they don't want anyone left on the island if they're all killed or must sacrifice themselves. When you are called to come to the Pit, hurry up the mountain to your cave and take your wife and my sweetheart to the deep jungle and stay there until the war is over. But don't tell the women beforehand for the women will talk and we will both be killed for it. This, my friend, is what I have to say to you. I go now. If I die, remember me for it, but while we live let us never speak of it again, even to each other,' and he bowed to me in his most formal Japanese way and left—though on the following night we climbed the mountain together just as we were in the habit of doing and continued to do until the very night before he died."

Sequence and time and place have no meaning for Manuel Ogo when he tells a story, and he transports his listeners effortlessly from war years to the present and back. Today Gerald Calvo and I are following him through the rubble that was once Tatachog Military Camp, but now so overgrown by Rota's waste jungle that I, if by myself, would pass through it without suspecting that here were enacted events of intense human interest. But not Manuel Ogo! Though he had not visited Tatachog since war's end, it takes him only a false start or two before he heads briskly through the jungle, his machete slashing a path for us . . . and suddenly we are following him through the 'well-ordered' streets of Tatachog Military Camp. Now I see the camp clearly through the jungle's deep shade of tangled lianas, boulders, ferns, and trees heavy with epiphytes—and with loathing, 'this stark, efficient, hungry, immaculate' military camp surrounding us in the sun!

"Here," says Manuel Ogo, "is entrance to the tunnel I worked in—right down these rock steps—but watch your head if you go into it, for it's small at this end which is an emergency entrance for the kitchen crew, but at the other entrance down by the coral pit, it's so large that all the soldiers in this camp can hide and sleep in it.

"And here is Katashi's kitchen," he says, pointing to a demolished foundation that is scarcely visible beneath thick moss and dark overgrowth, "and see the special cups and dishes Katashi used for special guests," as he unearths pieces of shattered Japanese porcelain, some of them exquisite—and, to my surprise, a metal spoon made in Japan. "And here is the tree I stand behind waiting for Katashi to steal food from the kitchen, that we will carry up the mountain tonight. And here beside the kitchen is the pile of sweet potatoes Katashi has just unloaded from a bull cart. Yes, he's just unloaded them and he's walking toward this tall banyan tree (it's gone now but it stood right here) to climb and take his turn as lookout for enemy planes. Yes, he is at the foot of the banyan tree now, all of 50 feet from the sweet potatoes, when (right now) a black bomber comes in so fast and low and mean that no one sees it until it's right overhead and drops a bomb—square on the sweet potatoes which disappear as if they'd never been there. And somehow, though he's 50 feet away, a rock, or maybe a piece of the bomb, flies at Katashi and smashes his head off.

"I come running up from the beach where I've been making salt and see him with almost no head left on him and see him being carried away on a stretcher, and I see the bull that brought the sweet potatoes thrashing about on the ground and bellowing and dying.

"That was the end of Katashi, and almost the end of my story. . . .But how did I feel about seeing my best friend killed like that?" Manuel Ogo asks himself, "Oh, I was pretty sorry about it at the time, but maybe no sorrier than I was when I couldn't find a piece of one of those sweet potatoes, not even a piece of sweet potato skin to chew. But once the war was over and I got well-fed, then and ever since I've been feeling terrible about it, and wondering how come I didn't say a proper prayer for him.

"That's the way we were then. That's the way people anywhere get when all they can think about is how to stay alive until next week, and are scared and hungry all the time. Yes, we even stole food from each other and didn't get too upset when some one starved and died. We were even told by our honchos, 'It's OK for you to steal but don't get caught doing it for then we'll whip you.' That was the way I felt in December, 1944 when Katashi was killed, and it was the way I kept on feeling right up to the day the war stopped. Every month I got hungrier and weaker and less concerned about others. Some days I walked around like I was dreaming or a ghost, and can't remember much that happened."

This statement of Manuel Ogo surprised me, for in my files I have a detailed Japanese military assessment of nutrition on Rota during the war. This states that the greatest hardship from hunger occurred during the period from September, 1944 to January, 1945 before food production had been increased by the four hundred Japanese civilians who were then impressed into work crews to produce an abundant crop of sweet potatoes, and to harvest coconuts and mangoes and bananas and African snails—snails that 'providentially' and for just such an emergency, had been introduced prior to the war into Rota gardens to feed and multiply. The military account regarding its nutrition program ends on a happy note: Though the attempt to store sweet potatoes ended in failure, the spoiled potatoes were used for production of shochu, a rough, low-grade liquor. Thus, one success in a multitude of failures.

The war is not yet over for Manuel Ogo, at least not so long as we are walking with him through his reconstructed Tatachog Military Camp, and he says, "Let me show you where I make salt, and he led us down to a stretch of beach where great boulders of coral stand up like totems in the shallow, narrow lagoon, save for one narrow entrance through the reef where ocean currents have made a tortuous channel among the boulders and finally lap on the beach itself.

"Here is where water comes in pure from the ocean, and this is where we collect it to pour into these vats that stretch from here to there," he said, pointing to an empty space, "and which we keep fires under to boil the sea water down to salt, just the two of us, my coworker and me. We keep the fires burning just right and scoop the salt out when it's finished or else it'll start popping and sort of exploding and getting ruined. And that's just what happened the last day we worked at it, for a fighter plane picked us out as something special to shoot at.

"Watch me now and I'll show you how things went. I have a bucket of sea water on my shoulder and when the plane comes at us I toss it one way and dive the other way under this rock. So does my friend. We peek around the rock and see the plane wheeling around and heading for us again. "Scrunch down,' I yell. And each time we start to get up to tend the vats, the plane comes roaring back at us and spraying the place with bullets.

"We can hear the salt popping and exploding in the vats but can't tell which are from the fire and which are from the bullets, but we know that we'll have some explaining to do for letting the salt get ruined. And when the plane finally leaves for good and we get up to look at the vats we see that they are shot full of holes and will never be any good again.

"And it isn't long after that I am here trying to patch up the ruined vats when many American planes come over, one after another, mostly following the beach road right over there where it leads to the airport, and dropping sheets of paper written on in Japanese, that get blown every which way, some into the woods, some into the ocean, but most of them staying right on the road. "Don't touch that stuff, it's a trick' we yell at each other. But nothing happens and some people are beginning to come out of where ever they've been hiding, and some of them actually risk picking up the papers and reading them and then looking happier than I've ever seen anyone look, at least during the last two years.

"Now I see a sheet of paper on the ground right in front of me beside the salt vats, and I start to pick it up but a Japanese soldier rushes out of a bush where he's been hiding, knocks me out of the way, and picks it up, reads it without acting the least bit interested, and does the only practical thing he can think of doing: he rolls it carefully into a cigarette and smokes it just as if a good smoke is what he needs now that the war is over.

ALBERT TOVES AND THE PIT

War as experienced on Guam and Saipan, never came to Rota, and the history of the devastating siege that substituted for invasion has never been written. Events which were once livid and specific and horrible have sometimes faded in Rota's collective memory of the war until they are scarcely discernible from folklore, and the contradictions that are beginning to cloud the accounts have become sources of angry disputes.

No better example to illustrate this point can be found than among those who recall details of Rota's Pit (or Pits). In the previous chapter I stated the predominate recollection of the Pit that was dug in the Sakayo area. It was, according to that version, for the purpose of genocide, a place for throwing the bodies of Chamorros who were to be slaughtered outright at time of the expected invasion—this interpretation based on a warning whispered into the ear of Manuel M. Ogo by his trusted Japanese soldier-cook friend, Katashi.

But there is another version that stands solid in the memory of a Chamorro man who lived and worked sympathetically with the Japanese military, even to war's end: not genocide, according to his view, though just as mortal and brutal, but actually of noble and self-sacrificing intent. But let Albert Toves (Kondo Akira was the Japanese name he used then) tell the story for this is the drama of the Pit that he learned as it unfolded before his amazed eyes, and that he passionately believes and fiercely defends.

My first interview with Albert Toves, my eventual friend, got off to a poor start, and after fifteen minutes or so of futile questioning he stood up and indignantly refused to continue—Albert Toves, this Rota Chamorro patriarch whom I had seen occasionally in Rota's Songsong village but had rarely spoken to. "Yes," he said, "I know about the Pit but I disagree with the stories you've been hearing and I'll have no part in spreading the lie that the Pit was just for the purpose of killing Chamorros. True, it was for killing, but there was a war going on and killing is what a war is all about. Unless you can put yourself in the position of my military friends who believed they were failing in their duty, failing to save 4,000 Japanese civilians and 800 Chamorros from hunger and probable torture and rape and death by American barbarian invaders, unless you can put yourself in their position you have no right to judge them. I ask you who were the nobler ones: the six taichos (district military commanders) who voted for the Pits to be promptly used, or the two taichos who effectively vetoed their use? You, of course, will say the two who vetoed it, but I, who was there and heard all their arguments and saw them shake and tremble and lower their heads as they cast their votes…I still don't know.

"They were all my friends and some of them still are. See this letter," and he showed me a page of scrupulously written Japanese Kanji script, "that I have just received from Eiichi Saito in Japan, one of the two taichos who voted against the Pits. He writes to me regularly and comes to Rota once each year to show his respect. He is my friend and I will not allow him to be embarrassed and dishonored by lies." Then Albert Toves led me to his front door in preparation for me to leave; and Gerald Calvo, who had been translating for me and had arranged the interview, and I took our departure, beaten.

But only temporarily, for after several months' cooling off and reconsideration Albert Toves told Gerald that he would be willing to continue the interview so that his views, admittedly minority views, would be placed on record.

This time we are sitting about the dining room table in Albert Toves' new, modern house that overlooks Sasanhaya Bay, Albert Toves, Gerald and I. Albert Toves' Chamorro wife scurries about the adjoining kitchen to prepare lunch and two grandchildren are playing a rambunctious, noisy game about us, up and over Albert Toves, under the table, back and forth through all the rooms of the house, screaming and laughing, but he remains undisturbed as patiently he seeks, as a good stage manager should, to find ways for transfiguring this congenial family scene into the reality—the craftiness and cruelty and pain and panic and havoc—of a worn-out, failing war.

"We were different then and you've got to understand how we thought and acted. There was an official executioner who was kept pretty busy; but we got so we didn't pay too much mind to what he was doing, for terrible things were happening to each of us; for instance, my Japanese wife and our son and my Japanese mother-in-law!. I tried to save them from the expected invasion by putting them on a freighter to go back to Japan but it was sunk before it got past Saipan by an American submarine of the 7th Fleet and everyone was drowned; and there were deaths from starvation and malnutrition in almost every Chamorro family.

"But to start off I want you to know about some of the executions. First, there was my old uncle, Ignacio Manglona, 84 years old, mild-mannered and kindly and maybe a little senile. He had once worked on a whaling ship and had gotten a whaler's favorite design tattooed across his chest: a large heart containing an American flag. So far as I know that was his only crime, but that was enough to get him tied to a tree up near where Rota Hospital now stands, right out in the sun with a Japanese soldier standing nearby in the shade to see that no one brought him food or water. And in about a week he was dead. It was hard on me to walk by him and hear him beg me for a cup of water, 'Albert,' he would plead, 'for Christ's sweet sake bring me water, for sake of Christ on his cross, for sake of our ancestors...' but the soldier would threaten me with his sword and there was nothing I could do but explain to myself that this was the way things were and had to be accepted, just like you don't argue with earthquakes or typhoons—you just try to live through them.

"Then there was Ignacio Cruz, light-skinned Chamorro and a former seaman who had the same kind of tattoo on him, which was enough to prove that he was a spy and he was executed. Brother Miguel Timoner, who had assumed the duties of a priest after the death of Father Juan Pons, was executed as a spy for waving a handkerchief at an American plane. And Bonifacio Estebes! Poor Bonifacio Estebes! He was beheaded because he pretended that he could read a Japanese newspaper, which he couldn't for he, though in his late twenties, was retarded and could read nothing. But there he was pretending that he could read a Japanese newspaper at a time when death was the penalty any Chamorro had to pay who was caught informing himself of the war's failure. Did Bonifacio's younger brother, Sabino Estebes, try to defend him? I don't know, but, anyway, Sabino was beheaded at about the same time."

"Then there was the time I was almost beheaded, at least when I was scheduled for it. The Japanese were great on telephone communication and they were busy throughout the war stringing lines all across the island. Any place you looked up in the jungle you were likely to see a copper telephone wire. But they ran out of insulators so it became a patriotic thing for us, when we were off from out regular duties, to go out in the jungle to find empty sake bottles and break off their necks to take to the military so they could be used as insulators. And that was just what I was doing when a Japanese soldier (probably the only one on Rota who didn't recognize me, for, as I will tell you later, I had become well known and respected by the military) saw me searching through the brush, and arrested me for spying. 'Damn spy,' he shouted at me, 'We'll hack your damn head off,' and he rushed me, sometimes knocking me to the ground, to Tonga Cave for execution. His name was Tokugawa. The officer at the Tonga Cave was new and didn't know me either, and he sent for the official executioner who had gone to Machong for the day.

"Fortunately, at that time, I was cook and general helper for Hatori, the 'mayor' of Songsong village who, with all the other Japanese from that bombed-out village, had moved up to Ka'n near the present water tower; and, fortunately, he got hungry at about this time and came looking for me. But even his word was not enough and he had to send for five other Japanese to identify me and vouch for my loyalty. Then all of us—Hatori, four honchos (civilian administrators), a retired Buddhist priest, and I—went up to the big cave at Ka'an and got drunk together, singing, laughing, patting each other on the back, far into the night. True, though there wasn't enough food for celebrating, there was always enough sake and hawamore to make us forget the bad things that had just happened."

Albert Toves pauses for a moment. Perhaps he recognizes that the passions of war have entered his home and that I have become their helpless observer. Which was true. Then he continues, "I want you to know my background and how it gave me special rank during the war; for instance, how come I could get drunk with the 'mayor' of Songsong village, as I have just told you, at a time when social relations between Japanese and Chamorros were strictly forbidden, and Chamorros were strictly forbidden to touch liquor? So bear with me while I give the details.

"Like most Chamorros I have relatives on all the populated Mariana Islands, but I was born in 1913 on Saipan and lived the first years of my life there. I was a good student in the Saipan Chamorro school, and when I was 13 the Japanese Government selected me to go to Japan to complete my education. My name was changed to Kondo Akira and I was treated as a Japanese citizen. My sponsors were a Catholic Japanese family who watched carefully over my religious training and my education, even sending me to compete in poetry contests all over Japan. I was there for thirteen years, during which time I married a Catholic Japanese girl whose name was Aiko (in our Catholic family we called her Lucy) and we had a son whom we named Tomas. At age 27 the Japanese government sent me and my family to Tinian where I worked for the Kohachu Company as agriculturist. My work still stand there today and if you look down as you fly over Aguihan (Goat Island), just six miles off Tinian, you will see parallel rows of Australian pine trees that I and the crew I worked with planted as windbreaks for the sugar cane we grew and harvested.

"But my wife tired of Tinian and I asked to be transferred. That was in 1936, and we were moved to Rota where I was employed by a private company that grew and harvested castor beans. Here I was in charge of 165 families of Chamorro, Korean and Okinawan workers, and my pay was the equivalent of $2.50 a day which conformed to the standard salary for high-grade Japanese supervisors.

"My wife and I and our son and my mother-in-law lived in the company's office in Songsong village. All other Chamorros had previously been evicted from Songsong village and sent to live in Tatachog, a newly created, apartheid-type village on the way to the airport; but my credentials as a Japanese (my name, my Japanese family, my status as a supervisor, my good salary, my Japanese education) allowed me to stay on in Songsong, comfortably housed and respected...until June 11, 1944 when bombs first fell on Rota, and Songsong village was demolished."

"That was when the war began for us. It was then that the military took full charge, and those of us in civilian employment were hastily transferred to jobs (mostly menial jobs) that supported the military. All Japanese civilians moved up to the ridge on Ka'an (site of the present water tank), to find shelter in caves and under overhanging rocks. Castro bean cultivation was immediately abandoned and I changed from an important supervisor to cook for Hatori, the former 'mayor' of Songsong village and now the mayor' of these displaced Japanese civilians at Ka'an."

"I still maintained the status of supervisor because two Japanese women and one Okinawan woman worked under me in the cave that was our kitchen. But in addition to these prime responsibilities I took on other duties. One of these was to act as master of ceremonies for a troupe of twelve dancing girls who once-a-month traveled to all military camps on Rota to perform for the soldiers. Once, when we had given an especially lively performance at As Manila (Japanese military headquarters high on Sabana), Sentosirebo Imagawa, the highest ranking officer on the island, congratulated me warmly and gave me a bottle of American manufactured Scotch whiskey. But these performances were finally abandoned when increasing bombing made them too hazardous.

"The military organization, as I remember it, consisted of twelve or more taichos (field commanders) who served under Sentosirebo Imagawa whose headquarters, as I have just said, was at 'As Manila, on the highest point on Rota where it commanded a splendid view of the ocean in all directions, but it was not readily accessible to the taichos, so often times staff meetings were held at the entrance to the big cave at Ka'an, 'mayor' Hatori's home and my kitchen; and it became my job to cook for all of them. Usually I was there cooking just a few feet from them when they met—I at the entrance to the cave and the taichos sitting on a tree's great roots that sprawled across the entrance, the Sentosirebo sitting on the highest root not more than ten feet from me, facing his subordinates. It was in this way that I was able to keep track of the war and how it was failing on all sides of us; but I didn't need to listen very closely to know what they were saying, for just looking at their faces told me all I needed to know. It made me remember the signs that Japanese war-protesters used to put up along the highways in Japan that showed a ferocious fighting cock (America) shaking a tiny baby chick (Japan) to death, and that had words printed under it that said, 'a chick must not attack a rooster', but I kept my feelings to myself though I loathed the war, even at the start and all the way through.

"Well, that was the background for this last meeting of the taichos and sentosirebo at Ka'an which is what I've been getting ready to tell you about. By this time Saipan had fallen, Guam had fallen, American planes were spying and dropping bombs on us almost every day; warships were passing on all sides of us, and everyone expected the invasion to start within days. Not more than six or eight of the taichos were present at this last meeting as best I can remember, and they were a dismal lot with their long faces and short sentences and the embarrassed way they tried to keep from looking at each other.

"Sentosirebo Imagawa took charge in his usual brisk manner and described the military situation on the basis of the last night's radio dispatches. So far, so good, for this was just what I had expected to hear, but what followed came as such a shock that I couldn't even remember it very well the next day. But I think it might have gone something like this:

"Sentosirebo Imagawa: 'Gentlemen of the emperor's Military, we are as prepared to defend Rota against invasion as we can hope to be. For more than a year we have been busily constructing fortifications and developing our defense strategies, all with the constant approval and support of this staff…that is, we have had unanimous agreement on all plans save one, and that is the purpose of this meeting: to reach a decision about the Pits, to decide if and when they are to be used. This is the most painful decision we have been required to make for it involves not only our loyalties and devotions to the Emperor but also the lives of our families, but we must make this decision today. Our own lives are no longer important and each of us knows what to do with his life when our defenses fail. That is not the problem. The problem involves the civilians, and, of course, the local residents, all of whom must be protected against dishonor and disgrace even at the expense of our sacrificing their lives. As soldiers we know this and we know that at moments of supreme peril, noncombatants must not be allowed to interfere with our military efforts or drain our few resources. As you know, the Pits for water were started early in the war, one at Sakaya and two more at areas on the Sabana. When they failed to produce water we continued their excavations with the idea that they could serve as graves in case large-scale sacrifice of the civilian population should become necessary. We are now at that point and a decision must be made today, but I must warn you that for me to proceed with the plan, I can accept only a unanimous decision.'

"There was a long silence," Albert Toves recalls, "and I stopped cooking expecting to hear an exciting military debate, but that didn't happen for the meeting had turned suddenly into a funeral. One taicho, his voice trembling, asked 'But are we sure the Americans will act like savages?' And another, without raising his head, said, 'Yes, that is well established.' And another added softly and hesitantly, 'We are soldiers of the emperor, we must never forget that. Our allegiance, our loyalties are to him; our lives are his, so are the lives of our families, and death should come to us—to all of us—as a noble sacrifice. Death shall be our glory and it must not be profaned by the barbaric acts of savages. No, there is no alternative; we must use the Pits as we have planned.'

Others made similar speeches, all in hushed, painful voices. Only two taichos said nothing. They sat there just like the others in deep thought and sorrow—one of whom was Eiichi Saito, who eventually became my good friend. When the speeches were finished and Sentosirebo Imagawa asked for a vote, all voted for the pits to be used and used at once—all except those two taichos. All looked at them in astonishment, but they said nothing except to shake their heads sadly as if in pain; and Senosirebo Imagawa closed the meeting by making a formal statement that the planned use of the Pits as mass graves was canceled . . . and from the formal tone of his voice I couldn't tell if he regretted the veto or was relieved by it.

"But I did learn how Eichi Saito felt about it for, much later, he said to me, 'That moment! It was a terrible moment! I wanted to do the right thing and I would have voted for the Pits if I had known for certain that the Americans would commit atrocities, but Americans are strange people and you just can't tell what they'll do. What if, I told myself, they come and ignore all noncombatants or even treat them kindly . . . or would except that all would then be dead? I just didn't know, so I cast my vote against the Pits . . . and felt like a traitor.'

"And that was the way this whole Pits story ended. There was nothing more to it, and I'm telling it to you today because I want you to know that there was something about it—the way it was planned, voted on, and canceled—that I think we should all understand."

This interview with Albert Toves completes the information that I have been able to unearth regarding Rota's Pits. Though my two informants (Manuel M. Ogo, in the previous chapter and Albert Toves in this one) contradict one another emphatically on the motive for their use, they do agree (also emphatically) that Pits did exist and were for the purpose of mass execution and burial. Those who accept Manuel M. Ogo's story of intended genocide point to the similarity of this explanation with the mass execution of Chamorros in Guam's infamous cave at Merizo which, unquestionably was for genocide; whereas a minority of Rota citizens who accept Albert Toves' account and explanation point to the fact that there were comparable situations (Saipan's Suicide Cliff and Banzai Cliff) where humane and rational intents—even noble intents—went outrageously berserk under the stress of extreme tragedy. These two dissenting explanations we cannot reconcile, but we can say with confidence that the Pits were not wartime myths or fantasies, as some historians suspect, but must be accepted as historically validated fact of that terrible war that devastated the Marianas.

TO BE CHAMORRO

Several years ago, three of us, Dr. Dirk Ballendorf, George Anderson and I, under a grant from the American Association of State and Local History, completed a study of the impact of thirty-one years of Japanese occupation. The study was an effort to discover how those years of intense indoctrination may have—or may not have—changed a culture that was the amalgam of centuries of autocratic Spanish influence with sturdy ancient Chamorro amenities and loyalties and that had passed unscathed through sixteen years of careless German colonialism. The opportunity for doing this on a first hand, eye witness basis is disappearing as elderly Chamorros are dying off at an increasing rate and taking with them the stories of life during those formative years.

We analyzed these histories methodically and rigorously, and came to the conclusion—contrary to established conventional wisdom—that the cultural impact of thirty-one years of intense Japanese tutelage, both in school and in the work force, though temporarily effective, was evanescent, and that there is now almost nothing to show for those three decades of Japan's supreme effort to transform a culture—save for a few artifacts in the jungle. That study has now been printed and is available at the Micronesian Area Research Center at the University. In this study we tried to maintain strict, sometimes tedious, detachment; but here I can simply relax and marvel at the story-telling abilities of these Chamorro elders, and the faith and sardonic good humor they maintained through this period of exploitation. Here we can unabashedly celebrate the strength of an ancient cultural heritage that is now endangered, but that once strongly protected the people from acculturation and gave them solace and faith even as their world was being shattered.

Let us start with Ursula Atalig, as strong and determined and articulate today at 85 years of age, as she was as a third grader attending the newly-formed Japanese school (*kogakko*) for Chamorro children. She sits in Rota's Office for Aging and, in Chamorro, recounts events which occurred only several blocks from us, grisly events at the time, but that amuse her now as she relates them, and she laughs as she talks. Gerald Calvo translates.

"I was born in 1909 on Rota. My father died when I was a year old and I was raised mostly by my godfather, Batermero Mendiola; I started at the *kogakko* school when I was seven. There was another school for Japanese children, the *shogakko* school, but there were not many Japanese children on the island in 1916, and segregation had not become strict; for instance, Pedro Manglona, who now works in the elementary school, went to the *shogakko* school, and Zukamato, the Japanese *secho* [governor], sent his two children to the *kogakko* with us. I don't think that this was a satisfactory arrangement, for they played by themselves and ignored us most of the time. I didn't like them.

"I don't think our Japanese education, which went only to the third grade, was very good. We did learn to speak and read and write *katakana* [simple Japanese], and we learned addition and subtraction, but we were not taught multiplication or division at that time. Discipline was strict, and I consider most of it to have been good for us. Was I ever disciplined? No, not quite. Here is the story of how I *almost* got disciplined.

"One day when I was in the third grade, I came late. Saporo, the younger son of the *secho*, who was in the school with us, asked me why and I told him that I had been at Mass. "That's wrong,' he lectured me, 'because your God is not as important as our Emperor.' I argued with him, and he went home and reported me to his father, and the next thing I knew, Mr Uasaka, the teacher, told me to come to his house that evening and bring my godfather. We went there and found the *secho* and the teacher talking excitedly to each other. They told me to stay outside while they took my godfather in and started scolding him. Just then, Father Edward Rodez, our priest, came along and asked me why I was out in the street after curfew. I told him, and he thought about it for a moment and said, 'Don't worry, I'll stay here and watch out for you.'

"Then the *secho* called me in. He was sitting in a chair and holding a rifle. At first he scolded me in a loud voice. I don't remember what he said, but I am sure it was insulting. Then he pointed his rifle at me and said, 'I'm going to shoot you unless you tell me who said your God was more powerful than our Emperor. Your teacher has taught you that you must never lie, so tell me who it was or I'll shoot you right now.'

"This scared me, of course, but not as much as you might think it would scare an eleven-year-old girl because I knew the priest was there listening at the window. I knew the *secho* would shoot me if I refused to answer, and that he would shoot Father Rodez if I gave his name, so I said, "No one told me. My heart told me that our God is more powerful than any man, and my heart never lies.'

"At that moment Father Rodez came into the house. He was angry and told the *secho* he had no right to frighten me with a gun, and that he was ashamed of him. Up to that moment the conversation had been in Japanese, but then it switched to Chamorro because Father Rodez spoke almost no Japanese. The *secho* said, 'She has profaned the Emperor by saying that he is inferior to your God.' And then they got into an argument about religion. I remember the priest saying, 'When you go to Japan you see the Emperor's picture everywhere, and that's because he is a human being like you and me, but you will never see a picture of our God because he has no body but exists in all places: in heaven, on earth, in our souls, our hearts, our brains and our conscience.'

"This went on for some time. Then the priest said, 'If we are to live together in peace on Rota, we must learn to respect each other's beliefs, otherwise our God will punish you.' That seemed to quiet the *secho* down, and my godfather and I went home.

"But that's not the end of the story. Here's the way it ends and it's the part that I like best: Saporo, the boy who squealed on me, returned to Japan to finish his education and then he returned to work in the sugar mill. He was here during the war and had a leg blown off by an American bomb; and he was being treated for this injury in the Japanese hospital when the American military came and took over the administration of the island. This, of course, included running the hospital. Saporo remained in the hospital as a bed patient. One day I took lunch up to my daughter, Maria, who was working as a nurse, and on this particular day she was in charge of the ward that he was in. As I handed her lunch to her I glanced down the ward, saw him and I said, 'I know that man' and I marched right down to his bed and said, 'Saporo, do you know why you got your leg blown off?' He looked shocked and said that he didn't know why, and I said, 'Our God did it because you said that your Emperor is more powerful than our God.' Saporo apologized but said that he couldn't remember the incident. But I felt better than any time since the war.

"I was happy during Japanese times and I considered some Japanese to be my friends, though I had no social contact with any of them. When the Japanese military first arrived there were more jobs and more money. I had no objection to the soldiers being here except that they were too noisy. During the war times were tough for all of us, and two of my children— one nine years old and the other a year old—starved to death. Of course, we liked the American troops because they brought food and clothes and gave us jobs.

"You ask me what Rota would be like today if there had been no war and the Japanese were still here, and I answer by saying that things would be even better than they are now, for the Japanese would have been more ambitious about developing industries than the Americans have been."

Edward T. Dela Cruz, a high-ranking official in the Commonwealth of the Northern Marianas' Department of Natural Resources, tells his story:

"My father was Chamorro and my mother was Japanese. This was an ethnic combination that was intolerable to the Japanese on Saipan, so soon after their marriage they were exiled to Pohnpei. But after my sister was born they were allowed to return to Saipan without further punishment or harassment.

"I was born there in September of 1935. My Japanese name was Toshiwo Tamaoki. I went to the Japanese school which was called *kokumin kakko*. I liked school, but used to get into fights when I was called *tomin babaoy*, native pig. I was not considered Chamorro, either, and I got into fights with Chamorros. I fought everybody. I couldn't speak Chamorro until after the war because I was required to speak Japanese.

"During the invasion I lived in the mountains with my family. We watched the war from there—a sort of safe, privileged gallery—and we could see battleships shelling the island and airplanes bombing and strafing everything in sight, but we were in no personal danger. But all of us were immensely frightened and baffled when the American soldiers came, for there was my father running across the field toward them, calling to them in English and embracing and kissing them. None of us children knew until then that he could speak English, but he had been born on Guam, where he had learned English and also that Americans were not the ruthless barbarians they had been portrayed to us.

"Soon after that I started learning Chamorro and going to an American school. My father is dead now, and my Japanese mother has moved to California and has become a full-fledged American."

And here is Rudolfo Mundo, Rota's leading exponent and singer of its traditional Chamorrita songs. During the war he was a supervisor for the construction of the military tunnels that honeycomb subterranean Rota. Rudy is at his best when he is the lead singer in a hilarious Chamorrita songfest: he is also very good at recounting events such as this one:

"This happened when I was about twenty-five years old when I was on the way to my ranch to tend my hogs. As usual, I would ride my bike to the place where the road ended, which was near a little store, and then walk on through the jungle to my ranch. This time I met an ill-tempered

Okinawan man at the store. He looked me up and down, made an ugly face, spit in my direction and said, 'You Chamorro pig, you're a third-class nothing, a *santo-koluming*, and all I've got to do is pay the Japanese five yen and they'll let me kill you.'

"I tried to pretend I didn't understand him, and parked my bicycle and walked on to my ranch. When I came back I hoped that he wouldn't be there, but he was standing by my bike, and when I started to get on it, he knocked it to the ground. I couldn't hold back any longer, so I said, 'Do you really want to kill me?' 'I sure do,' he said and looked like he meant it. But he didn't look like much of a fighter, so I said, 'Go ahead and try me, but if you miss you'd better look out, because I'll get you on the first hit.' He struck at me, I dodged and he missed, so I let him have it several times and knocked him down all covered with blood from his forehead, which I had cut up pretty good.

"I knew that I had done something against the rules, so I went straight to the *secho* and told him what had happened and offered to pay him thirty yen to cover the Okinawan's salary while he couldn't work. But the *secho* said no, that three yen would be enough. I didn't pay him anything, but then the Okinawa brought suit against me, and I heard that he might sue me for five million yen, which seemed like a lot of money. That scared me—especially when the guy went to an artist to get a sketch made of the cuts on his forehead to show the authorities. So I went to the artist and told him I would give him a pig if he would give me the picture. This pleased him and he gave me the sketch. I gave him the pig, tore up the sketch, and that was that."

Maria Sablan Reyes, of Saipan, who died not long ago, was a remarkable person. An accomplished musician, she composed a chorale of singular beauty and complexity for the recent ordination of a Rota priest. She was born October 15, 1922 in a Saipan Chamorro family of intellectual distinction. But let Maria Reyes speak for herself, first of her education and later of her wartime experience.

"There was a merit system in our school in Saipan which, unfortunately, always placed me at the bottom. The system was as follows: Those who came to school and worked in the school garden from five to six in the morning were of the highest order. Those who worked from six to six-thirty were of the second order. And those who worked from six-thirty were classified as third order. My grandfather did not approve of the system and did not let me come to school until seven, shortly before the classroom activities started at seven-thirty. The teacher's argument for encouraging early morning work was that Saipan was a farming community and we must learn how to get up early and get to work on our ranches. Besides, he said, we would feel better and be more alert when we got up early.

"At seven-thirty all children gathered in front of the school to sing and do calisthenics and march and listen to an inspirational lecture on morals and good manners. This was called *choikai* and it included saluting the Emperor and reciting commandments of proper behavior which we were required to memorize. One of the commandments was to strive constantly for perfection and to do each job perfectly. This included saluting the teachers in a stiff, prescribed manner, and we were trained to act all times as if we were soldiers on a parade ground.

"Much of our time was spent in learning Japanese and memorizing the vocabulary. We were also taught to write Japanese. In the first grade we learned *katakana* , in the second grade we learned to write *hiragana*, and in the third grade we were introduced to a smattering of *kanji* [increasing grades of complexity of Japanese]. Memorization was the way we learned: multiplication tables were mastered rapidly, and we memorized geography and Japanese history. I thought the manner of teaching was good, very conscientious and thorough. Most of us learned willingly.

"Discipline was strict, not only in school but also in the way we behaved outside of school. For instance, we were told that we must keep a picture of the Emperor, or at least a scroll of *kanji* that proclaimed the sacred state of the Emperor, in our homes, and that we must bow to it each morning. Teachers came occasionally to our homes to check on this and to ask us if we bowed. Actually, I didn't bow very often. My father thought the idea was silly.

'You can bow if you want to,' he said, 'but I'm not going to do it.' So I learned to lie about it when the teacher asked me. Also, the teachers would ask us if we bowed to the Shinto shrine when we passed it on the way to school, and even assigned student monitors to check on our bowing.

"By the time the war was imminent, the military took over our lives and all our activities. It took for its own use an auditorium next to the convent. The soldiers, becoming increasingly suspicious of the Spanish sisters, came to inspect the convent one day and to tell the sisters that all of their letters must be written in Japanese so they could be censored. The sisters were terrified and so I became the spokeswoman on the inspection tour.

"In 1934 everyone, including the nuns were told to leave Garapan. The soldiers changed the convent into barracks, and I went with my family to our farm, thus terminating my ambition to become a nun. It was there on the farm that I spent the rest of the war.

"Our safety there, however, was more threatened by the Japanese than by the eventual invasion, for my father, probably because he was educated and had many books—some in English, came under suspicion as a spy. Soldiers came to our farm, searched it, discovered the books and arrested my father and me. Why did they arrest me? Because I possessed and played an old-fashioned reed organ. The soldiers had never seen such an instrument and decided that I was using it, or would use it, to transmit my father's spying messages to the Americans.

They took us to their headquarters and interrogated us, and threatened my father with a bayonet and slashed the skin on his neck. They released me in twenty four hours, but kept my father for a week, constantly threatening his life. And they dismantled my reed organ in an effort to prove that it was some newfangled subversive devise.

"And what are my reflections now, some forty years later? How do I weigh the value of the educational system and the consequence of our intense indoctrination? Unquestionably, we learned more rapidly than students do now. I believe that kind of personal discipline that was drilled into us was good for us and our society. Compare the delinquency and the terrible crimes that are now occurring and you must see that something good has gone out of our system. Compare the manners of average citizens then and now, and you can see the difference; or compare the stability of our family life then and now, and you must admit that children today are being reared and educated in ways that do not produce a happy, secure community. On the other hand, I know now that we were being systematically brainwashed, and that brainwashing is not good for anyone.

Augusto Barcinas Atalig of Rota recalls his job as messenger: "When I finished the third grade, which was all we had on Rota, my uncle, Alexander Barcinas, was able to persuade the *secho* that he needed me for a messenger, and the next day I was called to his office and given a job. He asked me my name and I said it was Augusto Atalig. He tried several times to pronounce it but couldn't, and gave up, saying 'I will call you Taro.'

"He introduced me by that name to his cabinet, and ever since, even today, that is the name my best friends call me. The only problem was that I had trouble remembering it at first. The first time he called me: 'Taro, Taro, come to my office at once,' I just sat there at my new desk thinking how fine it was to be a messenger to the *secho* and his secretary had to come and get me. But he just laughed, and instructed me that I must learn to respond rapidly and to move fast, which I did from then on.

I spent my time carrying messages from him to cabinet members and to companies like the Nan-bo [a shipping company and store] and to various shops, using a government bicycle. I particularly liked to carry messages to the sugar mill and distillery, for no other Chamorros were allowed to enter it. All the employees there wore formal white and black uniforms, and the men wore neckties—the first I had ever seen—and acted as if whatever they were doing was the most important thing on the island."

Nicholas M. Leon Guerrero, who is now the director of the Department of Natural Resources in the Commonwealth of the Northern Marianas, told us about the American invasion: "On June 12, 1944 the Americans began to bomb Saipan. I remember that day because the pilots came in low to bomb and strafe, and I remember looking up at them and seeing their faces. Once I waved to one of the pilots and he waved back at me.

"After the invasion, we went first to a place behind the Japanese naval hospital, but the Americans were moving north so we went farther north, back to an area near Bird Island. We were a group of civilians, Japanese and Chamorro, including my aunt and her daughter. We met some Japanese soldiers, and one of the civilians asked them to shoot us and spare us the fate of falling into the hands of the Americans. However, the soldiers said it wouldn't be necessary yet since there was still time to escape. We made a small shelter against a rock and hid under it. The Americans came on and we could hear them shouting and cussing, even above the roar of small arms and mortar fire.

"I hid in the shelter under a blanket. I was very scared as the fighting advanced and surrounded us. But a sudden feeling of lightness, even under the blanket, made me realize that our shelter had been blown away, and moments later my blanket was jerked off me and I was looking into the muzzle of an M-1 rifle held by a marine. He motioned to me with his hand to get up and follow him. As I got up I noticed that one of the civilians, who had a rifle and had been lying near me, had the top of his head blown off.

"My auntie and her daughter and I and the others went along with the marine, confident that we were to be killed, and I said, 'Well, Auntie, I guess this is good-bye,' and when we walked through a clearing where the marines were digging trenches and fox holes, we thought they were preparing our graves, but the marine took us past them and into a truck that all of us got in to but my Auntie and her daughter, and I never saw them again or learned what happened to them.

"In the truck we were given candy and water. The Japanese civilians refused refreshments, thinking they were poison, but I took the risk and drank some water. As I drank it, all watched me closely, expecting me to drop over dead; when I didn't, they drank the water and ate the candy eagerly. And that was the way I got through the war."

This is a small but representative sample of the oral histories we got from Chamorro elders. These interviews constitute a memorable statement of the strength of a Chamorro heritage that was so deeply rooted in the hearts and souls of these islanders that it guided them through three decades of exploitation and subjugation, and through a war that used their property as battle fields and their lives as pawns . . . . Chamorro they were when history first encountered them, and just as Chamorro they remained up to war's end. These tales are a celebration of this sturdy people. Only now, with peace and prosperity assured, has their way of life become really endangered, this time not by exploitation and war, but by coping with and adapting to the challenges and pressures of a new, aggressive, 'resplendent' kind of world.

⊕ ⊕ ⊕

This is the way many remote islands appear: relaxed, carefree and friendly. This strip of island scenery is from an island in the Chuuk Lagoon.

THE MAKING AND THE UNMAKING OF A VAGABOND
FINAL REFLECTIONS

Whithersoever the fates drag us to and from, let us follow
—*Virgil*

The Alpha and Omega of an Odyssey: the beginning and, who knows, almost the end of my wandering about overseas! Why did I do it and without let up for more than 30 years? Why does anyone do it? Why, in this day of abundant amenities back home in the U. S. mainland does one choose to become a vagabond? The question didn't interest me much because I was too involved in the capers that have kept me hopping from island to island and in and out of an impoverished, rebellious continent (Africa) —That is, not until recently when I came upon a dissertation that I had prepared in 1958 to describe the middle-aged restlessness that had begun to pester me; and compared that three-decade old, faded, torn document with a statement I have just written to describe how I have gone about retiring on a quiet, ancient island—how I have tapered down and almost ceased to be a vagabond, and how I have come to reflect on those early, sometimes excessive years...from my genesis to my revelations

In the previous chapters I have documented those years by quoting magazine articles that I have published and speeches that I have given. Let me now try to give cohesion to these by filling in gaps that now exist. Let me start where my 1958 document left off where it describes me as a 47 year old pedantic, probably stodgy fellow who had somehow developed a 'look of eagles' in his eyes; and how, to his own amazement, stepped directly into the most adventurous event that existed on this post-war planet: bomb testing in the Marshall Islands; an event that is now seen as disreputable, but then was a noble, grand enterprise that would redeem mankind from the scourge of war; a violent, magnificent crusade in which I could partake, I, Galahad. And its nasty implications never occurred to me until I was involved in it. There was only one threat to serious catastrophe while I was there and it occurred in this solemn, but ridiculous way. I quote from my notes:

John, the handsome young Magistrate on Rongelap, came to me, "We mak' big Four July celebration, much singin', canoe races, maybe throwin' peple in lagoon for joke, much flag an' Uncle Sam stuff, but got no firecrackers. Council ver' sad. Says we gotta have big, bad boom on Four July. Flabbergasted, since I thought they were as frightened of bombs as I (of all people in the world they were the ones most entitled to panic), I agreed to do what I could, which, of course, was nothing. But by coincidence an especially big bomb—as big and bad as anyone could have wished for—was detonated on Bikini in the early hours of July 3rd, lighting up the sky and shaking us in our beds for we had not been notified of its schedule. But I got credit for having arranged such a spectacular, 'patriotic' performance, and the slight error in timing was not held against me. Hours later radio messages started coming in to warn me that winds were shifting ominously in our direction and that I should report radiation readings every hour. In dismay I watched the radiation counter's needle creep up bit by bit, not to a point of recognized danger but high enough to make me consider what I should do if it continued rising.

The most critical moment coincided with flag-raising on the morning of the Fourth of July. There we all stood in solemn alignment, heads bared to fallout, hands over hearts, swearing allegiance to the flag. In retrospect I think that the moment of greatest chagrin coincided with actual flag raising when John, confident of my abilities in all things, announced, "Dr. Peck, he now led us to sang Stars Spangled Bannered." Bravely I started the first line only to realize that was all I knew of it. . . . Raising the flag during fallout, baring our heads, forgetting the national anthem on the Fourth of July!—"What kind of American is that?" I asked then, and have been asking ever since.

A strange way to start an Odyssey! Though it turned me against bomb testing and bomb testers, it gave me such profound respect for islands and island people, and such passion for adventure and discovery that it has determined my subsequent career. I returned home briefly at the end of my tour, but in December, 1959 my wife and daughter and I went to Guam where I became Administrator of Public Health.

I was in Guam until June, 1964 when the University of North Carolina sent my wife and me to Malawi, a small, mountainous, mostly jungle country in Central Africa, where I conducted a program in tuberculosis detection, treatment, and control. Malawi, of course, was not an island, but I thought of it as an island—so isolated was it by surrounding, unfriendly neighbors—and I often mistakenly called it an island. Three revolutions occurred while we were there, and, soon after we left, there was a public hanging of the leading rebel with his corpse dragged behind a car through the streets of Blantyre. . . . But the program itself was successful, the patients and villagers were a delight to work with, the climate perfect (we lived at four thousand feet elevation), the myths and traditions and legends fascinating. My wife and I loved it, but for some reason that is not clear to me, I never wrote about these things: perhaps, because they overwhelmed me.

After three years in Africa my wife and I reentered the Western Pacific where I was assigned the position of Commissioner of Health Services for the Trust Territory, a position of grave responsibility but of few resources for there was only one other M D. in that entire, vast area, and he was a pathologist on a distant island—the others having quit in disgust a year previously. Much humbled by my new responsibilities, I gave a speech to an International Meeting of the World Health Organization in Miami in which I recalled with horror my introduction to my new job. Then I said:

I arrived in Micronesia, fresh from three years in a very small country in Central Africa, on a Monday morning in June, 1967. On Thursday morning I received a radio message at my Headquarters' office in Saipan informing me that a serious obstetrical complication involving an arm presentation had occurred in the dilapidated sub-district hospital in Kusaie [since renamed Kosrae], twelve hundred miles away. The radio reception was bad and it took half an hour of shouting for the young Micronesian physician in Kusaie to make me understand that he needed help from the district hospital in Ponape [since renamed Pohnpei], along with such surgical supplies as he would need, and fly them to Kusaie. So here is what transpired, as with considerable remembered agitation I will try to retrace with you the series of misadventures that introduced me to the ways of medical practice in Micronesia.

A large DC-4 plane from Guam flew a seaplane crew 554 miles to Truk [renamed Chuuk] where a Trust Territory seaplane was kept in readiness. But on arrival at Truk the crew was unable to get the SA-16 to fly. So a message was sent back to the Navy at Guam which dispatched one of its own seaplanes for this mercy mission. It made it successfully over the same 554 miles to Truk and then over the next 362 miles to Ponape, but when it tried to alight in Ponape's lagoon it missed a channel marker and piled up on a reef. Then a long wait for change of tide before it could be floated, and then nightfall with an interminable waiting for daylight. All this time, from Thursday morning to Saturday morning, a woman in labor with an infant's arm protruding as grotesquely and as horribly, it seemed to me as I waited nervously in Saipan, as in a somewhat similar H.G. Wells moon-based fantasy, which was the only precedent, medical or otherwise, I could call to mind. But on Saturday morning the seaplane did complete its mission to Kusaie where the senior and junior Micronesian medical officers successfully performed a Caesarean section, the mother and infant surviving with no complications. . . . A further note on the ingenuity of the staff: when the electric generator failed to function, most of the surgery was actually performed under the illumination of flashlights. This was my first humbling lesson in the magnitudes that were to confront me, my first sure insight into what happens when a fragile technology—our David—is matched against the surliness and strength of this Pacific Goliath.

Later, out of curiosity, I calculated the cost of transportation for this one Cesarean section. This alone cost $7,000 (an enormous amount in the late 60s). And what was the cost of transportation plus medical and hospital fees to the patient? It was $10.00, the highest fee that could be charged to a Micronesian for any surgical procedure performed within the Trust Territory. But even so, it was never collected.

In that same speech I read a letter from Ebeye Island hospital as example of problems that inundated me almost immediately, some with beguiling gentleness that is shown in this letter.

Dear Dr. Peck:
The hospital roof leaks, practically all the windows are falling out and need to be repaired. The air condition unit for the operating room is completely shot for almost three weeks. Oh, yes, I almost forgot to mention that the hospital ambulance has bro-

ken down and we are unable to transport patients in an emergency . . . so maybe the air condition unit in the operating room
isn't important after all.

Respectfully yours,
Medical Officer
Ebeye Hospital

As a former Guam resident I had thought I knew something about
the vastness of this part of the world, having crossed it many times by jet-
flight, usually asleep. But its extent cannot be comprehended by anyone
until he starts trying to arrange medical evacuations, orderly delivery of
medical supplies, and continuous supervision of hospitals thousands of miles
apart; for Trust Territory-Micronesia stretched through three time zones,
approached Japan and Hawaii on its northern and eastern reaches, abutted
New Guinea on the south and the Philippines on the west (it is on the
shores of the Philippines that Micronesian lost boats and their boatmen
are apt to turn up), sprawled through its 3,000,000 square miles of ocean as
if inaccessibility were its only motive. So far as I know no one person has
yet been able to visit all of its 92 inhabited islands, let alone another thousand or so that are uninhabited. For me to make ward rounds in the hospital at Majuro in the Marshalls (two hours of medical work) required ten
days getting there and back—or did before improvements in air schedule. I
had to cancel an important, brief meeting on Rongelap Atoll in the Marshall
Islands for it would have taken nearly six weeks time.

It took me several months of undependable air-plane travel and slow,
uncomfortable trips by field-trip freighters to discover the islands themselves
and the people who lived on them. Once, on an over-booked plane, I held on
to my arm rests and dared the pilot to throw me off, for that was the only way,
in those days, to keep a schedule. But it was worth it, and I wrote:

It comes to me almost as a revelation that this area contains
some of the most nostalgically beautiful islands in the world:
Kusaie, for instance, as fiercely rugged and jagged as the
Matterhorn, though green as an emerald; Ponape, always half-
hidden in clouds, soft and Elysian and dream-like with great
mountains folded into valleys that contain rain forests and the
sound of waterfalls; Truk with its Tol Lagoon as misty and as
mystical and as remote as a 17th Century Japanese painting;
and the Marshalls, flat, fungating, coral ring-worm atolls that
look as if they had been passed through a mangle and laid out

on the ocean to dry, but so ornately and miraculously transfig-
ured from a plane that one thinks of an over-turned jewel box
containing necklaces—and what I have just said becomes libel—
where the surf thunders ecological warfare almost up to your
doorstep and there is a feeling of sharks in the living room; and
the northern-most islands of the Marianas! How can I speak of
them since boat schedules and typhoons have, thus far, prevented
my making this northern trip, except vicariously to observe that
co-workers returning from Pagan and Anatahan and Agrihan
and Alimagan, though they have wonder in their eyes and eagerness to speak, seem to be struck dumb, as if they had beheld
the Taj Mahal—'mine eyes have seen the glory' sort of thing;
and Palau whose rock islands stand up, grotesque as the mush-
rooms they resemble, crowding Palau's great lagoon and protecting its precious corals and sponges and rare reef fish that
date back to this ocean's earliest memories; and tiny Yap, once
the center of a great ocean empire, still guarding its relics of
stone money and its memories of ancient ways. These improbable glories hidden behind nearly a century of restrictions are
now wide open to me and have become my daily ambiance.

Nor did I have reasons for knowing, before making these trips,
that human beings with compassion and dignity, and some with
actual greatness live here and work and aspire here, and succeed
or become fouled up in their frustrations just like anywhere else.
I will mention two medical incidents for illustration. Before coming here I had heard—and have since confirmed as acceptably
true—that Dr. Mac Donald, a former brain surgeon from Boston and one of my predecessors, once participated by radio in a
brain operation many sea-miles away: he at one end of a radio
frequency, a Micronesian Medical Officer (trained at the Fiji
School of Medicine) who never before had seen the inside of a
living cranium, at the other end; but with a scalpel in his hand
and the courage to cut and trephine and tie-off bleeding vessels
when Dr. Mac Donald's radio voice told him to do so. Of course
the patient survived as patients always do in tales that become
legends. And once while I worked on Guam I arranged for a
plastic surgeon to come from Honolulu for one week to repair
the cleft palates or harelips of twenty-four Guam children. Because of the unique training opportunity, I invited four or five
Micronesian Medical Officers to come to Guam Memorial
Hospital to assist in this week of marathon surgery. I recall the

awe with which Dr. Fernandez, the plastic surgeon, spoke of these Fiji-trained medical officers, "These men are excellent surgeons, *they handle tissues with reverence.*

Then, after gaining confidence of the islanders, plans were developed and completed: New hospitals were built and others planned, professional staffs were fully recruited, extensive training programs were created; and after five and one-half years I stepped down and Hawaii's School of Medicine sent me to develop a MEDEX (physician's assistant) Training School in Truk (Chuuk). There my wife and I lived, not in Moen where my office and classrooms were, but six miles away on Dublon Island—a wonderful way to continue a vagabond existence; for there we were the only state-siders among 2,400 Trukese. Each morning I conducted sick-call in our living room and then drove my Trukese-built boat six miles across the lagoon to work on Moen, the capitol of Truk. And on weekends I went diving and spear-fishing with our Trukese neighbors, as described in my *Letters to Dorothy.*

But time came for me to taper down, so we moved back to Saipan where I worked part-time in Public Health and began to learn to relax a bit and to adapt myself to the amenities that were transfiguring once-stable life on Saipan. And several years later (1982) we moved to Rota...this time for full, unremitting retirement. And it was here, just several weeks after coming to Rota that I composed the following dissertation that concludes this Odyssey and that may even redeem my thirty-some year as a vagabond. Here it is:

Why did I decide to retire on Rota, I am asked? Why on this not-much-favored (if one believes impatient people on Guam or Saipan), small, sequestered, jungle-farm island of gentle folkways and myths? I will try to answer this question but first I must state that 'decide' is not the proper word to elicit a frank answer for it suggests that I went through an intellectual process of rationalization and of weighing Rota's worth with that of many other locations, but I didn't do that, for the idea of coming here simply emerged without prompting—subliminal I think—and appeared as an unfolding destiny that was meant for me and that I shouldn't resist. Philosophically, then, I might answer: "I am here because this is where I came," or, more to the point, "I am here because this is where I feel comfortable."

My active professional life was lived in both hemisphere as far east and as far west as one can readily get, and from 'antipode to antipode'. This far-flung way of living suited me well when I was younger and my young world's universe was expanding and its details needed to be seen, felt, and sometimes suffered; but such a universe is too big for an old man, and the universe I now feel capable of coping with fits easily inside Rota's reef. A manageable universe is what I need in my declining years, one whose geographic limits I can actually see, one in which I know every person, where we all wave at each other, and in which there are few surprises.

Nostalgia is an affliction of old age, and I have a fairly severe case of it. The simple horse-and-buggy village in southern Iowa in which I was born and raised! It must really have been a disaster at that time, at least I never returned to it after I left for college. But now in my dotage, as I nostalgically reconstruct it, it glows with the spirit of my pioneer ancestry: firm, simple, stalwart, upright, and I can hardly tell it from Songsong village on Rota. Once when I stepped off an old Trust Territory plane—this incident occurred in Majuro (Marshall Islands) in the 1960s rather than on Rota but the emotions were similar to my frequent Rota emotions—as I stepped off the plane at the airport which, at that time, was at the very edge of the village, I saw almost the entire village waiting, waiting not for me but just to see the plane come in, and I was transported back 50 years to Fourth of July celebrations at Union Grove, several miles outside of my Iowa village, and the dusty road lined by corn fields and bluegrass pastures that led to the village. Of course this is silly and can have no meaning for anyone but me, but for me it reclaimed, for one wondrous moment, a universe that I thought was gone forever, and it established a kind of kinship with island life that has endured. Had Majuro's airport been indistinguishable from one in Des Moines, Iowa, this would not have happened. The magic was in the fact that Majuro, and especially Rota, have not moved forward very much beyond my comfortable childhood.

Those were some of the powerful motives that made me look initially toward Rota. True, they were (and still are) ephemeral and probably matters of my own fiction, but I'm sure they were at the root of my initial decision. Since then other reasons, not at all ephemeral nor fictitious, have emerged; for instance, there is 20th Century Guam just 45 miles away, and this makes living in Rota like living in two different centuries. Where else can this happen? Or like living on a prairie and downtown at the same time. And these are not fiction, for I use Guam's University frequently for intellectual stimulation. I tend my garden patch up on high, cool Sabana or explore a forgotten tunnel one day on Rota and the next day I am in Guam at the University visiting my friends and working with them, or I am in downtown Guam shopping in its modern department stores. Thus in retirement on Rota one can cheat a little in both Time and Space, almost as if one were a magician drawing rabbits and flags from a hat. Where better can I spend my declining years? Where better can I terminate this odyssey?

⊕ ⊕ ⊕